W9-CKK-579

BASIC MICROSCOPIC TECHNICS

BASIC MICROSCOPIC TECHNICS

BY RUTH MC CLUNG JONES

BASED ON MICHAEL F. GUYER'S *ANIMAL MICROLOGY*

THE UNIVERSITY OF CHICAGO PRESS

CHICAGO & LONDON

This book is based on *Animal Micrology* by Michael F. Guyer. Originally published 1906 (Fifth Edition 1953) by The University of Chicago Press.

Library of Congress Catalog Card Number: 66-20579
THE UNIVERSITY OF CHICAGO PRESS, CHICAGO & LONDON
The University of Toronto Press, Toronto 5, Canada

PREFACE

Guyer's *Animal Micrology*, on which this book is based, filled a special need for a good many generations of students and teachers. Its author's aim was to provide a useful guide both for students beginning the study of microtechnic and for instructors who make microscopic preparations for their classes. The five editions through which it passed and the popularity which they enjoyed are indications of the success of the author's aims.

The present writer has followed the general plan of Dr. Guyer's book with some modifications in method of presentation. The references, formulae, reagents, and notes concerning equipment are placed in separate sections for easier reference. It is hoped that this arrangement, and the cross references in text and index, will help in making information easily accessible.

Many of the older methods are not included. This is not only because so many new and excellent technics have been published and have superseded them, but also because a considerable number of new and better reagents are available which make new technics possible and preferable. More than half of the methods described here have been published in the past fifteen years. It is interesting to note, however, that several of the older ones are still in constant use, without modification; some of these have been included, such as the iron hematoxylin staining method and some fixation technics.

Some of the new methods make work easier both in preparing material and studying it. The whole preparations of cells for karyotype analysis are examples. Once the technics are mastered, these are easier to make and more satisfying to study than the beautiful hematoxylin preparations which were once used exclusively. Histochemical methods produce results which could not previously have been obtained and are changing microtechnic from its old status as an art to that of a science. It is hoped that the very brief introduction to these methods which is offered here will make the student aware of their great interest and importance, and that he will attempt to master many more. His attention is directed to the texts mentioned in the chapter on histochemistry and to the journals which are concerned with these methods.

Several methods for vital staining have been described because they are instructive and are quite simple.

It has been difficult to select the technics to be included in this volume since there are so many excellent ones available. The criteria used in making the choices were excellence of results which the writer and her students have been able to obtain and the relative simplicity of the procedures. A number of technics are presented which have been developed in the laboratory of the writer.

RUTH McCLUNG JONES
Corvallis, Oregon

ACKNOWLEDGMENTS

Several persons were of material assistance in the preparation of *Basic Microscopic Technics* and to them the writer tenders her gratitude. They include Mary Conner and Lana Bryan Shewey, recent graduates of Winthrop College, who spent much time and conscientious effort in trials of various technics. Mr. Jay Fox, of the department of chemistry and physics at the same college, kindly read Dr. Guyer's chapter on microscopy and criticized minor changes which had been made by the present writer. Dr. Miriam Albertson, director of the student health service at Winthrop College, has been a helpful colleague throughout the preparation of the book. She has criticized the writing and made valuable suggestions for its improvement, typed a part of the manuscript, read proof, and helped in all parts of the work. It could not have been completed without her invaluable assistance.

INTRODUCTION

These remarks are directed principally to student users of *Basic Microscopic Technics*. The directions in the text assume some knowledge of chemistry and of biology. They presuppose that the laboratory is supplied with such reference books as the *Handbook of Chemistry and Physics* (Chemical Rubber Publishing Company) or some other equally useful handbook; *Biology Data Book*, published by the Federation of Societies for Experimental Biology; a good medical dictionary; and *Webster's New International Dictionary*. In addition to these books, there should be available as many as possible of the following manuals of microtechnic; if these are cited in the bibliography, their entry number follows the title; otherwise their publishers are noted.

Baker, J. R. 1945. Cytological technique. Methuen's Monographs. London: Methuen and Co., Ltd.

Conn, H. J. *et al.* 1960. Staining procedures, Ed. 2 (*72*).

Cowdry, E. V. Laboratory technic in biology and medicine, Baltimore: Williams and Wilkins Co.

Davenport, Harold A. 1960. Histological and histochemical technics (*83*).

Gage, S. H. 1941. The microscope. Ithaca, N.Y.: Comstock Publishing Co.

Gatenby, J. B. and Beams, H. W. 1950. The microtomist's vade mecum, Ed. 11 (*119*).

Gomori, G. 1952. Microscopic histochemistry (*129*).

Gray, Peter. 1954. The microtomist's formulary and guide (*131*).

Gurr, Edward. 1959. Methods of analytical histology and histochemistry (*140*)

Guyer, Michael F., 1953. Animal micrology, Ed. 5 (*142*).

Jones, R. M., editor, McClung's microscopical technique (*164*).

Lillie, R. D. 1954. Histopathologic technic and practical histochemistry (*193*).

Lison, Lucien. 1953. Histochemie et Cytochemie animales. Paris: Gauthier-Villars.

Romeis, B. 1948. Mikroskopische Technik, Ed. 15 (*269*).

Other useful references are given in most of the chapters.

It is very important that students learn to use authoritative manuals and handbooks and that they become acquainted with journals and form the habit of consulting original sources. A good first choice of journal for microtechnicians is *Stain Technology*. Both the technics and the extensive bibliographies which accompany major articles are valuable.

The attention of the reader is called to the following points in the use of the book.

All references are numbered. The numbers that refer to authors are in italics and may be found in the Bibliography, pp. 296–312. References to reagents are preceded by R and are found in Appendix I; formulae (F) are in Appendix II; equipment and supplies (E) are in Appendix III; and addresses of dealers in equipment, reagents, and supplies (A) are in Appendix IV.

When formulae or directions call for water, this must be understood to be distilled water; if tap water is to be used this is always indicated.

CONTENTS

Contents   *xiii*

CHAPTER I

GENERAL STATEMENT CONCERNING METHODS IN MICROSCOPIC TECHNIC

Before it is examined with a light microscope, all material must be treated in some way. Probably the simplest preparations are temporary mounts of living organisms in a suitable medium on a slide. Permanent mounts are prepared by more complex methods which may be both laborious and difficult. A properly prepared, permanent microscopic preparation usually consist of these parts: a glass slide, or suitable substitute, a specimen mounted on the slide, a cover glass, and a label. The label carries either a number which refers to an entry in the technician's records describing the specimen and its method of preparation or a brief description of the preparation indicating its source and treatment, initials of the technician, and the date of preparation. Modifications of this pattern will be described later in appropriate sections.

Acceptable methods for making any type of permanent preparations for microscopic study must meet several requirements. They must (a) preserve the material in a condition as lifelike as possible; (b) provide for the separation of the tissues into masses thin enough to be studied with transmitted light; (c) include treatment which permits the demonstration of cell and tissue parts that would otherwise be optically homogeneous or which indicates the chemical composition of cell and tissue elements by microchemical reactions.

There is a bewildering variety of permanent microscopic preparations, but they may be divided into two principal categories. The first consists of preparations of animals, or parts of animals, of such size that they must be prepared for study by being cut into thin slices or otherwise subdivided into small pieces. The second is made up of preparations of animals or parts small enough to be studied as whole objects.

In the following pages are brief descriptions of procedures commonly employed in making slides. Not all of these are used for all kinds of preparations, nor are they always carried out in the sequence in which they are presented here.

ANESTHETIZATION is generally the first step in preparation. If the specimen is small and contractile, the relaxation produced by anesthesia may be necessary to prevent distortion in the fixing fluid. If it is larger, anesthesia is not only necessary for humane reasons, but it is also easier and more satisfactory to work with an anesthetized specimen. There is a wide choice of suitable methods, including the use of conventional ether and chloroform, several hypnotics, certain poisons, and agents producing hypothermia. When anesthesia is complete, the desired parts are removed and usually placed in fixative.

FIXATION is intended to preserve, as well as possible, the form of cells, cell organelles, and tissue elements, to produce optical differences in their microscopic structure, or to react with the tissues in such a way that parts or substances can be demonstrated by subsequent treatment with stains and/or other reagents. To accomplish these ends the fixing agent must possess certain properties, which are discussed in chapter III.

WASHING.   Although some fixatives are also good fluids for storing specimens, most of them must be washed out to prevent overfixing or to remove such substances as crystals which interfere with subsequent processes. Aqueous fixatives are usually washed out with running tap water; those made with alcohol are frequently removed with alcohol solutions of similar concentration.

PRESERVATION.   This step is omitted if the specimen is prepared directly after fixation. If, however, the material is to be stored for some time, it must be left in a preservative that, like the fixative, will not distort the tissue elements. Most preservatives are not mixtures but single reagents, usually diluted with water.

STAINING.   With few exceptions, microscopic preparations are stained. The stains are chosen according to the purposes of the study. Those staining technics for sectioned material, sometimes called oversight methods, are useful in exploring unfamiliar specimens. If a particular type of cell or tissue constituent is to be examined, a dye is employed that stains it characteristically. If an exhaustive study of a specimen is to be made, a wide variety of staining methods will probably be necessary.

DEHYDRATION.   Specimens to be mounted whole in aqueous media and those to be sectioned after freezing or embedding in gelatin or in water wax are not dehydrated. All others must have all, or almost all, of the free water in the tissues removed. Numerous dehydrators are available. Ethanol has been most commonly employed but, although it is often satisfactory, it may under many conditions be replaced by others.

INFILTRATION. Material to be sectioned must be supported by permeating it with a medium which will attain a consistency that permits the cutting of thin, even slices. From the various possible media including nitrocellulose, paraffin, water waxes, gelatin, agar, and ice, a choice is made according to the nature of the specimen, the speed necessary in making the slides, and the equipment available.

CUTTING (SECTIONING). Sections are cut on precise machines called microtomes at thicknesses ranging from 1 or 2μ to 50μ or more. Frozen material is usually cut on freezing microtomes; nitrocellulose-embedded blocks, on sliding microtomes or paraffin microtomes; and wax-embedded material, on paraffin microtomes.

CLEARING is the process of rendering specimens translucent. The term correctly describes the effect of glycerol on whole, small animals, of xylene on sections after dehydration, and of certain mountants used for small animals without preliminary treatment. Many reagents have excellent clearing properties. The term clearing is also used in a somewhat different sense in some of the paraffin technics in which it means the interposition of a reagent between the dehydrator and embedding medium.

MOUNTING is accomplished by placing a mountant on the specimen and adding a cover glass. Many mountants have a base of gum or resin and are dissolved in water, alcohol, or xylene; benzene is sometimes used in place of xylene. The choice of a mountant depends on the previous treatment of the specimen and the refractive index most suitable for the study in hand.

DRYING, CLEANING, AND LABELING are the final steps in the preparation of a slide. Drying refers to the evaporation of the solvent of the mountant, so that the slide may be handled without displacement of cover or specimen. Cleaning is the removal of any excess mountant from the edges or surface of the cover; it also includes the removal of any foreign material from the surface of the preparation. Labeling is the addition of identification information to the slide.

GENERAL DIRECTIONS

CHOOSE WITH CARE THE MATERIAL TO BE PREPARED.
Make a thoughtful and informed choice of specimens for each technic
to be tried. If somatic mitoses or meiotic divisions are to be demonstrated, choose an animal which has a small chomosome number and
large chromosomes and which is at a suitable stage in its life history.
For a study of mammalian kidneys, select an animal so small that longitudinal and cross sections of the entire organ will give a clear idea of
its anatomy as well as its cellular structure. For a study of bone formation in mammals or in embryos, use parts, such as the foot, in which
both diaphysis and epiphyses may be seen in a single longitudinal section. When details of cellular structure are to be studied, choose animals
such as urodele amphibians which have large cells and tissues that stain
brilliantly. *Necturus, Amphiuma,* and various small salamanders are
particularly suitable. It is both wasteful of time and disappointing to
prepare slides from material in which structures cannot be seen as
clearly as they can in other available specimens.

PLAN WORK CAREFULLY before beginning. Make a timetable for
the whole process or a discrete part of it which can be completed as a
unit, such as the dehydration and infiltration of a piece of tissue in
paraffin. Enter the timetable on a calendar which can then be consulted
each day. Assemble the materials needed; make up solutions well in
advance, except those which deteriorate on standing.

WORK NEATLY and keep equipment and solutions clean and in
order. This involves, among other things, keeping the work space un-
cluttered, washing and drying glassware after each use, and filtering
all solutions after or immediately before use unless there is some specific contraindication. Make clean, well-arranged slides with the covers
and labels properly placed; print the labels plainly with India ink and
a fine pen.

BE CONSISTENT in the methods you use. For example, consider the
placing of label and specimen on the slide. There are several acceptable
and conventional ways. The label may be at either the right or the left
end. Since it is usually about 24 mm square there remains 51 mm of
space for the specimen(s). The material may be centered in this space
with its midpoint about 25 mm from the right or left end and 12.5 mm
from top and bottom of the slide. An alternative is to place the specimen
with its center in the middle of the slide. After trials to determine

which method is most satisfactory, follow consistently the one chosen with only such modifications as are made necessary by the type of slide being made.

KEEP ACCURATE RECORDS and make them while the work is in progress, not waiting to do so later from memory. Select a system for records according to individual preference or prescribed class procedures. We prefer a bound notebook with numbered pages and a carefully made index. Large or small loose-leaf notebooks or card files are satisfactory also. Include in the records the identifying number of each specimen and the origin of the formulae used or the formulae themselves. In the latter case, identify the reagents used as exactly as possible, by chemical formula if necessary, or by grade: C.P., Pract., or A.C.S. If a choice of equipment was possible, indicate in the record the selection made. Such information will make it possible to repeat a successful operation or to discover where the fault lay if the result is not satisfactory or is atypical. Include in the records personal comments, ideas, and questions. In repeating a procedure previously recorded, give only the date of the second trial and a reference to previous notes. Record fully any deviations from a standard method, whether planned or accidental. Many technics are, at least in part, empirical and superior results may sometimes be obtained by modifying them, but always master a method fully before attempting to make changes in it.

CHAPTER II

STUDY OF
LIVING ORGANISMS

It is desirable to study not only fixed but also living material. Living preparations provide information impossible to obtain in any other way and will repay the time and care needed to make and study them. It should be emphasized that the most important factor in the study of living material is the attitude of the observer. He must have patience, objectivity, skill in manipulation, and willingness to spend, if necessary, long hours in observation.

GENERAL INSTRUCTIONS

There are several general requirements for making living preparations. Most of them are simple and all are essential for successful study.

GLASSWARE MUST BE CLEAN AND NONTOXIC. All equipment used in handling living material should be cleaned without the application of any of the various dichromate mixtures in common use in most laboratories. Even minute traces of potassium dichromate which remain after prolonged washing in running water are toxic to many animals and to their gametes (264). All equipment used for study of living materials should be marked in some distinctive fashion and used for no other purpose. It should be cleaned with a nontoxic detergent such as Tide (E–75), and thoroughly rinsed after cleaning, first with tap water and then with distilled water. If bacterial contamination must be avoided, sterilization should follow the rinsing.

THE MEDIUM IN WHICH THE SPECIMENS ARE STUDIED IS IMPORTANT. It must be chosen both with regard to the physiology of the cells or organisms and to the purposes of the study. Small aquatic organisms are usually left in the water in which they were collected or in the medium in which they have been cultured. Parasites or symbionts are studied either in the fluid in which they lived or in a medium isotonic with the host tissues, such as normal saline or Ringer's fluid. Natural liquids such as cerebrospinal fluid, amniotic fluid, aqueous humor (eye), or blood serum are often satisfactory.

MOUNTING TO PERMIT PROLONGED OBSERVATION without distortion or without loss of specimens is often necessary. Depression slides or slides carrying chambers cemented to them are usually necessary if the preparation is to be observed over a period of several hours to several days. For such a preparation, the specimen is placed on the cover which is then inverted over the chamber or the depression in the slide. See Figure 1. The edges are sealed with Vaseline or with mineral oil.

Fig. 1.—Depression slide with a hanging drop on the cover which is inverted over the well.

A PROPER TEMPERATURE FOR OBSERVATION IS ESSENTIAL. If the specimens are invertebrates or the cells are from cold-blooded animals, the main problem is to prevent overheating. This is not difficult if the light source may be moved away from the microscope, and the illumination provided by a mirror. But when the light source is built into the base of the microscope, the stage will usually become too warm. Heat filters of glass, which may be interposed between the substage light and stage, may usually be purchased from microscope manufacturers, but they are relatively expensive. An acceptable substitute is a piece of 4-mm Plexiglas cut to proper size. This is usually laid on the stage. If it interferes with critical lighting it may be mounted below the stage.

LIGHTING MUST BE ADJUSTED TO THE TYPE OF SPECIMEN. Small and transparent organisms may be seen best with light of low intensity. Light filters are useful adjuncts; dark-field illumination is frequently helpful. If the specimens are thin enough, skillful use of a phase microscope may be essential for the observation of certain structures.

RELATIVELY INACTIVE SMALL ORGANISMS AND CELLS which need no restraint may be placed on a cover glass in a drop of suitable fluid and the cover inverted over the well of a depression slide. Or they may be put directly on a slide and covered; the cells or organisms will remain in good condition for several hours or longer. Or specimens may be placed in shallow wells made by cementing rings to slides, and covered. Again a seal of Vaseline or oil will prevent evaporation of fluid.

RESTRAINT OF ACTIVE SMALL ORGANISMS is often necessary
and may be accomplished in several ways. Among them are the following:

A.   Methocel 10% aq sol, or polyvinyl alcohol (F–170) may be used
      to make a ring or a square of suitable size and shape to support the
      cover glass; the animals are placed within it, in their culture fluid,
      and covered. Both Methocel and polyvinyl alcohol will diffuse
      slowly into the fluid and will decrease the motility of the organ-
      isms so that observations can easily be made. Neither of these
      materials affects the specimen or its activities adversely.
B.   Nickel sulfate is recommended by Bovee (43) to anesthetize pro-
      tozoa. He prescribes for paramecia the addition of one drop of
      stock solution (F–155) to one drop of culture or pond water, which
      makes a 0.02% solution. The anesthetic effect is not immediate; it
      slows the swimming rate to about one-sixth of normal in 15 min-
      utes and similarly reduces the pulsing rate of the contractile
      vacuole. Tartar (308) recommends the same strength of nickel sul-
      fate solution for relatively quick anesthesia but finds that a
      weaker solution, 0.002%, acting for about 12 hours produces even
      better results. This agent is effective for other ciliates and for
      some flagellates such as *Euglena,* although the concentration may
      need to be altered for each species.
C.   Films to quiet small metazoa are recommended by Carame-Vivas
      (56), who gives directions for making a thin collodion film to place
      over small aquatic organisms on slides as a means of holding them
      relatively quiet for microscopic observation. It is a satisfactory
      technic, but preparation of the film is time consuming. Dean and
      Hatfield (85) use Saran Wrap (E–58) as a substitute for the col-
      lodion film. It serves the same purpose, is easily obtainable, and
      is inexpensive. Specimens which are to be viewed from two sur-
      faces are placed in a suitable medium between two small squares
      of the film which is then laid on a slide; the whole sandwich may
      be turned over when necessary. The authors report that even an
      immersion lens may be successfully used with this restraining de-
      vice and that the specimen is unharmed by the light pressure
      exerted by the film.

STAINING ORGANISMS WITH VITAL DYES. There is a fairly
large group of dyes that will stain parts of living protozoa and small
metazoa. These do not stain nuclei unless they are used in toxic concentrations and kill as they stain. Some of these dyes are phagocytosed

and appear in the cytoplasm of protozoa as food vacuoles. Others stain certain cell organelles effectively. Mitochondria will be deeply colored with Janus green B, and neutral red is taken up by cytoplasmic vacuoles. Methylene blue appears to stain various parts of aquatic metazoa in sequence.

Wenrich and Diller (*164*, p. 439) report a number of vital dyes that may be used on paramecia, together with a guide to safe concentrations. Some of these are Bismark brown, 1:150,000; methylene blue, 1:100,000; neutral red, 1:150,000; toluidine blue, 1:105,000; Janus green B, 1:180,-000; brilliant cresyl blue, 1:50,000; and Nile blue sulfate, 1:30,000. For other genera of protozoa, the concentrations may need to be changed. A simple way to determine useful concentrations is to make up 100 ml of a 0.1% solution and to make trials with various dilutions, with this as a stock. For metazoa in which it is difficult to distinguish various parts, experiments with vital dyes may produce informative preparations.

DEMONSTRATIONS OF ACTIVITIES OF CELLS AND ORGANISMS

II–1. MOVEMENT AND EMPTYING OF FOOD VACUOLES IN PARAMECIA. Kempton's method (*167*) is simple and effective. It is designed for class use. As many slides as are needed can be prepared in about 20 minutes.

1. Place a few milliliters of a rich culture of *Paramecium* in a petri dish. Stir in a very few grains of powdered carmine. Examine at once to see whether the protozoa are feeding and forming vacuoles. From a minute amount of the stain a *Paramecium* should form 10–15 carmine-filled vacuoles in 5–10 minutes.
2. Centrifuge this culture as slowly as possible 1–2 minutes. Transfer the sludge, with a mouth pipet, to a fresh culture medium and centrifuge as before. Repeat 2–3 times, until the excess carmine is removed.
3. Transfer the sludge to an equal quantity of well-hydrated 10% aq sol of methyl cellulose (R–123) and mix.
4. Place a small amount of the mixture on each slide and cover. Prepare an appropriate number of slides.

Results: The paramecia are practically immobilized and no further feeding occurs; cyclosis and the elimination of carmine from food vacuoles at the anal pore can be clearly observed. Yeast in a Congo red solution (F–66) (*11*) may be substituted for carmine.

II–2. CELLS IN LAMELLIBRANCH BLOOD. Breder and Nigrelli (*48*) give the following directions:

1. Remove one valve from a lamellibranch: *Ostrea, Venus,* and *Ano-*

donta are good genera to study. A single specimen will provide enough material for a laboratory section.

2. Thrust a capillary pipet into the heart and withdraw some blood. Place a drop or two on a slide; cover and seal with melted Vaseline.

3. Observe the initial clumping of leucocytes, and then the active ameboid movement which separates them.

Oysters may be used without opening. Place a specimen in water, warm it slightly, and harvest the large quantity of leucocytes which the oyster emits. If returned to a cool place, the oyster may be used several times for this purpose.

II–3. CELLS IN FROG LYMPH.

1. Add a drop of Higgins' India ink (R–106) to a few milliliters of normal frog saline (F–180).

2. Withdraw some lymph from the dorsal lymph sac of an anesthetized frog (II–8), using a luer syringe and 25-gauge needle.

3. Place a small drop of the diluted ink on a slide and add a larger drop of lymph; cover and seal. Make several preparations, varying the proportions of ink and lymph. Study to observe the ingestion of carbon by leucocytes.

II–4. CELLS IN OTHER BODY FLUIDS OF VARIOUS ANIMALS.

Peritoneal fluid of most coelomates and of many mammals may be used. The coelomic fluid of large annelids, particularly earthworms (*142*, p. 302), is made readily accessible by exposing the worms to the vapor of chloroform for 1–2 minutes. The fluid will exude from the dorsal pores between segments and may be picked up with a cover glass. Fluid in the hemocoele of many insects is sufficiently abundant to be satisfactory for the study of its cells by the methods outlined above for frogs and for lamellibranchs.

II–5. LIVING NEMATODES.

Cobb (66) recommends free-living species, either from water or soil. A summary of his directions follows:

1. Mount each specimen, which has been starved for a day or two, in a small drop of its natural medium and put a thin, round cover glass over it.

2. Withdraw enough fluid with bibulous paper so that the cover glass slightly compresses the worm but still permits slight movement; seal with very hot soft paraffin, using a small camel-hair brush.

3. Keep some of the worms overnight in a weak solution of methylene blue and mount these as above to demonstrate parts of the peripheral nervous system.

Results: Most important structures can be clearly seen if the animal is able to move slightly, "because various nemic organs reveal their contours more readily when sliding slightly, one on another."

Potts (253) has found neutral red useful in the study of small free-living nematodes. He immerses soil nematodes in a solution of neutral red just strong enough to show color. The solution is rapidly ingested and stains the gut pink to purple; after about 12 hours other organs color also, with muscle showing the color last.

Parasitic nematodes may usually be secured from the anterior pairs of nephridia in earthworms and studied in the same way as free-living forms. Larger numbers may be provided by cultures (XVII–20).

II–6.   THE STRUCTURE AND FUNCTIONING OF SMALL CRUSTACEANS are illustrated by *Daphnia magna* or *Artemia salina.* The following directions can be adapted to either animal *(11).*

1.   Mount the specimens in culture water in a cell shallow enough to partially compress them. Cover, and seal with melted Vaseline.

2.   After studying the organisms in pure culture water, make other preparations to show the effects of reagents. For *Daphnia,* Viehoever (317) recommends adding the following reagents: cascara 1:15/vol of nonalcoholic fluid extract; Glauber salts, 1% sol; yeast; ammonia 28%; digitoxin, sat aq sol; chloroform 3% sol; phenobarbitol, sat aq sol; neutral red in low concentrations. Viehoever also recommends studying the effects of various temperatures on *Daphnia* preparations.

II–7.   LIVING GREGARINES in cricket gut may be prepared as follows. Parrish and Parrish (244) provide these directions:

1.   Sacrifice a cricket known to be infested (XVII–4) by cutting off its head. Remove also the legs and the thoracic and abdominal sterna.

2.   Dissect out all of the gut posterior to the gizzard. Place it on a slide in insect saline (F–180), tease with dissecting needles, and spread out its contents in a thin film. Cover and seal with melted Vaseline.

3.   Put the gut wall in saline on another slide; cover, and seal this also.

Results: It is usually possible to see attached trophozoites, free sporadins, syzygy, cyst formation, and cysts. The slides may be made permanent with the aceto-carmine technic (V–4).

Another source of gregarines is mentioned by Packard (241). He notes that Adams and Travis (2) found two new species in *Thermobia domestica,* which is one of the common silver fish, and that more than half of the specimens examined were parasitized. The gut may be prepared for study in the same way.

OBSERVATIONS ON CIRCULATION

II–8.   IN THE WEB OF A FROG'S FOOT.   This study may be made with simple equipment: a binocular dissecting microscope or a compound microscope with provision for substage illumination, a few paper towels, and a plastic slide (E–34) or sheet of cork in which a window has been cut a little smaller than the web of the hind foot. If the stage of the microscope is not large, provide a glass jar of about the height of the stage and place it, bottom up, beside the microscope to partially support the specimen.

Anesthetize the frog by placing it in a 0.2% solution of Chloretone (F–56) 4–8 minutes or until it is relaxed. Wrap it in a paper towel saturated with the solution. Pin out the web of the foot on the slide or on the cork sheet, making as flat a preparation as possible and avoiding injury to blood vessels. Arrange the specimen on the microscope stage with a part of the web favorable for study in place under the objective. Keep the surface of the web moist with the Chloretone solution while studying it.

Results: Many observations on circulation may be made on this type of preparation: diapedesis may be observed as well as the reaction of the capillaries to raised and lowered temperatures. The specimen will remain anesthetized for 3–6 hours and may be returned to water, where it will recover completely in 24 hours.

II–9.   IN A FROG'S URINARY BLADDER (McNeil *et al. 216*).
This is a superior structure for demonstrating circulation.

1.   Inject 3–5 ml of frog Ringer's solution (F–175) into the dorsal lymph sinus to distend the bladder.
2.   After 30 minutes, inject 2–6 ml of 5% urethane into the dorsal lymph sinus to act as an anesthetic.
3.   When the withdrawal reflex has ceased, open the body cavity by a 2–cm incision parallel and lateral to the midline and ending about 1 cm anterior to the hind leg.
4.   Extrude the bladder carefully by holding aside the intestine and ovary (if the frog is a female); use a blunt instrument, and apply pressure to the body wall on the side opposite the incision. If the bladder is not well filled, gently force Ringer's solution into the cloaca with a medicine dropper before extruding it; in this process, avoid the introduction of air.
5.   For observation of circulation, place the frog on a glass plate in such a position that light is transmitted through the bladder with-

out obstruction. Soak a paper towel in water and cover the frog, cutting a window in the towel to expose the bladder. Keep the towel moist with water and the exposed bladder moist with Ringer's solution. It is possible to maintain a functional preparation by these means for as long as 10 hours.

5a. If experimental modification of the circulation is to be studied by topical applications of various reagents, place the frog in a clear plastic tray (E–82) containing 0.5–1.0 % urethane in Ringer's solution. Keep the bladder almost, or just barely submerged. Apply any of the following reagents, dropping them on the surface of the bladder: 0.001% sol histamine, 0.1% acetic acid, 0.0001 M or 0.001 M epinephrine.

6. Study, if possible, with a dissecting microscope and at a magnification of at least 40 diameters. If necessary, a compound microscope may be used.

Results: It is possible to distinguish, with the frog on a glass plate, arterioles, capillaries, venules, the axial column of red blood corpuscles in arterioles, peripheral white blood corpuscles, and the reversal of flow in anastamosing capillary systems and functional arteriovenous shunts. With the frog in the plastic tray, it is possible to demonstrate vasodilator effects of histamine or acetic acid and the vasoconstrictor effects of epinephrine.

Cowdry (77) points out that circulation in human capillaries can be studied in the skin at the base of the fingernail. He advises that the epidermis be treated with a drop of highly refractile oil to make it translucent. This simple method is excellent with a binocular dissecting microscope capable of high magnification. Terpineol (R–188) proved an excellent reagent for rendering the epidermis translucent.

KNISLEY'S QUARTZ ROD technic is an essential method for studying the circulation in internal organs of large animals. It requires a brilliant light source and quartz rods of various types (*164*, p. 477, and *175*).

CHAPTER III

KILLING, FIXATION, AND STORAGE

INTRODUCTION AND GENERAL DIRECTIONS

In chapter I it was stated that the purposes of fixation are preservation of cells, cell contents, and tissue elements; production of optical differences in miscroscopic structure; and reaction of certain constituents of the fixatives with tissues in such a way that parts or substances can be demonstrated by appropriate later treatments. These objectives cannot be completely attained. The best methods have faults, but it is possible, by a suitable choice of reagents, to achieve results that give a trustworthy representation of the normal conditions. It is also possible, unfortunately, to fix tissues in such a way that the normal condition is obscured rather than revealed.

A few fixatives are vapors but most of them are liquids. The specimen is usually excised and placed in a large volume of fixing fluid. When very rapid fixation of a part is desirable, the whole animal is perfused with fixative as a preliminary step before the desired part is removed and placed in the same reagent. For some purposes, freeze-drying or freeze-substitution precedes fixation.

There are numerous formulae for fixatives in the literature; many of them are needless duplications since they contain the same ingredients and vary only in the proportions of each. An example of this is the group of formalin-alcohol-acetic mixtures, of which there are at least fifteen; most of these could be used interchangeably since, within certain limits, the proportions are not critical (83, p. 166). But it should be noted that in some formulae, the quantities of the constituents are of critical importance and changes may produce disastrous results.

Some mixtures, of which neutral 10% formalin is an example, preserve most parts of animal tissue adequately and are accordingly called general purpose fixatives. They are useful for preliminary studies and in the preparation of material in which every part should be preserved as well as possible; examples are serial sections of embryos, sections of a whole organ for a study of its architecture, typical sections of an animal such as an earthworm or a small vertebrate, and unknown material taken during a collecting expedition. Other fixatives may give a good picture of only one kind of cell or even of a single cell organelle or constituent and do violence to the rest of the specimen. In spite of this their use for special purposes is mandatory. Acetic-orcein, a stain-fixative which demonstrates clearly the chromosomes of a cell but destroys the cytoplasmic constituents, is an example. An important consideration is that excellent staining of some structures is possible only if correct fixation has preceded the staining. A fixative compatible with the required stain must therefore be chosen. Originators or reporters of a staining technic usually specify one or more satisfactory fixatives. For new types of material or new technical methods, trials leading to the choice of a suitable fixer are essential.

Thus before choosing a fixative it is necessary to consider carefully the purpose of the study: whether the microscopic structure of all parts of the animal is to be shown as well as can be done with a single fixative, or whether the best possible preservation of a given tissue is to be attained. For the former purpose, a general fixative should be used; for the latter, a fixative particularly suitable for the intended study. It is often desirable to employ a general fixative first; after preliminary studies of the morphology of the animal or part have been made, a series of special fixatives can be applied (see index, general fixatives).

Both for humane reasons, and because of the disorganizing and other adverse effects of agonal struggles on the structure of organisms, it is desirable to anesthetize or narcotize animals before removing tissue or before immersing the animal in fixative. A particularly good example of the need for preliminary narcosis may usually be seen in prepared slides of cross sections of earthworms. These commonly show the longitudinal muscle layer in an injured condition: the cells look frayed and resemble small feathers. But if the worm is first immersed in weak alcohol (2–5% in tap water) until it relaxes and is then properly fixed, the preparations will show muscle cells smooth in outline and undistorted.

The temperature during the period of fixation is sometimes important. For most purposes room temperature is suitable, but heated or cooled solutions may be used for small, contractile animals such as hydra and some protozoa. Occasionally the hot or cold solutions are used to fix very thin blocks of tissue. There is an increasing tendency among histochemists to specify fixation at low temperatures. This retards the rate of penetration but tends to preserve cell products or organelles which might otherwise disappear before the fixative reaches all parts of the specimen.

The duration of application of a fixative may be unimportant or critical. Specimens put in 10% formalin may be left overnight or several weeks. This is also true of Bouin's PFA. But for Fleming's fluid, the period should be no longer than 24 hours, and for Zenker's, no longer than 18 hours.

One of the requirements of good fixation is that it be applied to the material while it is still living or as soon as possible postmortem. It is therefore particularly necessary that before anesthetization all reagents and equipment be assembled in good order. Nothing facilitates rapid work more surely than adequate preparation.

As soon as the animal is well anesthetized or killed it should be dissected both rapidly and carefully. If the organs to be removed include the alimentary canal, it may be dealt with first, since its mucous membrane soon begins to undergo autolysis.

The organs should be fixed *in situ,* if the animal is small. Parts must be excised with great care from a larger animal; they are rinsed in normal saline and transferred at once to an adequate quantity of the fixing solution, which is changed at least once during the period of fixation. The pieces of tissue should not be large: 5-mm cubes and even thinner slices are adequate for many purposes. Since they should be surrounded on all sides by the fixative, it is well to support the specimens above the bottom of the container (E–76–80).

A convenient method of keeping specimens labeled is to write the necessary information for each with pencil or India ink on one end of a small slip of heavy paper, put the specimen on the unlabeled end in a flat dish, and add enough fixative to completely cover it. In a few minutes the tissue should adhere to the paper which may then be put in a bag of cheesecloth or in one of the various types of tissue carriers. Whether or not the specimen is so attached, the label should accompany it.

Hollow organs are conveniently filled with the fixer as well as being immersed in it. For example, the urinary bladder may be distended with fixative, its neck and ureters tied off, and the organ transferred to a container of the fixing fluid. The gut is better treated by irrigating it with normal saline to remove its contents and cutting it into short lengths which are dropped into the fixative; or a segment of the alimentary canal may be slit lengthwise and pinned with plant thorns to a flat sheet of cork which is floated, specimen side down, on the fixative. A stomach may be ligated beyond the pyloric sphincter, filled with fixative, the esophagus tied off, and the whole transferred to the fixative.

If particularly careful fixation is essential, the anesthetized animal may be perfused with normal saline and then with fixative (III–10–12).

The technician should carefully note the specified duration of application for the fixative used and, if the time is critical, should avoid exceeding it. If there is a little latitude allowed and if there is plenty of tissue available, it is desirable to try time variations. For instance, if 4–12 hours are suggested, 4, 6, 8, 10, and 12 might all be tried.

SPECIFIC DIRECTIONS FOR LARGE ANIMALS

Anesthetization

III–1. HYPOTHERMIA. Reactions to anesthesia are not uniform from one species to another. It is often necessary to make several tests before finding the most suitable agent and dosage. A good method to try first is hypothermia, because it is effective for many animals. G. H. Parker (*243*) recommended that fishes, amphibians, and reptiles be placed in water and cracked ice, or simply in cracked ice, 10–15 minutes. They are also kept cold during dissection and removal of tissues.

III–2. COLD NARCOSIS FOLLOWING ANESTHESIA is described by van Breeman and Marx (*314*). They point out that, in addition to other advantages such as reduction of muscle contraction, chilling reduces enzyme activity, hence, autolysis. Their procedures for a large animal such as a dog follow:
1. Induce light ether anesthesia to inhibit movement and place the specimen in an ice-water bath. As cold narcosis increases, discontinue the ether and allow the animal to breathe air or oxygen. If necessary, use a respirator.
2. Remove the animal from the bath when its temperature reaches 20–18°C and while respiration and heart action are normal.
3. Dissect and place specimens in fixative at 18–20°C. Smaller mammals may be treated in the same manner or allowed to remain in the water bath until breathing and heart beats have just ceased or until their temperature has reached 5–0°C.

III–3. THE SODIUM AMYTAL TECHNIC of Nicholas and Barron (*236*) for anesthetizing rats is very good.
1. Provide 10 ml of a 10% aq sol of Sodium Amytal (R–180). This is stable for 7–10 days.
2. Weigh the rat and calculate the required dosage by the following formulae:
    a. for all females and for immature males, 10 mg/100 g body weight;
    b. for maturing males, 15 mg/100 g;
    c. for adult males, 20 mg/100 g.
3. Using a luer tuberculin syringe with 0.01 ml graduations, inject the required amount subcutaneously.
4. Determine when deep anesthesia is reached by noting increase in the rate of heart beat, rise in blood pressure, and disappearance of eye reflex. These will occur in 15–20 minutes. Dissect and re-

move the desired tissues. If the anesthetized animal is still living when the necessary material has been removed, kill it by opening a large artery.

III–4. ANESTHESIA FOR CERTAIN LARGE INSECTS. For many insects, a type of self-anesthesia may be used; we have applied it particularly to *Periplaneta* sp. and other Orthoptera.

1. Place one or more specimens in a wide-mouth bottle and cover its top with gauze. Fill the bottle completely with water or with insect saline (F–180) and cork.
2. When the insect ceases to struggle and has been under water at least 30 minutes, remove it, place in saline, and dissect.

If there is some sign of returning movement, add to the saline a small amount of club soda or carbon dioxide gas from a small capsule. The anesthesia results from an accumulation of carbon dioxide in the trachea, since the spiracles close when the insect is submerged. This method is useful not only for removal of tissues for fixation, but also for studying peristalsis and other physiological processes.

Killing

If little dissection is required to remove the desired parts, it is often as satisfactory to kill an animal, by a suitable technic, as to anesthetize it.

III–5. WITH ETHER OR CHLOROFORM. Gunthorp (*138*) gives a simple method for killing cats by anesthesia:

1. Select a bell jar just large enough to cover the animal and with a bottle-like top whose opening is not more than 1 inch in diameter and at least 1 inch long.
2. Cover the cat with the bell jar and wrap a moist towel around the base to reduce the entrance of air.
3. Pour into the top a small quantity of ether or chloroform, letting it run down the inner surface of the neck from which it spreads in a thin film over the sides of the bell jar and evaporates into the chamber almost immediately. Stopper the jar top at once with a cork. The animal dies very quickly.

III–6. WITH DRY ICE. One of the most humane methods of killing mammals is also the easiest, if dry ice is available. For a mouse, put a small cube of dry ice in the bottom of a deep jar; cover and allow the vapor to accumulate for a minute. Lower the mouse to the bottom. It dies almost at once and with no evidence of distress.

III–7. WITH ILLUMINATING GAS. Work in a well-ventilated room or under a hood with no open flame near. Confine the animal in a large glass jar with a lid; a gallon jar is suitable for small mammals. Run in a piece of soft rubber tubing attached to a gas jet, with its delivery tip touching the bottom of the jar. Compress it as little as possible between jar and lid and turn on the gas. When the animal shows clearly that the gas is taking effect, close the jar after withdrawing the tube. Remove it from the jar when it appears to be dead. It is always a good precaution to saturate a piece of gauze with ether and keep it at hand in a closed jar to be used if the animal shows some signs of life.

Dissection and Fixation

III–8. A MALE FROG PROVIDES SEVERAL SPECIMENS. *Supplies:* Dissection instruments including sharp, small scissors, straight and curved forceps, a narrow section lifter, and needles; a luer syringe with an 18-gauge needle; a dissecting board with pins and/or retractors; frog saline (F–180); jars with straight sides and broad bases for fixatives; syracuse watch glasses; labels carrying the name of each part and the fixative to be used in each jar; bottles of the following fixatives: 10% formalin, Gilson's fluid, Bouin's PFA, PFA$_3$, Perenyi's fluid, Zenker's fluid (*see* formulae, Appendix III).

1. Anesthetize the frog with Chloretone (II–8) or with urethane (II–9). When it is well relaxed lay it, ventral side down, on the board; put a forefinger in its mouth under an eye; push enough to cause the eye to protrude. With sharp scissors, sever the oculomotor muscles and the optic nerve and place the freed eye in saline; make a small opening in it through the sclera, transfer it at once to Perenyi's fluid, place the appropriate label in the jar and cover it.

2. Tie the frog to a dissecting board (E–7), ventral side up. Open the abdominal cavity with an incision to one side of the midline. Remove a segment of the duodenum, rinse it in saline, and cut it longitudinally in two pieces; affix each piece to a thin sheet of cork, serosa side down, preferably with sharp thorns (E–74) rather than metal pins. Place one piece in Bouin's PFA and the other in Gilson's fluid. Change both fluids in 1 hour.

3. Dissect out a portion of the pancreas; lay it flat, but without stretching, on a small piece of bibulous paper in a syracuse watch glass and drop on Zenker's fluid until the specimen is covered; then fill the dish. This should attach the specimen to the paper and make it easier to handle. After 30 minutes, transfer the specimen and paper to fresh fixative in a jar.

4. Remove a testis, rinse in saline, and immerse in PFA$_3$. At the end of 15 minutes, cut the testis transversely into two pieces for better penetration of fluid. Change to fresh fixative in 1 hour.

5.   Pass a metal cannula or large hypodermic needle with a blunt
     point from the cloaca into the urinary bladder and secure it firmly
     with a ligature which encircles the bladder neck. Attach to the
     needle a luer syringe filled with Bouin's PFA; distend the bladder
     with the fixative. Withdraw the needle gently and tighten the
     ligature. Keep the bladder surface moist with frog saline. After
     5–10 minutes, sever the bladder from the cloaca and remove it to
     a container of the same fixative.

6.   Remove one kidney, dissecting it out with care; rinse in saline
     and lay it on bibulous paper in a syracuse watch glass. Pipet on
     10% formalin until the specimen is covered. In not less than 15
     minutes cut the kidney transversely into 3 pieces, with a sharp
     razor blade, and transfer the pieces to a fresh dish of 10%-for-
     malin.

7.   In the meantime, pipet Gilson's fluid on to the other kidney, cover-
     ing the adrenal gland. Remove this kidney to a dish filled with
     Gilson's fluid and in about an hour dissect off the adrenal and
     transfer it to a jar of fresh fixative.

III–9.   POST-FIXATION TREATMENT for specimens fixed in III–8.

1.   Eye in Perenyi's fluid: After 4 or 5 hours of fixation, wash in water
     and transfer to 30% alcohol and then to 50% alcohol, 1 hour in
     each; store in 70% alcohol.

2.   Duodenum in PFA: After 24 or more hours up to several weeks
     in fixative, store in 10% formalin; or wash briefly in water, transfer
     to 50% alcohol, 2–4 hours, and store in 70% alcohol.
     Duodeum in Gilson's fluid: After 12 hours to several days in fixa-
     tive, wash briefly in water; store in Cellosolve. Complete dehydra-
     tion later in Cellosolve.

3.   Pancreas in Zenker's fluid: After 2–4 hours wash briefly in water,
     then in 70% alcohol, several changes; store in alcohol of the same
     grade. Complete dehydration in Cellosolve to remove mercuric
     chloride.

4.   Testis in PFA_3: The specimen should remain at least 24 hours in
     fixative. Then transfer to 30% and 50% alcohol for a short period,
     10–15 minutes; store in 70% alcohol; or transfer directly to
     triethyl phosphate for storage.

5.   Bladder in PFA: Release the ligature; cut the bladder in strips
     and treat these as in step 4.

6.   Kidney in 10% formalin: After at least 24 hours, change to a
     fresh solution of 10% formalin for storage until ready to prepare.

7.   Adrenal in Gilson's fluid: Fix for a minimum of 4 hours; over-
     fixation does no harm. Rinse briefly in water; store in Cellosolve.

Fixation by Perfusion

III–10. METHOD OF ALLEN (6) for the injection of an adult white rat.

Equipment: A funnel held by a retort stand 60–70 cm above the laboratory bench where the injection will be done; a rubber tube with a screw clamp connecting the stem of the funnel to a cannula; a heating pad, without its fabric cover, placed under a cooky sheet (E–16) of appropriate size; several cannulae (E–10) of various sizes; a heating device which will keep fluids at about 45°C; dissecting instruments.

Reagents: Normal saline and fixative at 40–45°C.

1. Test the equipment: put saline in the funnel and allow it to flow through the cannula until there are no air bubbles in the system; warm the heating pad to body temperature; if an extra experimental animal is available, follow the procedures in steps 3, 4, and 5 to determine the proper size of cannula.
2. Anesthetize the rat lightly (III–3); tie the hind legs together and the front legs behind the back.
3. Open the abdominal and chest cavities; avoid cutting the internal mammary arteries. Remove the left side of the diaphragm and, if necessary, the ventral ends of the ribs to provide a large enough opening in which to work.
4. If the entire animal, except the lungs, is to be preserved, place a large cannula in the left ventricle and open the right auricle; if only the posterior part of the body is to be fixed, place the cannula in the thoracic aorta and open the posterior vena cava. Open the screw clamp slightly and let the saline flow through the circulatory system until the liver becomes pale; this indicates that the blood is almost washed out. Close the clamp, place the desired fixative in the funnel, and continue perfusion until about 100 ml of the fixative has been used.
5. After perfusion is completed, remove the parts desired and place in fresh fixative. Cut large organs such as the kidney and testis into several slices after they have been in the fixative 30 minutes. Transfer them to fresh fixative.

III–11. METHOD OF KOENIG, GROAT, AND WINDLE (177).

This method was designed particularly for fixation of the central nervous system, but is also useful for other tissues which must be fixed with a minimum of distortion. It is designed to prevent, as far as possible, injuries due to changes in hydrostatic pressure in the capillaries of the animal.

The general preparations for the operations are similar to those for Allen's method. The saline and fixative, (F–179 and F–93), are placed in reservoir bottles connected by rubber tubes with clamps to a Y-tube joining them with the tube to which the cannula is attached. If the animal to be fixed is a guinea pig, the reservoir bottles should be 82–90 cm above the animal. For cats and monkeys, the height should be about 156 cm. These heights provide pressures equivalent to the mean arterial pressures of the animals.

1. Make an incision in the wall of the right auricle; place the cannula in the ascending aorta through an incision in the left ventricle.
2. Open the clamp on the saline reservoir tube; continue the perfusion until the fluid escaping from the right auricle is free of blood.
3. Perfuse with fixative until the muscles are stiffened.
4. When perfusion is completed, remove brain and other desired parts to 10% formalin containing 0.9% sodium chloride; leave overnight or longer.

The success of this method in preventing edema of the tissues may be tested by weighing the animal before and after perfusion. There should be little alteration in weight. The authors record a change of about 2%.

III–12.   HAUSHALTER AND BERTRAM'S (150) PULSATING PERFUSION METHOD for fixing the central nervous system is warmly recommended by several competent neurological workers. They point out that the pulsation dislodges small clots which might otherwise interfere with the free flow of fluids through the tissues, and that by perfusion all parts of the brain are quickly preserved. The essential feature of their method is that the perfusion occurs at a pressure and rate about equal to the arterial pressure and pulse rate of the animal.

Solutions: Normal saline-acacia (F–179) and formol-saline-acacia (F–93).
Equipment: Pulsator in cannula line; 2 reservoir bottles at a height to provide proper pressure, both connected by a Y-tube (with clamps) to the cannula tube.

1. Administer deep anesthesia (or a lethal dose of ether). Cannulate the arch of the aorta through an incision in the left ventricle. Provide an exit for escaping fluid by making an opening in the right auricle.
2. Exsanguinate and wash out the circulatory system with the saline-acacia.
3. Perfuse with formol-saline-acacia until the brain is properly hardened.
4. When perfusion is completed, dissect out the brain and spinal cord and transfer to 10% formalin.

If equipment for pulsating perfusion is not available, the usual methods of perfusion can be followed with a preliminary injection of heparin as an anticoagulant and of sodium nitrite as a vasodilator. Pulsation can be simulated by regular interruptions of the flow of fluid.

FIXATION OF SMALL WHOLE ANIMALS

III–13. PARAMECIA IN LARGE NUMBERS may be fixed without discharge of trichocysts by the method cited by Wichterman (334, from 58).

1. Strain 150–200 ml of a rich culture of paramecia through 4 thicknesses of handkerchief linen into a finger bowl. Add 6–12 drops of ethanol to the edges of the culture.
2. Put the finger bowl in a refrigerator freezing unit for about 10 minutes; add 6–12 drops of ethanol and return to the unit.
3. After 10 minutes repeat the addition of alcohol and leave in the freezing unit; examination of the culture with a dissecting microscope shows that the paramecia are nearly immobilized.
4. Rotate the finger bowl with a gentle steady motion, under the microscope, until the specimens are concentrated in its center. Remove them with a pipet, discharging them into 100 ml of 50% alcohol of the same temperature as the culture. Continue to remove the paramecia thus, rotating the dish when necessary, until most of them have been collected.
6. After about 5–10 minutes, add 100 ml of PFA or other fixative. Let the specimens settle and withdraw enough fixative to leave a concentrated suspension.

III–14. SMALL NUMBERS OF PARAMECIA or other protozoa may be fixed as follows:
1. Smear a cover glass of appropriate size with Mayer's albumen (F–7) and add a drop of culture fluid and organisms.
2. Allow the fluid to evaporate until only a small quantity remains.
3. Lower the cover, specimen side down, on the fixative until it floats on the fluid.
4. When fixation is complete, usually 10–20 minutes, transfer the cover to washing fluid in a cover glass staining dish.

III–15. A SINGLE HYDRA may be fixed as follows: Place in a warm watch glass and leave it in only a few drops of water. When it has expanded, apply either corrosive-acetic (F–67) or Bouin's PFA at 80°C by squirting it into the watch glass so that it sweeps over the hydra from aboral to oral end. Then fill the watch glass with the hot fluid.

III–16. HYDRA IN LARGE NUMBERS may be fixed with little contraction.

1. Collect hydra in clean, shallow containers with enough filtered pond water to cover.
2. When they are attached and the bodies and tentacles are expanded, quickly dash on them about one-third as much PFA as there is pond water in the dish.
3. Replace the diluted fixative with full strength PFA, in the course of 10–15 minutes; leave the specimens in the latter several hours or overnight.
4. Remove the fixative and replace it with 50% alcohol; change as it becomes colored, until the hydra have lost their yellow tint.

III–17. HYDRA ATTACHED TO PLANTS

1. Select the parts of plants bearing the most hydra and immerse them in 0.1% Chloretone solution. Test for reactions to the touch of a needle and when they react only slightly, transfer the plants and hydra to a large dish of formalin-alcohol-acetic (FAA) (F–89), leaving 1 hour or overnight.
2. Transfer hydra and plants to 5% formalin, or remove the hydra and preserve them alone.
    Results: In an hour, several thousand hydra may be killed in a fairly extended condition.

POST-FIXATION TREATMENT

Washing is the process of removing the fixative. The fluid used depends on the composition of the fixative from which the material is taken; if it is an alcohol mixture, alcohol of suitable strength is used; if the fixative is aqueous, water is applied.

III–18. WASHING IN WATER may be a long process if some of the constituents of the fixative are relatively insoluble. The equipment used depends on the number of specimens or specimen containers to be treated. If there are only a few specimens, they may be tied in a square of cheesecloth and suspended by a string in a large container. Water is run in from a piece of tubing so placed that it discharges near the specimens.

It may be convenient to enclose the material to be washed in floating tissue carriers (E–76–78). If they are fixed in such carriers, they should remain in them. Following the use of mercury-containing fixatives, metallic carriers should be avoided. A large jar such as a gallon mayonnaise or pickle jar is filled with water; the specimens are placed, in their carriers, in the jar which is covered with a layer of cheesecloth firmly attached to its top by a rubber band. The jar is placed under a faucet from which a small stream is allowed to run into it and to wash its contents overnight. There are numerous methods of washing described in the literature, and ingenious students will contrive still others. The important feature is a slow and steady flow which continually replaces the water near the specimens.

III–19. WASHING AFTER NONAQUEOUS SOLUTIONS calls for different treatment, and is usually more simple. For example, if Carnoy's fluid has been used, it should be followed first by 2 baths of 95% alcohol, then by 70% alcohol. This brings the material quickly to a suitable storage fluid. Or, if a formalin-alcohol-acetic mixture was the fixer, the washing fluid should be alcohol of approximately the same concentration as in the fixative followed by transfer to 70% alcohol for storage. The fluid for washing is usually indicated in the recipe for each fixative.

III–20. REMOVAL OF MERCURIC CHLORIDE CRYSTALS. Since crystals of mercuric chloride may injure the specimens during sectioning, every endeavor should be made to remove them before infiltration. The classic method is to add enough Lugol's solution (F–132) to the alcohol series of dehydrators before storage to make each grade of alcohol a deep brown color. The iodine in turn must be completely removed before storing. The 70% or 80% grade should be changed until no traces of iodine color remain in the alcohol.

A second method has been proposed by González (*130*), who reports that when Cellosolve is used in the dehydrating schedule it removes all traces of the deposit. This method is satisfactory and much easier to use than iodine. It may follow the washing directly; specimens may be passed through several baths during 24 hours and then transferred directly to alcohol for storage or they may be cleared and infiltrated in paraffin.

If the tissue has not been treated before infiltration, the crystals may be removed from spread sections by a 10-minute bath in Cellosolve.

III–21. BLEACHING. It is sometimes desirable to bleach natural pigments in specimens and to remove too dense deposits of osmic acid. For natural pigments, such as melanin, 3% hydrogen peroxide will often serve. It may be applied to the block or to whole specimens, following washing.

Mayer's chlorine reagent (F–137) is also a good bleach. Since it is a solution in 70% alcohol, it should be used after the 50% solution in the dehydration series; it is best to suspend the specimen in the solution. The specimen is well washed afterward in 70% alcohol.

Both bleaches may be used on sections, where they act much more quickly than on blocks or whole specimens. They have some tendency to make the sections separate from the slide; this suggests that it is advisable to infiltrate in nitrocellulose most material which must be bleached, and to apply the bleach to unmounted sections.

STORAGE

Proper storage after fixation and post-fixation treatment involves keeping specimens in such a way that they will undergo no changes and that their labels will remain legible. It is as important to give careful attention to storage as to the steps which precede it.

III–22. STORAGE OF EMBEDDED BLOCKS. If the material is to be prepared for paraffin sectioning and if time is available, the best and safest method is to embed the specimens before storing them. Specimens well infiltrated with paraffin can be safely kept at suitable temperatures for long periods or can be shipped without danger of injury. Material embedded in nitrocellulose also stores well if the blocks are kept in 70–80% alcohol.

III–23. STORAGE IN FIXATIVES. A few fixatives are suitable for storage for extended periods. Among them are 10% neutral formalin, Bouin's PFA, Allen's B_3 modification of PFA, and Gilson's fluid. The convenience of fixation and storage in a single solution should be considered in choosing fixatives for collecting trips, when the time and labor saved thereby are important.

III–24. STORAGE IN ALCOHOL. The most common method of storage is to place the specimen(s), together with a properly made label, in containers with a generous amount of preserving fluid; this is usually 70–83% alcohol. The containers must be tightly stoppered. Sealing with molten paraffin helps to prevent evaporation.

Formerly glass containers such as shell vials were widely used and this is still a good method. It is satisfactory for material which does not occupy much space, or for numerous items of a similar nature, such as a complete series of developmental stages of the eggs of an echinoderm which have been dehydrated to 70% alcohol after fixation.

III–25. STORAGE IN SHELL VIALS WITHIN GLASS JARS. Select the proper number of shell vials (E–84) large enough to contain the specimens and at least 10 times their volume of alcohol. Press the label made with waterproof India ink, written side out, against the side of the vial, and with the end bent over its top; add the specimens in alcohol, and stopper with a plug of absorbent cotton, first dipped in alcohol. As each vial is filled, arrange it in proper order, label side out, in a wide-mouth mason jar an inch or more taller than the vials. Pack cotton loosely in the center to hold the vials upright, fill the jar to the brim with alcohol, apply a rubber ring, and screw down the top tightly. This is not a suitable arrangement for shipping, since the jars and the contents of the vials should remain undisturbed.

III–26. STORAGE IN PLASTIC CONTAINERS. Lightweight plastic containers for specimens should be seriously considered for storage; they are available in many sizes and shapes. The rigid plastic vials with polyethylene stoppers are particularly good; they may be sealed with paraffin to retard evaporation. See also E–13.

III–27. STORAGE IN GLASS CARTRIDGES with rubber stoppers at each end, that were made to contain dental procaine or Novocaine. This was recommended by Obrecht (239); Yunker (337) found them satisfactory for small specimens and supplied the name of a manufacturer who no longer makes them. The emptied cartridges can usually be obtained from dentists. They are particularly good containers for mites, fleas, lice, and other ectoparasites. Yunker used them on collecting trips and inserted the cartridges in blocks of Styrofoam in which he made holes deeper than the height of the vials; this provides excellent and lightweight protection in shipping if the vials are pushed to the bottom of the holes. It also provides storage space, in logical order, if the vials are placed so that one end projects above the surface of the block. The Styrofoam blocks are easily labeled.

When specimens are stored in liquid, they should be examined at intervals. If evaporation occurs, the fluid should be replaced.

CHAPTER IV

STAINS AND STAINING

Staining, in the broadest sense of the term, is the treatment of tissues and cells in such a way that their components become distinguishable by the colors they assume. Staining is usually accomplished by dyes, but for some purposes salts of metals are used. In histochemical methods the results of the chemical action may be demonstrable without special treatment. If they are not, they may be made visible by reagents which color or otherwise make apparent the end product of the reaction.

STAINING AGENTS

Dyes are the most commonly used of the staining agents, and will be considered first. In general, dyes are synthetic organic compounds, although there are some natural dyes in common use. Whether natural or synthetic, their suitability for a particular technic depends upon the methods by which they have been prepared. Unfortunately these methods are not always uniform or standardized and therefore different samples of dyes may vary in their effect upon the tissues, although they are used exactly according to directions. Because of this, one of the first steps in staining is to learn how to select and purchase reliable dyes.

CRITERIA FOR SELECTION OF DYES

Any specifications for a dye, provided in a given method, should be followed exactly; they may include:

    A.   Color index (C.I.) number(s);

    B.   Certification of the stain (C.C.) by the Biological Stain Commission;

    C.   Name of the manufacturer and the batch number of the stain used.

COLOR INDEX NUMBERS were first assigned in 1924, by the Society of Dyers and Colourists (292), to textile and biological dyes in general use. The numbers identify the dyes as possessing definite chemical and physical characteristics. There are now, unfortunately, two sets of numbers for the dyes which appeared in the first index. The original system did not permit the logical addition of new numbers as new dyes were introduced. A second and entirely new set of C.I. numbers, which does permit additions, has been assigned, and was published by this society and the American Textile Chemists in 1956 (*293*). These numbers supersede the old ones, but the older designations naturally appear in the literature published prior to 1956; both old and new numbers are often cited in catalogs of dealers, in directions for staining methods, and on the labels of bottles of dry stains. The older C.I. numbers run from one to four digits; the new ones are all of five digits; it is common usage to cite the older number first, in parentheses. The most recently developed stains may have no C.I. designation if assignment of numbers is still pending. In all cases if the directions specify the C.I. number, a dye bearing that number should be procured. Conn's book, *Biological Stains* (*73*), gives authoritative information on C.I. numbers, synonyms, composition, including chemical formula, and uses of biological stains as well as stain testing methods; all workers in microtechnic should have access to it. Gurr's *Encyclopedia of Microscopic Stains* (*141*) gives chemical formulae, solubilities in various reagents, and synonyms, but no C.I. numbers. It also is a valuable book for technicians.

COMMISSION CERTIFIED STAINS are those in common use which have been tested by the Biological Stain Commission both chemically and by application to appropriate biological materials. If their composition and performance are found to be satisfactory, they are certified for use. The containers of certified stains bear Commission Certified (C.C.) labels. Certified stains cost only slightly more than others. Certification is for a single batch of stain; the testing is repeated for each batch submitted by each manufacturer. Not all stains in common use are submitted by manufacturers for testing, nor are they necessarily certified after testing. But if Commission-certified stains are available, they should be used. Notice of certification of new batches of stain is published in *Stain Technology*.

SPECIFICATION OF STAIN BY NAME OF MANUFACTURER AND THE BATCH NUMBER may be valuable if the originator's directions for a staining technic included these data. If the technic is difficult and the originator's results cannot be repeated with other brands of the stain, it is worth considerable effort to obtain stain from the same batch.

SOURCES OF STAINS

NATURAL DYES are extracts from plants and animals. The list of those
in current use include indigo, saffron, brazilin, cochineal and its carmine derivatives, orcein, and hematoxylin. Of these, indigo, brazilin,
and untreated cochineal have found only limited application but the
others are of great importance. Hematoxylin, a purified extract of logwood, is one of the most commonly used stains in both histology and
cytology. Orcein, derived from lichens, is widely used in cytology. The
carmines have found extensive application. These last three stains are
primarily nuclear.

SYNTHETIC DYES are mostly anilines. There are perhaps sixty to
seventy in common use and a larger number available for special purposes. Generally textile dyes are not suited for biological staining without special treatment, but in recent years several have been found
excellent for certain purposes; chlorazol black E, C.I.No. (581) 30235,
is an example. Among the aniline dyes, there are a number of valuable
nuclear stains as well as numerous cytoplasmic stains and stains for intercellular substances.

METALS USED AS STAINS are generally applied as solutions of their
salts; some of these are silver nitrate, gold chloride, mercuric chloride,
and osmium tetroxide. They do not stain as dyes do but make deposits
of precipitates, which are often black, or very dark but are sometimes
colored. Staining methods with metals do not have wide application,
but some are essential in neurological technics and in the demonstration of certain characteristics of ciliate protozoa.

It is important, in procuring metallic salts for staining, to follow
recommendations exactly. None of them has a C.I. number, but specifications as to purity and type of compound are important. For example,
brown gold chloride is called for in some methods; in others, the yellow
salt is used.

SOLUBILITY OF STAINS. Some stains are soluble in a number of
reagents. Others dissolve in one reagent and only slightly, or not at all
in others. It is necessary to know dye solubilities, both to make up
solutions and to avoid passing stained tissue through reagents which
will dissolve the stain and impair the staining; or alternatively to know
what reagents will decolorize overstained slides.

STAINING PROCEDURES

The application of stain may be before or after the death of the animal. It is usually after death and preservation, i.e., postmortem, but it is also possible, by using relatively nontoxic dyes, to stain living cells and intercellular substances.

VITAL OR *INTRAVITAM* STAINING is accomplished if the stain is injected into an animal or ingested by it. For example, cells of the reticuloendothelial system become intensely colored when they phagocytose and store colloidal carbon or toluidine blue with which the experimental animal has been injected. The calcifying bones of a young animal are stained red if it is fed alizarin red S. Embryos may be stained by surface applications of vital dyes and the development of the dyed areas followed. Injection of certain aniline dyes will stain selectively some kinds of intercellular substance of connective tissue.

SUPRAVITAL STAINING is the term used when stain is applied to cells removed from the body but living *in vitro*. Leucocytes exposed to Janus green B and neutral red and kept at normal temperatures on slides exhibit supravitally stained mitochondria and neutral red granules. Both vital and supravital staining are useful adjuncts to the more common staining technics.

POSTMORTEM STAINING methods are numerous and diverse but may be classified according to whether staining is done before or after sectioning. Staining after sectioning may be done before or after the sections are mounted on slides. It is most often the only feasible method, but in some technics is neither necessary nor possible. Staining before sectioning, usually called *in toto* or in block staining, is essential in some neurological technics and inevitable when making whole preparations. It is desirable in other cases such as in preparing serial sections of embryos (XI–13) and decalcified bone (X–9). Since *in toto* staining is both timesaving and satisfactory, its use should be considered whenever recommended or suggested.

APPLICATION OF STAIN may be progressive; in this method material is placed in the staining solution until the proper depth of color is reached; the process is then stopped. In regressive staining, specimens are overstained and the excess extracted by a differentiator, which is usually the solvent or the mordant of the stain. Some stains are always applied regressively; for instance, in the Heidenhain hematoxylin technic, the material is overstained in hematoxylin and then differentiated, usually in the mordant, an iron alum solution. But other stains may be used either progressively or regressively according to the end desired or to the preference of the technician. This is true of many of the alum hematoxylin mixtures.

STAINING WITH AND WITHOUT MORDANTS. If there is a strong chemical affinity between a cell or tissue part and a dye, the dye may be applied to the tissue directly and staining will result. For example, granules in certain white blood cells, the eosinophiles, stain brilliantly when placed in a solution of eosin. When the affinity is weak, an intermediate substance, a mordant, which will unite both with the tissue and the dye, is applied to the specimen before the stain. For Heidenhain's hematoxylin, the mordant is iron alum; sections are placed in a weak solution of the mordant, the excess is removed by rinsing, and the slide is transferred to hematoxylin. Under this treatment the nuclei, which scarcely stain with the hematoxylin alone, color deeply after the bath in iron alum.

SINGLE AND MULTIPLE STAINS. For whole preparations, one dye, or at most two, is used. A flatworm may, for example, be stained with Grenacher's borax-carmine, which brings out its internal organs clearly, and is then subjected to indulin which makes its external parts very plain. Sections also may have a single stain, or two or more. Some of the triple and quadruple stains are very useful. Usually the stains are applied in succession, but there are some mixtures of more than one stain in a single solution.

STAINING FOR NEW METHODS OF MICROSCOPY. New types of optical instruments such as fluorescence and phase microscopes have called for new kinds of stains. Although the methods themselves are outside the scope of this book, they should at least be mentioned. Tissue and cell parts which are not auto-fluorescent can be treated with fluorescent dyes and will then be visible when studied with a fluorescence microscope.

With phase microscopes, many cellular details may be observed in unstained materials, but some may be clearer and more easily observed when the preparation is lightly stained with certain dyes.

CHAPTER V

NONSECTION METHODS

It is often desirable to study small animals or parts of larger animals, eggs, embryos, and cells as whole objects rather than in sections. Whenever the material is of such a nature that whole preparations are feasible, they may be valuable supplements to sections of the same material, or may make sections unnecessary. In some studies, particularly the analysis of chromosome complements, the nonsection preparations at present seem to be displacing section methods. Whole preparations may often be made more easily and quickly than sections.

There are many types of nonsection methods. They include the preparation of whole animals such as protozoa, flatworms, and nematodes, in which a disturbance of the normal relationship of all parts is carefully avoided; the separation of tissue into single cells; the spreading of loosely aggregated cell masses into a single layer of cells; the stretching of thin membranes into flat sheets; and the separation of a mass of fibrous tissue into its constituent fibers.

Whole preparations require a considerable variety of technics. This chapter describes some of those most generally used and gives references to the literature for information on less common ones. Those which pertain entirely to a field such as cytology, embryology, or histology are generally only referred to here; the specific methods are described in the appropriate chapters.

SMEARS, SQUASHES, PRINTS, AND SPREADS

SMEARS. If the material to be prepared is a liquid such as blood, it may be spread into a thin film in which the cells do not overlap. It is then fixed, stained, and mounted. Smears are made of blood and of blood-containing parasites, of coelomic, cerebrospinal, and ascitic fluids and of various exudates. The preparation of blood smears is described in VIII–13.

V–1. SMEARS OF COELOMIC FLUID OF EARTHWORMS.

1. Expose large earthworms to chloroform vapor 1–2 minutes. Coelomic fluid will usually exude through the dorsal pores. If it is not

produced in sufficient quantity, make a dorsal incision to the right of the dorsal vessel for a larger supply.

2. Collect the fluid on one cover glass, place a second one over the first with the edges not quite approximated, and pull the covers apart horizontally. Air-dry the two smears.
3. Stain with Giemsa's stain (VIII–16).
4. Mount the dry smears, specimen side down, on slides in xylene-resin.

SQUASHES are made of material relatively soft in consistency; they show cellular detail but not tissue architecture; they are indispensable for chromosome analysis. Because the relationships of cells to each other are disturbed, the squashes are usually supplemented by sections. At present the tissues most commonly prepared by squashing are certain parts of the nervous system, bone marrow, lymph nodes, soft tumors, seminiferous tubules, and the salivary glands of larvae of a few genera of Diptera.

V–2. EPITHELIAL CELL SQUASH.
1. Scrape the inside of the cheek gently with a clean toothpick or a sterile scalpel.
2. Place the material thus collected on a cover; drop another cover of the same size upon it, with the edges not quite approximated; press the upper cover gently with the eraser end of a pencil to make an even spread.
3. Quickly pull the covers apart horizontally, and air-dry with the specimen side up.
4. Stain in Wright's stain (VIII–15), dry, and mount in xylene-resin.

V–3. SPINAL CORD SQUASH.
1. Secure from an abattoir, as soon after death as possible, the spinal cord of a beef animal. Cut small segments from it.
2. From the ventral horn, take a small bit of gray matter, put it on a cover, place a second one above it, and press firmly but carefully upon the upper cover with the eraser on the end of a pencil; this squashes the soft tissue into a thin film. Slide the covers apart and air-dry at once, or dip into 95% alcohol for a moment before drying.
3. Stain in 1% aq sol of methylene blue, 2–3 minutes; or use any other dye suitable for demonstrating Nissl substance (p. 117); determine the correct staining time by microscopic inspection.
4. Wash well in tap water, air-dry, and mount in synthetic resin.

Results: The neuroglia and the large motor neurons are both stained;

many neurons show relatively long attached processes. The Nissl substance is deeply colored, and neurofibrillae are usually visible. The nucleolus is prominent, but the nuclear membrane is sometimes difficult to see.

V–4. SALIVARY GLAND CHROMOSOMES OF DROSOPHILA (*166*) are usually studied in squashes. Jump's method is an early one and simple. The preparation is permanent.

1. Select large, fat *Drosophila* larvae which have crawled up the side of the culture jar preparatory to pupation.
2. Place a larva on a slide upon which egg albumen (F–7) has been thinly smeared and dried.
3. Drop insect saline (F–180) on the larva; decapitate by holding the head with one pair of fine forceps and the posterior part of the body with another pair, pulling gently on the head which, with a part of the gut and the salivary glands, will separate from the body. Dissect the glands free from the gut and other tissue, leaving only the glands on the slide.
4. Remove saline from the slide with bibulous paper; put the slide on supports in a petri dish and drop on aceto-orcein (F–2); cover and leave 10–20 minutes.
5. Lower a cover on the glands and press carefully upon it with a pencil eraser so as to crush the glands and to separate the chromosomes in their cells. Examine microscopically and, if the chromosomes are not well separated, repeat the pressure somewhat more firmly.
6. When the chromosomes are well spread, place the preparation in a staining jar containing 95% ethanol in sufficient quantity to bring its surface just slightly above the lower edge of the cover glass. Leave the slide about 1 hour or until the alcohol has reached all parts of the preparation.
7. Remove the cover; the glands should adhere to the slide.
8. Dehydrate in fresh 95% ethanol, one or more changes, or in butanol; clear in xylene and mount in synthetic resin.

The glands may be treated with aceto-carmine (F–1) instead of aceto-orcein. In this case, make all manipulations with glass instruments or with metal instruments coated with paraffin.

For other methods of squashing and cytological technics for germ cells, see chapter XII.

PRINTS. Soft organs and tissues such as spleen, liver, bone marrow, and lymph nodes will give accurate pictures of their cells and even of cell arrangement if prints are made of them.

V–5. LIVER PRINTS, *Necturus.*
1.   Cut a small block from the tip of a liver lobe; holding it with forceps, press the smooth, cut surface lightly on a clean slide or, preferably, a rectangular cover glass. Lift the specimen and repeat, making a series of prints in a straight line and in serial order as long as a clear impression results. Air-dry and fix with 95% ethanol or methanol.
2.   If several preparations are required, cut off the used surface or take a fresh block of the material and repeat the printing.
3.   Stain with Wright's, Giemsa's, or Kingsley's stain (VIII–15,16,19), or use Peary's method for aceto-orcein staining of prints (V–6).
Results: Both the border of hemapoietic tissue and liver cells are well demonstrated.

V–6. PEARY (*248*) has adapted the methods of Blank *et al.* (*40*) to the staining of prints in aceto-orcein. He recommends it for staining prints of glandular organs, of tumor tissues, and of bone marrow. It can also be applied to smears of bone marrow and of ascitic and other body fluids.
1.   Have ready a mixture of equal parts of anhydrous acetone and absolute alcohol in staining jars. If smears or prints are to be made on covers, use Columbia jars or other cover glass staining equipment (E–23). Place the jars in insulated containers with dry ice (R–24). The temperature should be −20°C or lower.
2.   Make prints or smears on chemically clean slides or covers.
3.   Place in aceto-orcein (F–2), 5 minutes at 60°C or 10 minutes at room temperature.
4.   Rinse in water, 30 seconds, and drain briefly.
5.   Place in the chilled acetone-alcohol and keep in an icebox for 24 hours.
6.   Differentiate 30 seconds in 1% hydrochloric acid in 95% alcohol, if necessary.
7.   Counterstain in 0.01% fast green in alcohol for 10 seconds only.
8.   Place in *n*-butanol until slides or covers reach room temperature.
9.   Clear in xylene and mount in synthetic resin.
Results: Chromosomes, dark purple to black; interphase nuclei, red; cytoplasm, pale green. There is good definition of nuclear elements.
   This is an excellent and rapid technic to use if it is not necessary to study the material in temporary mounts.

V–7. SERUM-FILM TECHNIC FOR BONE MARROW. An alternative to smear or print technics for bone marrow has been devised by

Harris (*147*). It prevents the excessive damage to cells sometimes caused by smears or squashes.

1.   Anesthetize a guinea pig with ether; open the abdomen, expose the inferior vena cava, divide the vein, and partially exsanguinate the animal without killing it. Collect the blood, centrifuge it, and remove the serum.

2.   When the serum has been obtained, remove the humerus and cut off the ends of the bone. Expose the marrow cavity with bone-cutting forceps and remove the marrow by loosening its endosteal attachment with a fine needle.

3.   Place enough of the marrow in the autogenous serum to make about a 1:20 mixture, and suspend by shaking the tube in a mechanical shaker.

4.   Place a drop of autogenous serum on one end of a chemically clean slide and spread it with a similar slide.

5.   Before the serum dries, place a large drop of the marrow suspension in the center of the slide with a Pasteur or other capillary pipet. Allow it to spread by capillary attraction until it covers an area of about 15 mm.

6.   Spread the drop further by blowing gently and continuously until there is a dry central portion about 2 cm in diameter; the margin will be moist. The dry area is the useful part; remove the margin with filter paper.

7.   Stain with a blood stain. Harris used MacNeal's tetrachrome (F–134).

Results: The number of damaged cells is small and all cells show superior morphological detail.

V–8. SPREADS OR STRETCH PREPARATIONS. Thin membranes, stretched into flat sheets of tissue, are called spreads or stretches. Those made from mesenteries show cellular details of the loose connective tissue between the two layers of peritoneum and may also be stained with silver to show the epithelial cell outlines. Stretches of amnion can be stained to demonstrate the presence or absence of sex chromatin in metabolic cells. These preparations are most easily made with pairs of rings, one fitting inside the other (E–57). If rings are not available, the membrane may be stretched over the end of a short glass tube with a flanged top.

After fixation is completed the membrane is kept on the rings or tube during all subsequent processes and is removed for mounting only after it has been cleared. See XII–11,C for the method of staining amnion for sex chromatin masses, and VII–7 for methods to demonstrate the connective tissue of the peritoneum.

MACERATION AND DISSOCIATION METHODS

When it is necessary to study the shape of whole cells or of intercellular fibers in organized tissues, a macerating or dissociation fluid is applied. When skeletal parts covered by muscle or epithelium are to be studied, the fluid used is generally a corrosive mixture. There are many suitable solutions which macerate and dissociate. Most aqueous fixatives, diluted with 9 parts of water, will serve. Those cited in the directions below are suitable for many types of tissue. They do not preserve cytological details well, and the cells may supply incomplete information. Nevertheless, slides of macerated tissues are valuable and are often the only means of determining cell form. They should be supplemented by other types of preparations.

V–9.   MACERATION OF EPITHELIUM.

1.   Kill a frog and remove the posterior portion of the lining of the roof of the mouth. Cut it into pieces not more than 2 mm wide.

2.   Place the specimens in a stoppered vial in Gage's formalin dissociator (F–94) at room temperature, 24–48 hours. Shake the vial at intervals.

3.   Scrape the epithelial cells from the pieces of tissue with a scalpel and mount a portion of them in water on a slide. Apply a cover glass, preferably of unbreakable plastic, and examine.

4.   Separate the cell masses by tapping gently on the cover with the eraser of a pencil or the wooden handle of a needle. If maceration is not complete, put the material in a fresh lot of dissociator for another 24 hours.

5.   Remove the dissociator with bibulous paper and replace with water. Stain in Harris' hematoxylin, running the stain in under the cover at one side and withdrawing water from the opposite side with a slip of bibulous paper. Leave the slide on the microscope stage and observe the progress of staining. When the cells are well stained, withdraw the hematoxylin and replace with tap water.

6.   Dehydrate with Cellosolve, making several changes by adding and withdrawing fluids as before.

7.   Clear in terpineol (R–188), at least two changes; remove the terpineol and run xylene-resin under the cover.

Results: Cell outlines and nuclei are clearly defined; distribution of cells may be uneven.

   If more than one or two slides of epithelial cells are to be prepared, use V–12 for staining and subsequent steps.

V–10. MACERATION OF MUSCLE.

1. Macerate small bits of fresh smooth or striated muscle in a vial containing 20% aq sol of nitric acid or in F–138, 24–72 hours. At intervals after the first day, shake the vial; observe the progress of maceration under the microscope. When the cells begin to separate, remove the acid solution with a pipet and replace it with water, rinsing several times.
2. Stain in alum cochineal (F–13) or Harris' hematoxylin (F–16) until nuclei are deeply stained. Rinse in water. If the cells are not well separated, tease the tissue (V–11).
3. Dehydrate in Cellosolve, 3 changes.
4. Clear in xylene or terpineol, and mount in xylene-resin.
   An alternative method after hematoxylin staining is
3a. Dehydrate to 70% alcohol.
4a. Add about 5% of glycerol to the alcohol and place in an oven for several hours at about 40°C to evaporate the alcohol.
5. Mount by the method of Mitchell and Cook (V–21).

V–11. TEASING is a method applicable to cells and intercellular material of a fibrous character. Smooth and striated muscle, some neurons, tendons, and ligaments give good results. It is usually easier to tease tissues after they have been subjected to macerating fluids. After partial maceration and thorough washing, the material may be stained before teasing in Darrow red (F–71, 72) or Harris' hematoxylin (F–16).

1. Place the strips of tissue on a glass slide in macerating fluid; place the slide on the stage of a dissecting microscope. Use direct light and a white background if the material is stained; a black background if it is unstained.
2. With a pair of fine needles separate each bit into units, stroking delicately and carefully in a direction parallel with the long axis of the fibers.
3. When enough cells or fibers have been separated, remove unwanted material, cover, and stain on the slide following V–9, steps 5, 6, and 7 if the tissue has not been previously stained; follow V–9, steps 6 and 7, if it has been stained.

Results: Although not all of the muscle cells will be separate, enough should be isolated to indicate the cell outlines plainly. Striated muscle cells which are partially fragmented are especially useful to show the myofibrillae and their cross markings.

V–12. PREPARATION IN BULK BY CENTRIFUGING. If macerated and teased preparations are to be made in quantity, the staining and subsequent steps may be conveniently performed with the aid of a centrifuge. This is also a useful method for small metazoa, some protozoa, and for small marine invertebrate eggs and embryos. Material is transferred to a centrifuge tube after appropriate initial treatment; the reagents are then applied, in proper succession, for the required periods. At the end of each application, the tube is centrifuged at a low speed just long enough to throw down the cells. The supernatant is removed with a fine-tip pipet, the next reagent added, and the cells resuspended by shaking, or with a stream of fluid from the pipet. The process is repeated until the specimen is in the reagent in which it is to be mounted. This method, when applicable, is a good one. It saves time, also, especially when enough material is being prepared for class use.

If the specimens are so delicate as to be injured by this method or if a centrifuge is not available, the process may be carried out in a small glass dish with a rounded bottom such as an old-fashioned salt cellar (E–11) which is rotated by hand in such a way as to collect the specimens in a central concavity.

SCHEDULE FOR CENTRIFUGE PREPARATION of epithelial or muscle cells which have been previously macerated in an aqueous fluid. (Remove the supernatant each time after centrifuging.)
1.   Transfer cells in as little fluid as possible to a 5-ml centrifuge tube; fill the tube with water; centrifuge; resuspend in water; repeat twice.
2.   Suspend the cells in a suitable aqueous stain such as Harris' hematoxylin. Remove some of the cells at intervals, and examine for depth of staining; when this is satisfactory, centrifuge. Suspend in tap water, spin down, rinse in a second bath of tap water, and centrifuge again.
3.   Suspend in Cellosolve; spin down and repeat twice at intervals of 5–10 minutes or longer.
4.   Suspend in xylene-Cellosolve 1:1/vol and centrifuge.
5.   Suspend in xylene; centrifuge. Repeat twice.
6.   Transfer the now cleared cells to fresh xylene in a small covered dish. Add 2–5 ml of xylene-resin, a few drops at a time, mixing after each addition. Put the dish under a bell jar with its cover slightly raised until enough xylene has evaporated to make the solution of proper viscosity for mounting.
7.   Mount by method V–16 or V–17.

THE SEPARATION OF HARD PARTS from the softer tissues which surround them is also a dissociation process. It can be carried on by more drastic means than those used for the separation of soft tissues into cells and fibers. Corrosive fluids may be used to release spicules of sponges or to free exoskeletons from their contents. Various chitinous parts may be freed by nonchemical means.

V–13. TO REMOVE SPICULES FROM SPONGES. Place small pieces of calcareous sponges in 5% solution of potassium hydroxide and boil gently for a short time. Decant the supernatant, add tap water, and repeat this washing until all cellular debris has been separated from the spicules. Dry the spicules and mount as opaque objects (V–22) or in an aqueous or resinous mountant. It may be necessary to try several to see which best demonstrates the spicules. For silicious sponges, use strong nitric acid without heat. Wash, clean, dry, and mount in the same way.

V–14. SETAE OF EARTHWORMS. Harman and Corliss *(146)* have published a simple and useful method of releasing these structures. They place fragments of the body wall of the worms in flourishing but hungry cultures of *Tetrahymena corlissi*. The setae are cleaned in a relatively short time as the protozoa ingest the tissues. Other histophagous *Tetrahymena* are also useful and easy to obtain since most snails harbor one or more species.

COVER GLASS SUPPORTS FOR WHOLE MOUNTS

Prints, smears, squashes, macerated tissue, most protozoa, and some minute metazoa are usually mounted without cover glass supports. Delicate objects, however, such as blastulae and fragile eggs may be injured if the cover is placed directly upon them. Supports are also often needed to keep the cover parallel with the surface of the slide or to provide a neat border to the specimen and its mounting medium. The supports may be pieces of glass or plastic, or they may be chambers made of various materials, and of sizes to match the cover glasses which are to be used. Directions follow for making cover supports and chambers and for mounting specimens, using both types of supports.

V–15. THIN SUPPORTS FOR COVER GLASSES are neatly cut from plastic or glass covers, capillary tubing, or thin rods. Use a glass scriber (E–60) to cut the cover glasses; the size chosen will be determined by the dimensions of the specimen to be mounted. The supports may be attached either to the slide or to the cover. The material used for attaching should be well dried before the slide or cover is used. Capillary tubing should have its lumen filled with the adhesive material.

1. Provide 4 corner supports for each square cover; 3 for each circle.
2. Place each slide to which a cover is to be attached on a centering diagram (E–20) with the supports in the positions appropriate for

the cover to be used. If the supports are to be attached to the cover, the diagram is unnecessary.

3. Attach the supports with epoxy resin (R–73) or with a mountant. If the latter is chosen, use an aqueous, quick-drying kind for slides that will carry specimens mounted in xylene-resin; attach with xylene-resin if the specimens are to be in aqueous mountants.

4. Prepare in advance enough slides, or covers with supports, for the material which is to be mounted.

V–16. TO MOUNT SPECIMENS FOR STUDY WITH IMMERSION LENSES.

1. Have ready No. 1 cover glasses with supports made of pieces of No. 1 or No. 2 cover glasses.

2. Turn the cover with its supports uppermost and put on it a small drop of mountant containing the specimens; allow the specimens to settle and the drop to spread and to dry slightly. Add enough more mountant to fully cover the specimens and dry 24 hours in a dustproof container.

3. Center the cover glass on the slide; hold it in place with a needle and run more mountant in from the side, using a pipet with a fine tip. Dry for about 1 hour at room temperature.

4. Place the slide, cover glass side *down* in the grooves of a slide box, with the box in a vertical position, until drying is complete; *store the slides in the same way.*

Result: The specimens will remain close to the cover.

V–17. TO MOUNT SPECIMENS FOR STUDY WITH A 4-MM OBJECTIVE.

1. Use slides with attached thin No. 1 covers supported by pieces of No. 1 or No. 2 cover glasses or

1a. Use slides with attached supports of this size; place covers upon them, and hold the covers in place with a needle while mounting (V–16).

2. Run specimens, in mountant, under the cover using a fine pipet; the mountant will not spread beyond the edges of the cover if properly applied.

3. Examine the slides daily as they dry and add more mountant as necessary.

CELLS FOR WHOLE MOUNTS

V–18. CELLS MADE FROM RINGS OF GLASS OR PLASTIC.

The rings, of various diameters, may be purchased from certain supply houses (E–56). They may also be cut from tubing in the laboratory shop if the proper tools are at hand. Plastic rings may be inexpensively prepared from any type of translucent plastic tubing which is resistant to the solvent of the mountant to be used. To obtain a ring of any desired height, the tubing should be held in a slicing guide such as that devised for cutting sections of brain (E–64, 65) and cut with a very sharp knife or with a thin saw which has 64 teeth to the inch.

1.   Prepare or buy rings of the desired height and diameter; be sure that their upper and lower surfaces are parallel and moderately smooth.

2.   Using a centering diagram (E–20), attach rings to the slides with a good brand of epoxy resin. Follow the directions of the manufacturer exactly for mixing and application. If so recommended in package directions, heat gently to remove air bubbles; the resin thus treated will be homogeneous and transparent. Put a small weight on each ring while it is setting. Supports thus attached remain firmly in place even though subjected to rough treatment.

V–19.   CELLS OF BLOTTING PAPER are recommended by Fesco (*103*). He finds that specimens mounted in blotting paper cells develop few bubbles and that the cells seldom become detached.

1.   Select smooth white blotting paper about 1 mm thick and without watermarks or printing. Cut with scissors or paper cutter into squares or rectangles of a size to fit the covers to be used.

2.   Mark a margin 2–4 mm wide on each blank and cut out the central part with a razor blade or other suitable tool, leaving a frame to form the walls of a cell.

3.   Place the frames first in xylene, then in a 40% solution of mountant in xylene, until completely permeated. Fesco recommends mountants of the cumarone, terpene, or cycloparaffin polymer type. We have used H.S.R. mountant (R–96) with satisfactory results.

4.   Remove each frame from the mountant, drain well, and, using a mounting diagram, place it on a slide singly or in layers to make a cell of the desired depth.

5.   Press the frame gently to make it adhere to the slide, and press succeeding layers together if more than one is used. Dry well before use.

V–20.   TO MOUNT SPECIMENS IN CELLS.   After constructing and drying a cell of suitable dimensions, run a thin layer of mountant in the bottom. Put the specimen in position very carefully and avoid the introduction of air. Fill the chamber with the mountant; if possible, use enough so that its surface is slightly convex. Put on a cover glass very gently, beginning with one edge of the cover and lowering it carefully. If the cell has been well filled and no air is trapped beneath the specimen, there should be no air bubbles beneath the cover. If a bubble appears, remove the cover; add more mountant, and try again. It sometimes is useful to put a few drops of mountant on the lower surface of the cover. If bubbles appear as the preparation dries, add more mountant.

V–21. DOUBLE COVER GLASS METHOD. When it is necessary to mount whole specimens in an aqueous mountant, the use of supported cover glasses and cells may be replaced by the ingenious double cover glass method. It avoids the necessity of ringing a cover to protect an aqueous mountant. Several authors have described variants of this technic; see Mitchell and Cook (*225*) and Zuck (*341*). Usually the mounting is begun with specimens in glycerol (V–10, 4a). The article by Mitchell and Cook is the principal source of the following directions.

1. Lift the specimen from glycerol and place on a round 13-mm cover glass. Cover with a small amount of warmed glycerol jelly. Put aside until the jelly has set.

2. Add another drop of warmed glycerol jelly and cover with an 18-mm round cover glass. Allow the mountant to set. With the smaller cover glass down, place the mount in a drop or two of xylene-resin on a slide. The resin fills the space between the upper cover glass and the slide.

Zuck (*341*) suggests the use of the aqueous mountant Clearcol (R–46) rather than xylene-resin. This avoids a white line where the glycerol jelly and xylene-resin meet. Clearcol, although satisfactory and quick-drying, is expensive and might well be replaced by another aqueous mountant such as Abopon (F–190) or PVP–VA (F–173).

METHODS FOR PROTOZOA

V–22. MORRISON'S METHOD FOR OPAQUE MOUNTS (*228*) is applicable to tests of Radiolaria, Foraminifera, and *Globigerina*, which fail to show their structural detail when immersed in the usual mountants.

1. Using black phenol formaldehyde synthetic resin (R–160), paint a small circular area in the center of a slide, preparing as many slides as will be needed.

2. Heat the slides about 45 minutes in an oven at 175°C. They must rest in a horizontal position. Cool in the oven. This treatment produces a smooth and glossy surface unaffected by most solvents.

3. Put a thin layer of Duco or thinned, clear varnish on the black patch. Just before this is completely dry, cover the area with an excess of the material to be prepared and in a few seconds invert the slide over paper and tap off the excess.

4. Cement around the specimens a ring of plastic (E–56), hard rub-

ber, blotting paper, or other suitable material, and cover. Cellulose caprate (F–53) is an excellent material to use, both to cement the ring and to attach the cover, because it hardens quickly.

V–23. RELIEF STAINING FOR SURFACE MARKINGS OF CILIATES.

1. Place a drop of culture solution containing ciliates in the middle of a slide and add a drop of relief stain (F–174). Mix well, spread into a thin film, and air-dry.
2. Mount in synthetic resin without supports.

Results: The specimens are flattened; only one side of each can be seen. The ciliary rows are very clear and details of the buccal opening and cavity are plain in the individuals with these parts uppermost.

V–24. SILVER METHODS for ciliates show ciliary rows and other markings more plainly than relief stains. Klein's dry silver method, as modified by Gelei (*120*), is good.

1. Spread a drop of culture fluid containing ciliates on a slide and air-dry. Make several of these mounts.
2. Arrange the dried slides in a white-lined dish containing 2% silver nitrate; expose to strong sunlight. Reduction usually occurs in less than 10 minutes. Begin to check the intensity of the stain after 5 minutes, and remove the slides from the solution when the ciliary rows are clearly blackened.
3. Rinse well in distilled water, air-dry, and mount in synthetic resin.

Results: The specimens are flattened as in the preceding technic. The ciliary rows are marked by lines of black granules; the buccal apparatus, anal pore, and contractile vacuole pores are clearly shown in individuals fortunately orientated.

The silver impregnation method of Chatton-Lwoff is superior to the dry-silver method in some respects but more difficult. It has been well described by Corliss (*74*) and should be used when counting rows of cilia and when observation of polar structures is necessary.

V–25. LYNCH'S BORAX-CARMINE-INDULIN METHOD FOR PARAMECIA (*204*).

1. Fix in solutions that contain no chromic acid. Bouin's PFA, Da Fano's cobalt nitrate, and 10% formalin are particularly good. Wash after fixation.
2. Transfer to 30% alcohol, 2 baths, 15 minutes each.
3. Transfer to Grenacher's borax-carmine (F–39), 6–24 hours.
4. Drop a few drops of hydrochloric acid into the dish containing stain and specimens, with continuous agitation until a cloudy or flocculent pink precipitate appears; avoid an excess of acid, which

will redissolve the precipitate. Mix well the contents of the dish; cover and leave the specimens in the mixture 12–24 hours.

5. Transfer specimens to 50%, then 70% alcohol, both slightly acidified; leave 5–10 minutes in each.

6. Differentiate under the microscope by adding and mixing hydrochloric acid, a drop at a time, to the alcohol until the cytoplasm is colorless and the nuclei brilliant red.

7. Transfer to 80% alcohol, 10 minutes, with 2 changes.

8. Counterstain with a saturated solution of indulin[1] in 80% alcohol and remove the solution when cilia and cytoplasm are a clear blue. This may take a few minutes to an hour. (We prefer to use a pale blue, much weaker solution, since overstaining is almost impossible to correct.)

9. Transfer to 95% alcohol, 10 minutes with several changes; place in absolute alcohol, then alcohol-xylene, 5 minutes each.

10. Clear in xylene; make a weak mixture of xylene-resin, concentrate slowly and mount by the V–16 or V–17 method.

METHODS FOR PLATYHELMINTHES

One of the principal problems in preparing flatworms is their considerable contractility. The first necessity is to fix them in a relaxed condition and, as the directions indicate, several methods are successful.

V–26. LAVOIE'S METHOD FOR WHOLE MOUNTS OF POLY-CLADS (*186*). The species used were *Notoplana stomata* and *Stylochus zebra*.

1. Transfer worms from sea water to a flat dish with no more water than adheres to the specimens. Place dish in the freezing compartment of a refrigerator, 20 minutes.

2. Flood the worms with heated formol-acetic-alcohol (F–89).

3. Dehydrate with alcohol.

4. Clear and mount in Euparal in cells or under supported covers or

4a. Clear first with benzene, then with beechwood creosote, and mount in synthetic resin.

Results: The worms are relaxed by the freezing, there is no change in the natural coloring of the specimens, and shrinkage is minimal. They remain pliable enough for easy mounting.

V–27. TO DEMONSTRATE THE GUT OF PLANARIANS, feed them an opaque pigment mixed with an acceptable food such as liver.

---

[1] The C.I. number is not specified in the directions, but the context indicates that it should be No. (860) 50400.

Powdered carmine or Chinese ink in stick form are useful as pigments. If ink is chosen, a small amount is scraped from the stick with a knife or scalpel.

1. Select planarians with as little pigmentation as possible. Place them in small containers such as petri dishes, in spring water, and starve for a few days.
2. Prepare a small amount of liver by grinding it with pigment in a mortar.
3. Add a few small bits of the liver to each dish and allow the worms to feed for not more than 30 minutes.
4. Remove the worms to clean spring water and leave undisturbed 10–12 hours.
5. Anesthetize and, when they are relaxed, fix them in 10% formalin.
6. Make whole mounts without further staining; dehydrate in Cellosolve, clear in terpineol, and mount under supported covers.

V–28. ACETO-ORCEIN, USED AS BOTH FIXATIVE AND STAIN in Bergan's method (32), makes excellent whole mounts of both *Dicrocoelium dentriticum* and *Fasciola hepatica*. The specimens are relaxed by this solution. His schedule is as follows:

1. Fix in 1% orcein in 45% acetic acid, 1–14 days; optimum time is 3–8 days.
2. Differentiate in acetic-ethanol 1:3/vol until internal organs are clearly visible.
3. Remove acid by 4 changes of 70% ethanol during 24–48 hours.
4. Dehydrate, clear in clove oil (we prefer terpineol), and mount in xylene-resin under supported covers.

Results: The animals die in an extended condition. The internal organs are clearly shown.

V–29. DEMKE'S METHOD FOR CESTODES (87) is as follows:

1. Place in water fresh specimens of tapeworms still attached to short segments of intestine; store in a refrigerator. Leave *Taenia* about 4 hours; *Dipylidium* overnight. Remove scolices from the intestine by gentle traction.
2. Stretch the now-relaxed specimens, and wind each one spirally around a 50 × 75-mm glass slide. Put another slide on each side of the first and apply pressure by binding the slides at each end with rubber bands.
3. Immerse the slides, in a vertical position, in the fixative of Becker and Roudabush (F–28), 30 minutes to several hours. After immersion, insert a razor blade or thin scalpel tip between the upper ends of the slides to release trapped air bubbles.
4. Remove specimens from slides. Store in fresh fixative or prepare

to stain by washing in running water, 30–60 minutes, according to size.

5. Immerse the specimens in Riser's stain (F–177); leave scolices and immature proglottids of *Taenia hydatigena* and *Dipylidium caninum*, 5 minutes; mature and gravid proglottids of *T. hydatigena, T. saginata, D. caninum, Diphyllobothrium mansoni,* and *D. latum*, 10 minutes; mature *Fasciola hepatica*, 30 minutes.

6. Pass through 2 changes of water, 30 minutes in each, or until no further stain comes away.

7. Put into 2 successive baths of 50% isopropanol, 12 hours or overnight for the first bath and 2 hours for the second to remove further excess stain and to differentiate.

8. Dehydrate in 70%, 80%, 95%, and absolute isopropanol, 1 hour in each; equal parts of absolute ethanol and ether, 1 hour.

9. Transfer to a petri dish and cover with 3% celloidin or 3% LVN in ether-alcohol 1:1/vol. Arrange the pieces so that they are well separated; cover and allow the ether-alcohol to evaporate very slowly, thus avoiding formation of bubbles in the celloidin. When it is firm, flood it with 80% isopropanol 30–45 minutes.

10. Cut the celloidin into pieces, each containing a specimen; make each piece 1–2 mm smaller on each side than the cover glass to be used. Store in 80% isopropanol, or dehydrate in 90% and 100% isopropanol.

11. Clear in beechwood creosote (R–13) until pieces sink. Mount in xylene-resin without cover supports. Place slides in 37°C incubator, examine daily, and add fresh mountant as xylene evaporates.

12. When dry, clean and seal with fresh resin.

METHOD FOR NEMATODES

These worms are notoriously difficult to prepare and are often studied in the living condition with vital dyes. Grundmann has proposed a successful method for permanent preparations which follows.

V–30. GRUNDMANN'S METHODS FOR NEMATODES (*136*).

1. Heat living specimens gently in normal saline until they are relaxed and killed.

2. Fix in Kahle's fluid (F–121) 24 hours or more; formol-alcohol-acetic (F–89) or 10% formalin may also be used. Alcohol alone is an unsatisfactory fixative and preservative.

3. Transfer to tinted lactophenol (F–107), and make a small incision through the body wall of each specimen. Stain and clear, by heating the solution to 60°C, 30 minutes; or leave in the solution at room temperature 24–48 hours; or

3*a.* Transfer to tinted 50% glycerol (F–143), 48 hours; puncture the cuticle and body wall directly after transfer.

4. Transfer from the lactophenol solution or the glycerol solution, blot well, and mount directly in Hoyer's medium (F–101) using the double cover glass method (V–21).

Results: The mountant produces a further clearing action; the cuticle is almost transparent; in a short time the tissues become brownish, but the definition of cells and organs increases as the preparation ages.

PLASTIC PREPARATIONS

One of the most satisfactory technics for making whole preparations of embryos and metazoa of small to relatively large size is to embed them in plastic. Although both ethyl and methyl methacrylate may be used, they are more difficult to handle than Selectron, a thermo-setting resin produced by the Pittsburgh Plate Glass Company. It is sold to many biological supply houses which market it under names such as Ward's Bio-Plastic and Turtox Embedding Plastic. As far as can be ascertained the material, under whatever name it is purchased, is the same. It keeps in the refrigerator without polymerizing for several months but does not contain an inhibitor. When brought to room temperature and with a catalyst added, it sets in an hour or two. An accelerator added with the catalyst hastens the process. Among its many advantages are the superior clearing effect which it produces and the permanence of the preparation.

There are many publications on making plastic mounts: Roudabush, (*271*); Jones, (*164*, pp. 162–163). Directions for use of the plastic accompany each package if requested. The information given here is accordingly limited to general directions for embedding specimens.

V–32. GENERAL DIRECTIONS FOR PREPARING MATERIAL IN PLASTIC.

1. Fix and wash the specimens as usual.
2. Stain; dehydrate in alcohol using the usual percentages, with two changes of absolute alcohol. The timing will depend on the size of the specimen.
3. Transfer to ether (R–76), 2 changes.
4. Transfer to plastic monomer (R–178) which has been slightly warmed to permit bubbles to rise and break. Place in the dark and leave 24 hours. During a part of this period, place in a vacuum dessicator at reduced pressure.
5. Select or make a container (E–45) of suitable size and shape for the specimen. Rub its inner surface with a mold release compound (R–133). Pour plastic monomer into a disposable glass jar in a

measured amount sufficient to cover the bottom of the mold. Add the catalyst to it, determining the amount by the size of the block; if it is to be thick, use 0.1% of the quantity of plastic. For small blocks, increase the proportion up to 0.5%. Too much catalyst will cause the blocks to crack. Mix the catalyst and plastic together gently and pour carefully into the mold. If necessary, place near a lamp to raise the temperature high enough so that any bubbles will rise and burst. Do not warm longer than necessary. It should gel in 1 to 3 hours.

6.   Prepare enough more plastic to fill the mold, adding the proper amount of catalyst; allow for the volume of the specimen. Pour it upon the previously gelled plastic in the mold; lower the specimen with care upon the gelled layer to avoid introduction of bubbles. Again warm gently if bubbles appear, but allow the block to gel at room temperature. Cover the surface with a smooth sheet of aluminum foil.

7.   Leave the gelled block overnight; a longer period will do no harm.

8.   Cure in an oven, beginning with a temperature of 38°C and increasing it slowly to 112°C, 15–60 minutes.

9.   Cool and remove from mold. Polish any rough surfaces.

For making mounts of embryos in plastic see XI–12. The same method may be used for many small animals.

CHAPTER VI

SECTION METHODS

Most tissues are not firm enough to be cut into thin, uniform sections unless they are both surrounded by and permeated with a supporting material. The process of permeation is called infiltration, and the substance used for support is spoken of as the infiltrating or embedding medium. Media in common use include ice, gelatin, various waxes, several types of nitrocellulose, and a few plastics.

Specimens to be prepared for sectioning usually contain considerable quantities of water. This is easily displaced if the infiltrating medium is soluble in water, as are gelatin and water waxes. The process is more difficult if the water must be replaced by an embedding medium such as paraffin, which is not miscible with water.

Each of the various methods of preparing material for sectioning has its advantages and disadvantages which should be considered in making a choice of the technic to be used. One essential requirement is that the cells or cell substances to be studied must be well preserved and clearly demonstrated. The convenience and cost of the several possible methods should also be considered. The special applications of each commonly used medium are treated in the appropriate sections of this chapter. However, it seems desirable to note here, briefly, a few criteria for choices of method.

When it is necessary to preserve material stored in cells and afterward to stain it distinctively, reagents which dissolve it must obviously be avoided. Thus, in the study of fats in cells, one may make frozen sections or embed in a water-soluble wax. No fat solvents are used in preparing sections by these methods, but some are used in the paraffin and nitrocellulose technics, which should therefore be avoided. If shrinkage and distortion of tissue and cell elements must be kept to a minimum, embedding in nitrocellulose is the method of choice. It is of value for certain types of cytological preparations and often for embryo serial sections from which very precise reconstructions are to be made. If the purpose of the technician is to produce numerous slides of good quality with a minimum expenditure of time, the paraffin technic is usually the best choice.

FREEZING METHODS

The most rapid and uncomplicated method of preparing sections is to first freeze the specimen, sometimes as soon as it is removed from the body but more often after it has been fixed, and to cut sections on a suitable microtome. This method is of medical importance since diagnosis requires identification of tissue removed by surgery. It is also essential for certain histochemical technics because it preserves materials that are destroyed by reagents used in other methods; it is frequently employed in neurological procedures, and it is a timesaving method of sampling various kinds of specimens.

Preparing Material for Freezing

VI-1.   FREEZING WITHOUT INFILTRATION.   If the sections are to be prepared as quickly as possible, a small piece of tissue is removed from the animal, washed, placed on the freezing plate of the microtome, then frozen and cut. If sections are not required immediately, the piece is fixed. Formalin, in 10% solution, is a good choice for general purposes.

When fixation is complete, the specimen may be washed in running water and then frozen and sectioned without further treatment. Marshall (*210*), quoted by Davenport (*83*, p. 106), recommends soaking the tissue in 20% alcohol for several hours before cutting. He points out that since the freezing point of the specimen is lowered by this means, it is less likely to become excessively hard from over-freezing; he finds that blocks so treated produce sections which flatten readily when placed in water.

Sections prepared as above without embedding are delicate. They are difficult to handle, particularly if they are thin: the parts often fail to cohere. It is accordingly common practice to infiltrate the block with a water-soluble substance that can be hardened when the infiltration has been completed. Among the commonly used media are aqueous solutions of gelatin, various gums, and agar.

STAINING IN BLOCK.   If it is feasible, the infiltration may be preceded by block staining; certain neurological technics employ block staining to considerable advantage.

Infiltration before Freezing

If the specimen is to be infiltrated before sectioning, one of the following methods may be used.

VI–2. ZWEMER'S GELATIN METHOD (*343*) slightly modified.
1. Fix 24 or more hours in 10% formalin.
2. Wash at least 4 hours in running tap water.
3. Infiltrate in 5% gelatin, 24 hours at 37°C; transfer to 10% gelatin and continue the infiltration at 37°, 12–16 hours.
4. Orient and embed in 10% gelatin in a lightly oiled mold. Cool at a low temperature until hard.
5. Harden further in 10% formalin unless the stains to be used color gelatin heavily.
6. Freeze on the stage of a freezing microtome with carbon dioxide vapor (VI–6) until the block is white. Without further freezing, make test sections at brief intervals until it is possible to cut thin slices. Section rapidly when the block is at a suitable temperature; refreeze and repeat as necessary.
7. Store sections in 10% formalin or mount at once (VI–10).

VI–3. BAKER'S GELATIN METHOD (*15*) calls for a single, more concentrated solution of gelatin. It is applied after a 3-day fixation in 10% formalin containing 1% calcium chloride neutralized with calcium carbonate.
1. Infiltrate in a 25% solution of gelatin in a closed container at 37°C for about 24 hours and embed in a fresh portion of the same solution or
1*a*. Infiltrate in 25% gelatin solution in a dessicator over anhydrous calcium chloride at 37°C for about 30 hours; embed in the infiltrating mixture.
2. Cool the blocks; harden 24 hours in 10% formalin containing 1% each of calcium chloride and cadmium chloride.
3. Cut frozen sections. If infiltration is by the method 1*a*, the sections may be cut as thin as 5μ.
4. Attach sections to slides (VI–10) and stain.

VI–4. LILLIE'S AGAR METHOD (*193*, p. 56). Lillie recommends agar as an embedding medium for certain tissues. He uses a 2% solution, melted, and points out that a considerable advantage of this medium is that it does not take stain readily.

VI–5. LEWIS AND SHUTE'S ALGINATE GEL METHOD (*189*) permits infiltration at low temperatures so that heat-labile constituents are not destroyed. The authors find that at room temperature there is little apparent loss of activity of both true and pseudo-cholinesterase, nonspecific esterase, and alkaline phosphatase. The cutting properties are reported to be excellent.

Freezing and Cutting

VI–6. THE TECHNICS OF FREEZING AND CUTTING with the microtome shown in Figure 2 are given in the following directions for an unfixed block of tissue about 2 × 10 × 10 mm.

Fig. 2.—Microtome designed primarily for cutting frozen sections; it must be attached to a tabletop. It appears here with a nitrocellulose block in position for cutting. (Courtesy of the American Optical Company.)

1. Clamp the microtome to the tabletop. Connect the freezing attachment to the microtome and to the tank of carbon dioxide (Fig. 3). Put a small drop of water on the freezing plate. Close the valve to the freezing chamber and open the tank valve slightly; now open the chamber valve a little, three or four times in quick succession, and note whether the water freezes quickly. If it does, the apparatus is ready for use.

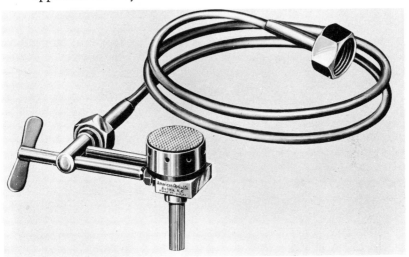

F<small>IG</small>. 3.—Freezing attachment for the microtome in Figure 2. The freezing head takes the place of the object carrier. (Courtesy of the American Optical Company.)

2. Raise the block holder until it is about the right height for the block which is to be cut. Set the screw which regulates section thickness. Screw the knife into its holder.
3. Place a large drop of water or gelatin solution (F–95) or a saturated solution of dextrin (R–63) on the freezing disc, and put the specimen in position; be sure that there is enough fluid to attach the tissue firmly to the disc when it is frozen. To freeze, open and close the chamber valve several times in quick succession until the specimen is solidly frozen.
4. Cut several sections by moving the knife obliquely across the specimen. The first ones may roll up and fly off because the block is too hard. When they begin to cut easily, allow several to collect on the knife and remove them together with a soft, moist brush to normal saline; or flush them off into a syracuse watch glass with saline or with water from a medicine dropper. Cut another group of sections. When the block becomes too soft to section well, freeze again. Continue cutting until enough specimens have been collected.

Specimens which have been fixed and embedded are placed on the disc, frozen, and cut in a similar fashion.

Anthony (*10*) recommends that a razor blade carried in a razor-blade holder be substituted for the usual microtome knife. He finds that for technicians who do not cut frozen sections routinely, this produces superior results. *See* E–50, –51.

These directions are for a clinical type of freezing microtome. Although it is relatively inexpensive in comparison with most rotary and sliding microtomes, it is not a part of the standard equipment of all laboratories and probably because of this, many substitutes for it have been devised. Those mentioned below are satisfactory when the technician has acquired facility in their use; a choice from among them may be made according to personal preference and the equipment at hand.

SUBSTITUTES FOR FREEZING MICROTOMES. If a freezing microtome is not available, the sections may be made by one of the following technics.

VI–7. GALTSOFF'S METHOD (*118*) is very simple; it was devised for making sections which would show the distribution of fat in oyster tissues.

1. Mount small pieces of tissue, fresh or preserved in formalin, on wooden blocks. Very loose or soft tissue should be embedded in gelatin. Orient as desired, moisten with water, and place in the freezing compartment of a refrigerator for about 15 minutes or until well frozen.

2. Insert the block in the holder of a rotary microtome and section as usual (VI–20).

3. As the block becomes too soft for proper sectioning, refreeze by spraying it with ethyl chloride (R–77). This reagent does not harm the tissue.

VI–8. PAULY'S METHOD (*245*) uses dry ice for freezing and cutting on a rotary microtome.

1. Make a hole with a hand drill in a block of dry ice. If necessary, use a screwdriver or a small chisel to enlarge the hole until it will receive the shank of the object carrier and allow the disc to rest on the surface of the dry ice. Place the block of dry ice in an insulated box with a cover.

2. Insert an object carrier in the prepared hole and allow it to cool about 15 seconds.

3. Drop water on the cooled disc and arrange the block of tissue on it. The time of freezing varies with the size of the specimen, but it is usually only a few minutes.

4. Place the object disc in the object clamp with a few chips of dry ice between disc and clamp. The chips may be held in place by a strip of flexible plastic and a rubber band. It is necessary to pick up the pieces of dry ice with insulated tongs.
5. Cut in the usual manner. Serial sections as thin as 10 μ may be produced by this method.

CRYOSTAT MICROTOMES. There are commercially available cryostats fitted with microtomes; they are cooled by compressors. They freeze blocks and provide low temperatures for sectioning, eliminating the use of carbon dioxide gas or dry ice. Where a great deal of frozen section work is done their high cost is probably justified, but they are rather expensive instruments if infrequently used.

TREATMENT AFTER SECTIONING

Treatment after sectioning depends on the method by which the specimens have been prepared—whether they are frozen fresh or after fixation; whether stained in block, or unstained; and whether they are unsupported or have been infiltrated.

FOR SECTIONS STAINED IN BLOCK, the procedures following sectioning are simple. It is only necessary to place a section on a slide, differentiate it if it is overstained, rinse, and mount, usually with an aqueous mountant (F–173). If mounting in xylene-resin is desired and is practicable, the specimen must be dehydrated. For an example, see Snider's method of block staining of Nissl substance (IX–9).

MOUNTING SECTIONS. The treatment of unsupported frozen sections after cutting is difficult since they tear readily; large ones are especially fragile.

VI–9. MOUNTING UNINFILTRATED SECTIONS WITH GELATIN, Albrecht's method (4), makes them easier to handle.
1. Soak washed sections 5 minutes or longer in a 1:1 mixture of 1.5% aq sol of gelatin and 80% alcohol. The solution should be at least 2.5 cm deep.
2. Dip the slide in the mixture and, with a fine brush, work the section to a suitable position. Place the slide at an angle which will promote rapid drainage; carefully wipe excess fluid from the slide surface.
3. Working rapidly to prevent complete drying, blot the sections well with smooth filter paper and immerse when almost dry in 95% alcohol.

4.   If the sections have already been stained, dehydrate and clear as usual; if they are to be stained on the slide, continue with step 5.

5.   Transfer the slide to absolute alcohol, then to a 0.5% solution of celloidin in alcohol-ether 1:1, 5 minutes. Remove the slide, drain, expose to air for several seconds, and immerse in 80% alcohol for 5 minutes or more.

6.   Hydrate, if sections are to be stained in aqueous solution, or pass to proper grade of alcohol for an alcoholic stain (see p. 88).

MOUNTING INFILTRATED SECTIONS. If the block has been infiltrated before sectioning, the sections may either be mounted on slides before staining or stained in dishes and then mounted.

VI–10. BAKER'S TECHNIC FOR MOUNTING SECTIONS (15).

1.   Coat slides with a warm 2.5% gelatin solution, drain, and dry.

2.   Arrange sections on the coated slides; remove most of the moisture by draining or blotting with filter paper. Expose to fumes of concentrated formalin in a staining jar until the gelatin is hardened.

3.   Stain at once or store in calcium-cadmium-formalin (F–26) until they are about to be stained.

4.   Stain by the same technics used for sections mounted in paraffin or nitrocellulose.

STAINING SECTIONS BEFORE MOUNTING. Frozen sections are more frequently stained before than after attachment to slides. They may be carried from one solution to the next in transfer trays (E–61).

VI–11. THE ALUM HEMATOXYLIN METHOD is an example of a commonly used technic.

1.   Rinse frozen sections in distilled water.

2.   Transfer to Harris' hematoxylin (F–16), 30–60 seconds, and return to water. Examine one section under the microscope; if nuclei are not clearly stained, return to the hematoxylin until staining is satisfactory. Rinse in tap water.

3.   Mount in a suitable aqueous mountant or

3a.   Dehydrate in dioxane by transferring the section to a slide and dropping the reagent upon it. Clear in xylene and mount in synthetic resin. If a counterstain is desired, omit 3a and use 3b.

3b.   Transfer to a solution of Cellosolve, well colored with eosin, until the desired color is attained. Rinse in Cellosolve, 2 changes; clear in xylene and mount in synthetic resin.

VI–12. METHOD OF JIMINEZ AND SCHNEIDER FOR CLARIFYING FROZEN SECTIONS (162).

1.   Cut frozen sections at 15μ and float on water.

2. Remove from water on a glass rod and dip into a dish containing 5 ml of Schain Clarifier (R–62), about 5 seconds; return to water.
3. Float onto an albumenized slide and dry with hot air.
4. Stain with alum hematoxylin-eosin or with a fat stain.
5. Mount slides stained for fat in an aqueous mountant such as glycerol jelly (F–101); mount hematoxylin slides in synthetic resin after dehydration and clearing.

Results: The sections show more cellular detail than the usual frozen sections.

PARAFFIN METHODS

Summary of Dehydrating, Clearing, and Embedding Methods

Various methods are available for preparing specimens in paraffin. The choice depends on the material and the studies for which it is to be used, as well as the preferences of the technician. It should be emphasized that some of the simplest methods may produce the most satisfactory results.

General Directions

A. Make an identifying label on heavy paper which will be carried with the specimens through all the reagents; mark it with a soft pencil or with waterproof India ink, and embed it with the specimen in such a way that the information is easily visible.
B. Make a careful schedule of the proposed method, in advance, noting when time limits for any step may be varied.
C. Have ready a series of bottles or jars of the reagents to be used; label each one and number it in the order of its use. Provide a closed container in which the specimen may be treated with the successive reagents. After use, systematically discard the reagents that are most contaminated. For example, in using a Cellosolve schedule with three changes of this reagent, discard the first bath, return the second bath to the first bottle, the third bath to the second bottle, and put fresh Cellosolve from stock in the third.
D. Suspend or support the specimen in fluid reagents.
E. If the specimen is light in color, add an easily soluble dye such as methyl eosin, C.I. No. (769) 45385, to the last dehydrating bath, so that it may be easily seen in the embedding mass.
F. Adopt some method for indicating the plane in which sections are to be cut, and follow it consistently. For instance, put the side which is to face the knife when mounted in the microtome at the bottom of the embedding dish.

REAGENTS FOR DEHYDRATING, CLEARING, AND INFIL-
TRATING. The conventional way of removing water from the tissue
(dehydration) is to replace it with ethanol. Following dehydration, the
alcohol is replaced by xylene; this process is called clearing. The term
clearing refers to the fact that xylene and certain other reagents cause
the tissue to become translucent as they replace the dehydrator. Since
all clearing agents do not do this, it is an inappropriate term. The alcohol
is best applied in gradually increasing concentrations; thus dehydration with ethanol is a rather time-consuming process; in the hands of
inexperienced technicians, it is sometimes unsuccessful. An alternative
method uses dioxane which is miscible with water, alcohol, and paraffin
and thus both dehydrates and clears. This is a good technic, since it is
simple, produces excellent results if a proper grade of dioxane is used
(R–68), and permits a flexible schedule of application; specimens may
be left in it for months. It has little or no hardening effect upon the
tissues as do both strong ethanol and xylene. It produces good preparations even in the hands of inexperienced students. In view of these advantages it seems surprising that it is not more generally used. It is
slightly toxic, but harmful effects are avoidable if work is done with
proper precautions (71).

   In addition to dioxane, there are several other reagents which have
few unfavorable effects on tissues, and which are simpler to use than
alcohol. Among these are Cellosolve (R–31) and triethyl phosphate
(R–80); both are miscible with water without the production of violent
diffusion currents; hence they can be applied full strength. Neither hardens tissue appreciably. Since they are not miscible with paraffin, they
must be followed by a clearing agent.

   Alcohols other than ethanol are useful for dehydration. Isopropanol
(R–107) is especially satisfactory since it, like dioxane, both dehydrates
and clears. Normal and tertiary butanols (R–21) are solvents of paraffin,
but they mix with water only in solutions that contain ethanol. They are
particularly good in seaside laboratories where the air is moist, since
the butanols are not very hygroscopic. They do not distort tissues.
Methanol (R–121) may replace ethanol in most paraffin schedules.

   Xylene and benzene are often used for clearing; toluene and chloroform are occasionally employed. Essential oils, such as oil of cloves, are
clearing agents but most of them make specimens excessively brittle.
For some purposes, aniline oil (R–6) is excellent when ethanol is used
as the dehydrator. It is miscible with 30% alcohol, and its use avoids
the hardening effect of stronger concentrations. Cedar oil (R–145) is
also useful for some purposes.

   Specimens may be infiltrated in paraffin produced for domestic use,
but with inferior results. There are various formulae which include

adjuvants that make cutting easier and produce superior sections. (F–163–165). In addition to mixtures prepared in the laboratory, there are several satisfactory proprietary mixtures (R–155).

METHODS OF DEHYDRATION AND CLEARING. Whatever reagents are chosen to prepare material for sectioning in paraffin, the methods of applying them are essentially the same. A single description will suffice for most of them. These processes are commonly carried out in one of two ways. In the first, the specimens are placed in a covered container, such as a short stender dish (E–25). Each fluid, after it has acted for the required length of time, is poured off and the next added. The specimens should be supported on crumpled filter paper to allow access of the reagent to all surfaces. Only small numbers of specimens should be treated at one time in this way.

In the second method, which we consider preferable, the reagents are kept in closed containers; for 5-mm to 7-mm cubes of tissue they may be of 50- to 100-ml capacity. The specimen is suspended about midway between the surface of the fluid and the bottom of the vessel. It may be enclosed in a small bag of cheesecloth or of lens paper, or in a piece of glass tubing covered with cheesecloth at one end. The enclosed specimen is attached to the side of the container or to the lid of the jar by a string. For several specimens, one of the commercially available tissue carriers, such as a tube of stainless steel with numerous perforations in sides and bottom, may be used. The tube is closed by a cork which gives enough buoyancy to support the whole. There are also several types of carriers made of inert, light plastic. One is weighted and floats upright below the surface of the reagent. The carriers are transferred from one solution to the next until dehydration and clearing are completed. Care must be taken to provide fresh supplies of the dehydrators and clearing agents at suitable intervals.

METHODS FOR INFILTRATING. Specimens are transferred from the clearing agent to molten paraffin and left until the clearing agent has been replaced by the paraffin. There are several methods of melting the paraffin, and of these the one which is probably most widely used is an oven with a thermostatic control that can be set at the melting point of the paraffin. Such ovens, which are expensive, are sold by most laboratory supply houses.

A simple and inexpensive technic for infiltration was devised by C. E. McClung (personal communication). He hung an electric light bulb with a metal shade over a glass jar of paraffin, adjusting its height so that only the upper inch or inch and a half of the paraffin melted. When the cleared specimen was put in the jar, it rested on the unmelted surface, in paraffin just at the melting point, and never too hot.

It is somewhat easier to use the adjustable desk lamps carrying a 40- to

50-watt bulb, which are now available, although the lamp suspended by a cord is quite satisfactory. For student use, or for the technician preparing only a few specimens at a time, either type of lamp is excellent. Curtin's oven (E–48), which makes use of the same principle, accommodates larger numbers of specimens at one time. Gray (*132*) describes a radiant-heat embedding oven which also employs the same principle; it permits infiltration of many specimens simultaneously and is very satisfactory. See also E–27.

EMBEDDING is the process of transferring the infiltrated specimen and its label from the molten paraffin to a mold, covering it with paraffin, and cooling it quickly. In this way the specimen is encased in a firm homogeneous mass. When the embedded specimen is detached from its mold, it is called a paraffin block. Blocks may be safely stored indefinitely at room temperature.

SECTIONING. The block is attached to an object carrier, which is unfortunately sometimes called a block. It is better to speak of it as an object carrier although one type is referred to as an object disc. The carrier with the specimen attached is placed in the object clamp of the paraffin microtome and, after careful adjustments have been made, the block is cut into sections which are stored in covered flat boxes or trays.

SPREADING. One or more sections, always slightly compressed in cutting, are placed on warm water. This permits them to expand to their original dimensions; they are neatly arranged after spreading. After removal of excess water, they are warmed and dried, and become firmly attached to the slides, usually with the aid of an affixative which was placed on the slide before spreading or mixed with the water on which they were spread. They may be stored in dustproof slide boxes (E–9) for a few days to a few weeks after spreading.

FOR STAINING, the paraffin is dissolved (deceration) and the slides carried through appropriate reagents to the solvent of the chosen stain. When staining is completed, the slides are mounted in water-soluble, alcohol-soluble, or xylene-soluble mountant after they have been transferred to the solvent of the mountant.

EXAMPLES OF PARAFFIN SCHEDULES

VI–13. ALCOHOL-XYLENE SERIES using ethanol, methanol, or isopropanol.

Reagents: A series of jars containing 30% alcohol (1), 50% alcohol (2), 70% alcohol (3), 95% alcohol (4), 95% alcohol (5), 95% alcohol and xylene 1:1/vol plus 10% by volume of tertiary or of normal butanol (6), xylene (7), xylene (8), xylene (9). Number the jars as above. Jar 9 should be smaller than the others and always contain fresh xylene from a stock bottle. After one use, add its contents to jar 7. Make up the series fresh after several uses. The butanol in jar 6 is particularly necessary in damp weather.

1. Place the specimen, which has been fixed and washed, in a tissue capsule or other carrier; the carrier should either have some device by which it will float in the solutions or be provided with a thread by which it can be held midway between the top and bottom of the dehydrating and clearing agents.

2. Put the carrier with its specimen and accompanying label in jar 1 if it has just been washed in water or in jar 3 or 4 if it has been stored in alcohol.

3. Transfer in succession to the jars of the next higher number, 30–60 minutes in each, until jars 4 and 5; leave the specimens in these 60–90 minutes. If a stain is to be used to make the specimen easily seen in the paraffin, it should be in jar 5.

4. Leave in jar 6, 60 minutes; in 7, 30 minutes; and in 8 and 9, 60 minutes each.

VI–14. THE DIOXANE METHOD. Since dioxane is mildly toxic as are many of the reagents used in a microtechnic laboratory, handle it with proper precautions. Carry out transfers in a hood or in a well-ventilated laboratory; keep containers covered; avoid unnecessary contact with the skin.

Supplies: A bottle of fresh, and one of used dioxane; a small covered jar; a dish with a cover into which discarded fluid may be poured; a square of lens paper about 40 × 40 mm and a stout thread of linen or cotton, or a tissue carrier.

1. Fill the jar with used dioxane.

2. Place a fixed and washed cube of tissue and its label on the lens paper, tie the specimen in the paper with the thread, and suspend the package in the container by catching the thread in the cork or cover; leave 2–8 hours.

3. Discard the used dioxane, pouring it into the covered dish; refill the jar with fresh dioxane and suspend the package of tissue as before.

4. After 4–8 hours, pour the dioxane into the bottle of used reagent; refill the jar with fresh dioxane.

5. If it is not convenient to infiltrate when step 4 is completed, put fresh dioxane in the container and store. The specimen may be safely left in the dioxane for several weeks. If infiltration is to be carried on at once, transfer to molten paraffin and proceed with the infiltration according to directions VI–17.

VI–15.   The BUTANOL SCHEDULE was proposed by Zirkle (*340*) for plant work. It is equally satisfactory for preparing very delicate animal tissues. Although it is somewhat more tedious than most paraffin methods, it is well worth using when other technics prove unsatisfactory.

TABLE 1

Solution	1	2	3	4	5	6	7	8	9	10	11
Water	95	89	82	70	50	30	15	5	0	0	0
Ethanol	5	11	18	30	40	50	50	40	25	0	0
Butanol	0	0	0	0	10	20	35	55	75	100	100

1.   Make up the solutions in Table 1 and put them in labeled and numbered jars. Use either tertiary or normal butanol and 95% or absolute ethanol. The numbers refer to parts by volume. Solutions 1 to 8 may be used many times; 9 and 10 should be renewed frequently; 11 should always be a fresh supply from stock.

2.   Prepare several vials by filling them about two-thirds full of molten paraffin; cover and allow them to cool.

3.   Suspend the specimen to be treated in the solutions, in succession, allowing 1 hour in each of the first five; 8–12 hours in 6; 1 hour in 7, 8, and 9; and several hours to overnight in 10 and in 11.

4.   Infiltrate by dropping the specimen into the vial of solid paraffin, covering with fresh butanol, and placing the vial in an oven set at the melting point of the paraffin, or in a hood beneath a lamp. When the paraffin is melted, pour it off and transfer the specimen to a jar of molten paraffin. Leave it in the jar 2–3 hours, according to size, and embed as usual (VI–17).

VI–16.   CELLOSOLVE AND TRIETHYL PHOSPHATE SCHEDULES.   These reagents are both used in the same way.
Supplies: A series of jars containing Cellosolve (or triethyl phosphate) (1), Cellosolve (2), Cellosolve (3), Cellosolve and xylene 1:1/vol (4), xylene (5), and xylene (6). Jar 6 should be smaller than the others and always contain fresh xylene from the stock bottle. After one use, its contents may be added to jar 5.

1.   Place drained or blotted specimen(s) in a tissue capsule or other container which will be suspended in the various reagents.

2.   Put the container in jar 1, 4–8 hours; transfer to jar 2, then to jar 3, for the same periods of time. If desired, add to jar 3 a few drops of a saturated solution of eosin, which will make the tissue visible in the paraffin.

3. Transfer to jar 4, 30–60 minutes.
4. Clear in jars 5 and 6, 60 minutes in each.
5. Infiltrate.

VI–17. INFILTRATING AND EMBEDDING IN PARAFFIN.

Supplies and equipment: Two jars of clean paraffin, a bunsen burner or a spirit lamp, forceps and a section lifter, a stainless steel spoon or a pipet with a rubber bulb and a wide tip, a small pitcher of molten paraffin from the same lot as that in the jars, a large shallow basin of ice water, a small dropping bottle of glycerol, and embedding molds (E–44).

1. Transfer the cleared specimens with their labels to a jar of molten paraffin, removing them at this point from their carriers.
2. Infiltrate 2–3 hours under the lamps or in the oven; transfer the material from the first to a second jar during this period, if the clearing agent used is not very volatile.
3. Prepare molds; if they are of glass, metal, or porcelain, rub them with a very small amount of glycerol; have ready the ice water, the pitcher of paraffin under one of the lamps, the lighted bunsen burner, and the tools listed above.
4. Remove the label of the first specimen to be embedded, choose a mold to fit the specimen, and place the label in the mold in such a way that the writing will be visible when the specimen is embedded. Transfer with heated spoon or heated pipet enough paraffin to cover the bottom of the mold and let it cool slightly.
5. With heated forceps or section lifter, place one specimen in the mold, orienting it according to some chosen plan. Cover the specimen well with paraffin since it contracts on cooling. If the paraffin has cooled until a film has formed on its surface, heat the empty pipet and draw up and expel the paraffin in the mold until it is liquid at the surface. Be sure that there are no air bubbles in the paraffin or under the specimen. Blow gently on the surface until a film forms, then incline the mold at a very slight angle and gently slide it beneath the surface of the water. This is a critical part of the operation; too steep an angle or too much haste may cause the surface film to break and some of the molten paraffin to escape. If this happens, permit the block to cool, trim off the excess paraffin, return the block to the melted paraffin, and try again.
5a. If there are a number of identical specimens, a larger mold may be chosen which will accommodate several. In general, follow the directions for 5, but use the spoon or the pitcher to transfer paraffin to the mold and take especial care to form a thick enough sur-

face film, so that it will not break when it is put in the cold water bath.

6. Leave the mold in the water until the paraffin button separates from it and floats in the water. If the block remains in the mold, loosen one edge gently with a scalpel tip; this will usually detach it.

SECTIONING METHODS

VI–18. ATTACHING BLOCKS TO OBJECT CARRIERS. An object embedded in paraffin must be mounted on an object carrier before sectioning. Several types of carrier are in common use (E–47) but whichever one is chosen, the method of attachment of the block to the carrier is essentially the same.

1. Cover the surface of the carrier with molten paraffin. If the wax does not seem firmly attached, heat a spatula or section lifter in a flame and press it firmly on the surface of the paraffin until it melts. It may be necessary to add more paraffin and repeat. The layer of wax should be about 3 mm thick.

2. When it has cooled, heat its surface again with a hot spatula and press the roughly trimmed paraffin block firmly into the softened paraffin.

3. With the hot spatula, press against the sides of the block so that there is no break in continuity of the wax between that of the specimen and of the carrier.

4. Cool in the refrigerator or on a block of ice.

VI–19. TRIMMING BLOCKS. The preliminary trimming before mounting is best done with a single-edged safety razor blade. Remove the wax in relatively thin slices; leave the largest amount of paraffin on the surface that will be attached to the object carrier. Trim the sides and top only roughly; be sure to leave enough wax for the final trimming, which is done after the specimen has been attached to the carrier. For this, one may rely on the accuracy of hand and eye or use a trimming jig (E–83). These directions assume that the technician is skillful enough to dispense with this aid.

Again using a single-edged razor blade, trim the opposite sides of the block that will become the upper and lower surfaces when mounted in the holder of the microtome. These should be the longer sides if the block is rectangular in outline. It is essential that these surfaces be made exactly parallel. The cuts made in trimming should extend a little beyond the lower surface of the specimen leaving a broad base to the trimmed portion by which the block will be supported. Trim the lateral surfaces neatly. Make these parallel to each other or make one lateral surface perpendicular to the upper and lower surfaces and the other at a slight angle. This is recommended by some microtomists and, if properly done, provides a helpful marker for arranging ribbons accurately upon a slide. Make the face of the block that will meet the knife relatively flat and leave enough paraffin above the specimen so that preliminary adjustments in cutting are possible before the knife reaches the tissue. It may be necessary to correct the trimming slightly when the block is in the microtome.

VI–20. CUTTING PARAFFIN SECTIONS ON A ROTARY MICROTOME. Before beginning to section, the inexperienced worker is urged to consult the directions provided with the instrument or Richard's book on the use and care of the microtome (265). See also Figures 4 and 5, and E–50–51.

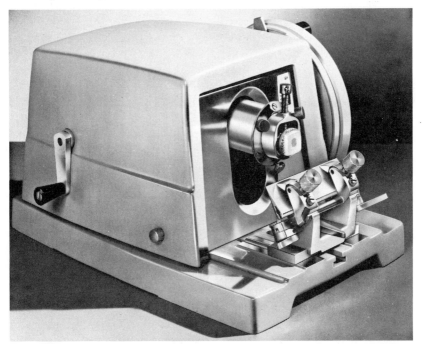

Fig. 4.—Rotary microtome designed particularly for cutting paraffin sections, shown with a carrier in the object clamp. It will also section frozen blocks and nitrocellulose-embedded material that has been cleared in clove oil. (Courtesy of the American Optical Company.)

1. Insert the mounted block on its carrier in the jaws of the object clamp; screw it tightly in place. Adjust the razor blade in the razor-blade holder, so that only the beveled surface of the blade shows above the holder top and fasten the blade tightly in place.

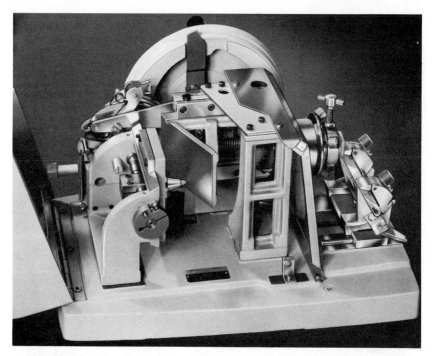

Fig. 5.—Rotary microtome of the same model as Figure 4, opened to show the simple but effective mechanism of the instrument. (Courtesy of the American Optical Company.)

Put the razor-blade holder or a microtome knife in the knife holder; fasten it firmly and adjust it so that it is tilted slightly toward the microtome: about 9 degrees from the perpendicular is usually satisfactory. The angle will vary somewhat according to the type of tissue and should be changed as necessary. Move the knife until it is less than a millimeter from the face of the block and turn the lever which locks the knife holder in place.

2. Adjust the object clamp so that the lower edge of the block is parallel to the knife edge and its face is perpendicular to it. If necessary, readjust the position of the knife. Set the feed indicator to cut at 10μ (this is a good thickness for practice); release the locking device and cautiously turn the wheel clockwise. Continue turning until sections begin to come off. The first ones are usually irregular. Note that as each new section is cut it displaces the last one and, if the paraffin is of proper consistency, it becomes attached by one edge to the displaced section. The first sections should be paraffin only.

3. By the time that the sections are complete and regular they should form a straight, slightly wrinkled ribbon.

4. When the ribbon becomes sufficiently long, support its free end by

a brush or wooden applicator held in the left hand. To prevent breaking the ribbon, avoid pulling it taut. When tissue begins to appear in the sections, discard all but a few of the nonspecimen sections by holding a slip of cardboard under the ribbon and cutting off the redundant part with a sharp scalpel.

5. If it is desired to section the whole block in a single unbroken ribbon, which may be necessary for embryological preparations, wind it on a commercially made roller (AO Spencer makes a good one) or on one made from inexpensive materials (E–54). When the entire block has been sectioned and the ribbon wound on the roller, cut it into segments which fit into a box (E–53) for storage. If shorter ribbons are preferred, cut pieces of a length which will fit easily into a ribbon box. Use a brush to remove each piece from the knife, carefully pushing from the undersurface of the ribbon at its attachment to the edge of the blade. Place each segment of ribbon in the box, keeping its upper surface uppermost, with the first section of the ribbon at the left and the last at the right; place in rows, from top to bottom, so that the serial order of the sections is comparable to the arrangement of letters and words on a printed page. While serial order is not always necessary, it is well to get into the habit of arranging ribbons in this way.

6. Identify the specimen, preferably by copying its label on the paper upon which the ribbons lie; cover the box. Store it in a cool place, if possible a refrigerator. Never leave sections where they will become warm or be exposed to dust or draft.

During the sectioning process it is sometimes necessary to clean the knife edge. For this purpose use facial tissue and wipe up, not down, on both back and front of the blade; avoid touching its edge. If necessary, moisten the tissue with a drop of xylene or benzene. It is good practice to clean a knife edge before beginning to section a new block.

VI–21. COMMON DIFFICULTIES IN SECTIONING AND POSSIBLE CAUSES.

(See a more extended list in Richards, *265*.)

A. The sections fail to form a continuous ribbon. Possible causes are:
    a. the paraffin is too hard;
    b. the microtome or the cutting room is too cold;
    c. the sections are too thick;
    d. the blade is dull.

B. The ribbon is not straight, but curved. Possible causes are:
    a. the blade is dull;
    b. the lower edge of the block is not parallel with the knife;
    c. the upper edge of the block is not properly trimmed: if the

left side is too high the ribbon will curve to the right, and vice versa.

C. The sections curl into a roll as they are cut. Possible causes are:
    a. the paraffin is too hard;
    b. the knife edge is dull;
    c. the angle of the knife is not correct.

D. The sections compress and wrinkle as they are cut. Possible causes are:
    a. the paraffin is too soft;
    b. the angle of the blade is incorrect.

E. There is a scraping or ringing sound as the blade passes through the specimen or as the block returns to position on the upstroke. Possible causes are:
    a. the specimen may be too hard to cut either because of the method of preparation or because of its natural characteristics;
    b. the angle of the blade is incorrect;
    c. the edge of the blade is too thin.

F. The sections vary markedly in thickness. Possible causes are:
    a. the blade or the blade holder is not held firmly in place;
    b. the specimen is not tightly clamped in the object clamp;
    c. the paraffin block is not firmly attached to the object carrier;
    d. if a razor blade is being used for sectioning, its edge projects too far above the razor-blade holder.

G. The sections vary slightly in thickness. Possible cause: the setting for section thickness is not exact. If, for example, it is set between 9 and 10, the sections will be cut alternately at 9 and 10μ, not at 9.5μ.

H. Splits and tears appear in the sections. Possible causes are:
    a. the edge of the blade is defective and has nicks in it;
    b. there is dirt in the paraffin;
    c. there is dirt in or on the embedded specimen; animals such as earthworms and many marine invertebrates which ingest dirt or sand often cause this difficulty unless the alimentary canal receives especial treatment, either before or after sacrifice. Inspection of the block with a hand lens will usually reveal the offending particles.

I. The material crumbles as it is cut or separates from the paraffin matrix. Possible cause: some part of the dehydration, clearing, or infiltrating process is at fault.

J. The ribbons are attracted to the metal of the knife or other parts of the microtome by static electricity which is generated by differences in consistency of specimen and paraffin. Possible causes are:

    a. the specimen is inadequately dehydrated, cleared, or infiltrated;

    b. the specimen is harder than the paraffin.

VI–22. REMEDIES. It may be seen by considering this list of difficulties that a single fault, such as a dull blade or improper blade angle, may produce several unfortunate results. It is, therefore, useful to try first to correct the faults that result in the most trouble. If the blade is dull, the condition may be corrected by moving it in the holder so that another portion will be used or by using a fresh one. If this does not have the desired effect, the knife angle should be altered. Several adjustments of the angle may be necessary before it can be determined whether this is the cause of the difficulty.

Excessively hard paraffin suggests warming the block by placing a lamp near it. To determine whether the paraffin is too soft, an ice cube may be held against the block surface and more sections cut at once. If the condition of the knife edge is not the cause of cuts or tears in a ribbon and the paraffin is found to be dirty, it may be worthwhile to reimbed the specimen; there is no good remedy for dirt in the alimentary canal of the specimen. Unless it is of great importance it should be discarded and others prepared, with dirt removed before embedding. Most of the other troubles suggest their own remedies except those caused by static electricity. These can be virtually eliminated by use of a Neutra-Stat (E–46).

To prevent the formation of static electricity, it is important to be sure that dehydration, clearing, and infiltration are complete and that the paraffin and specimen are of about equal density. The difficulty is also sometimes avoided if the technician, when sectioning, is careful to wear shoes that do not have rubber soles.

SPREADING PARAFFIN SECTIONS ON GLASS SLIDES

The process of spreading is relatively simple. The slightly wrinkled and compressed sections are extended or spread on water with gentle heat, arranged neatly on a slide, and again laid on a warm surface where the remainder of the water is evaporated. Uncomplicated as this seems, it may be a source of considerable trouble in making paraffin preparations unless it is carefully performed. The slides must be chemically clean, the sections must be completely extended, and they must make contact everywhere with the slide surface. If these three requirements are not met, the sections will not adhere well to the slide during subsequent treatment.

Although it is possible to spread slides successfully without the use of an affixative, it is routine procedure to use some material in spreading that will make the adhesion more sure. There are a number of available formulae for these affixatives. Those which we have found most satisfactory are Mayer's albumen (F–7) and Haupt's gelatin affixative (F–110). The albumen is either wiped on the slide in a thin film or mixed with the water used in spreading. The gelatin mixture is put on the slide as a thin film, and the sections are spread on a 2% formalin solution.

There are two technics for spreading. In one, a segment of ribbon is floated on the surface of water warmed to a suitable temperature; it is transferred to a slide, placed on a spreading table, and the process completed there. In the other method, water is placed on a slide, a segment of ribbon is added and the slide put on a warming table until the sections have extended fully.

Equipment and supplies: A tissue flotation bath and/or spreading table both, preferably, thermostatically controlled; chemically clean glass slides (E–66); one or more slide diagrams (E–20); fine-tipped forceps; a needle; a section lifter; a scalpel for cutting ribbons into segments (E–59); a glass scriber (E–60); rectangles of bibulous paper (E–5) about 25 × 50 mm; dropping bottles of affixatives; freshly boiled water or 2% formalin in a dropping bottle.

VI–23.   SPREADING SECTIONS ON A FLOTATION BATH (E–3).

1.   Set the heat control of the bath to maintain the water at about 40°C; if the sections do not become flat at this temperature, increase it slightly.

2.   Prepare the needed number of clean slides by smearing on a thin film of Mayer's albumen with a clean finger and wiping off any excess.

3.   Place a ribbon segment on the water of the bath. When it is free of wrinkles, lower one end of a prepared slide below the sections, hold it in place with a needle, and lift the slide. Add more water if necessary. Place the slide on a diagram and center the specimen carefully; move the section with a needle or with the edges of the bibulous paper.

4.   Lay the slide on a spreading table set at about 42°C. After 1 or 2 minutes, tilt it so that excess water collects at one side of the paraffin; remove it with an edge of a piece of bibulous paper. Return the slide to the table for several hours to dry.

5.   Label each slide, before it is spread, with a glass scriber.

VI–24.   SPREADING SECTIONS ON A SPREADING TABLE (E–69).

1.   Set the heat control so that the surface temperature will be about 42°C. This temperature may be raised slightly if the material has

been prepared in hard paraffin. The temperature must not be high enough *under any circumstance* to melt the paraffin.

2. Boil water for several minutes in an Erlenmeyer flask; cool. Mix 6 drops of Mayer's albumen in 100 ml of water and put the solution in a dropping bottle.

3. Place enough of the albumen water on a slide to float a section or piece of ribbon; put section(s) on the slide and the slide on the spreading table. When the section is fully extended, drain the water onto a piece of absorbent paper, put the slide on a diagram, center the specimen(s) with a needle and/or a strip of bibulous paper, and return the slide to the table. After about 2 minutes tilt the slide, allowing any surplus water to collect at the lower edge of the paraffin and remove it with a strip of the paper.

4. Lay the slide on the warm table to dry; it may be ready in a few hours, but it is safer to leave it overnight. Label each slide with a glass scriber.

Instead of Mayer's albumen, Haupt's gelatin affixative may be used by varying this schedule slightly. Prepare the clean slide for use by spreading on it a thin film of the gelatin solution. Add formalin solution and the ribbon; place the slide on a spreading table and proceed as in steps 3 and 4. If the material is difficult to affix to the slides, the sections may be transferred after drying to a 40°C oven and kept overnight, in a horizontal position, in fumes of strong formalin.

VI–25. SPREADING TORN SECTIONS. It occasionally happens that a valuable specimen has cut badly, and the sections are torn or distorted. If the ribbons are not to be mounted serially, it may be possible to obtain reasonably good preparations by using Speece's method of spreading (*296*). His procedure is:

1. Spread, with a glass rod, about half a drop of Haupt's gelatin affixative over a small part of a slide which has been cleaned with detergent or Bon Ami. Add a drop of full-strength neutral formalin.

2. Transfer one of the better specimens to the formalin with a brush; and add to it a drop of xylene. The xylene dissolves the paraffin, and the section expands immediately; no heat is applied.

3. Remove excess fluid with bibulous paper or smooth filter paper, pressing the section firmly against the affixative-coated slide. Before it dries, transfer the slide to a jar of xylene.

4. Run down and stain the slides as usual.

VI–26. SPREADING SECTIONS IN SERIAL ORDER. It is best to use a spreading table, not a flotation bath.

1. Cut the ribbon into segments which will fit under a rectangular

cover glass. Allow for an expansion in length of about one quarter during spreading. Thus, if you intend to use a 22 × 55-mm cover, each segment of ribbon should be about 37 mm long, since it will expand to almost 50 mm during spreading. It is unsatisfactory to measure each segment. Determine the average number of sections in 37-mm lengths of ribbon and cut each segment to contain this average number. Assume, for an example, that there are 15 sections in most 37-mm lengths of ribbon and cut segments with 15 sections in each. It is better to have too few than too many in a row, since those nearest the edge tend to show fading of stain in time.

2.   Determine the number of rows of segments that will fit a 22-mm space. If three rows will fit easily, each slide in the proposed series except the last one will carry 45 sections; the number of sections in a block seldom comes out even.

3.   Use or prepare a mounting diagram that centers a 22 × 50-mm rectangle in a 50-mm space at the right or left end of the slide. Number the slides that will be needed in serial order with a glass scriber. Place slide 1 on the diagram; add albumen water and the three segments of ribbon in proper order; section 1 will be at the upper left-hand corner, 16 and 31 below it, with section 45 at the lower right.

4.   With the slide on the spreading table, watch the sections as they extend. If the rows curve slightly, it is often possible to straighten them by holding a needle point against the curving part for a short time.

5.   When the wrinkles have disappeared, remove the slide from the spreading table, let it cool, drain off excess water and, replacing it on the diagram, arrange the sections so that they will be centered under the cover glass and will lie in straight lines. It may be necessary to cut the paraffin between a few of the sections if the ribbon is curved. It is very important to have straight rows which facilitate microscopic study.

6.   When the arrangement is completed, return the slide to the spreading table, remove surplus water, make any necessary final adjustments in position, and dry. Serial sections may be mounted equally well with Haupt's gelatin affixative.

SPREADING PARAFFIN SECTIONS ON COVER GLASSES

It may at times be desirable to attach paraffin sections to cover glasses rather than to slides. The spread cover glasses can then be treated as slides are, either singly or in staining dishes or racks designed to fit them. Several types of these are available (E–23). When the reagents used in any process are expensive, the cover glass preparations may well be considered, since smaller amounts of reagents are required. A further advantage is that more than one section from the same block, each with a different stain, and each on a separate cover, may be mounted on the same slide for comparison.

This method is described by Ashley (*12*). In discussing its advantages, some of which are cited above, he points out that focusing with an immersion lens is much easier when the specimen is directly beneath the cover than when separated from it by a layer of mountant.

VI–27. ASHLEY'S DIRECTIONS are summarized as follows:
1. Float single paraffin sections on water kept at about 45°C, until wrinkles have disappeared.
2. Dip a cover glass that has been thinly smeared with Mayer's albumen into the water and bring it up under a single section, holding the section in place if necessary with a needle. Center with the needle or with bibulous paper; remove excess water with bibulous paper, and place on a spreading table in a horizontal position overnight.
3. Carry out desired staining technics in a Columbia jar or a cover glass staining rack.

SPREADING SECTIONS ON 35-MM FILM

This technic, which was the result of the work of several persons in different laboratories, was introduced commercially in 1959 by the Carolina Biological Supply Company in an article in their publication, *Carolina Tips*. In addition to offering prepared slides on film, they gave directions for making them. For two purposes, at least, sections mounted on film are particularly desirable. (1) Serial sections of embryos may be spread in a single row on a piece of film as long as required. This avoids a considerable amount of trouble in study. The preparations are durable and easy to handle. (2) Single sections may be prepared on film and mounted in 2 × 2-inch slide binders. In these they may be projected with a 35-mm projector or with a microprojector. They may also, of course, be studied in the usual way under a microscope. We have found that many features of brain structure of small animals may be well demonstrated in such preparations, using sections cut through the whole brain at appropriate levels.

VI–28. THE METHOD FOR PREPARING SECTIONS ON FILM is taken from *Carolina Tips* (*59*) and does not differ in many respects from more conventional technics. The reader is also referred to this article for references.
1. Cut 35-mm film without emulsion (E–30) into 75-mm strips if a preparation of conventional size is to be made.

2.   Put a drop of albumen water on the strip, add a section, place on a spreading table set at about 42°C, and leave until the section is well extended; or

2*a*.   Rub a minute drop of albumen over a segment of film and place it beneath a section which has been spread in a container of water warmed to about 45°C. Lift the film, holding the section in place with a needle; place on a spreading table.

3.   Drain the water from the section, put it on a diagram (E–20), and arrange as desired.

4.   Return the film to the warm table, reheat, tilt, remove excess water with bibulous paper, and leave on the table until thoroughly dry.

5.   Decerate and stain in the usual way; dehydrate, clear in xylene, and spray with an acrylic spray or dip in plastic (R–28) before the xylene evaporates.

6.   Dry thoroughly.

Sections may be studied in oil, directly, with an immersion lens. It is better, when using a 4-mm lens, to place a drop of immersion oil on the specimen and add a thin cover. Before returning the preparation to its storage container, remove the oil and the cover by immersion in xylene. Drain the preparation, air-dry, and store.

WATER WAX METHODS

Water-soluble waxes (R–200), in which specimens may be infiltrated and cut, have come into limited use rather recently. They have a special application where the tissue constituents to be studied are soluble in the reagents used in paraffin and celloidin technics. They are thus useful in some histochemical methods. The most commonly used waxes are polyethylene glycols. In the Carbowax series there are a number of grades designated by numbers, which, with the exception of 1500, represent the average molecular weights of their components. The numbers are 200, 300, 400, 600, 1000, 1500, 1540, 4000, and 6000. The Carbowax brochure (57) states that as "molecular weight increases, water solubility, vapor pressure, hygroscopicity, and solubility in organic solvents decrease while freezing or melting range . . . and viscosity increase." Numbering of the Dow series (93) is similar, but does not always agree exactly with the molecular weight. Hartman-Leddon markets a water-soluble wax which they call H.E.M. Their catalog description says that it "has physical characteristics similar to those of Carbowax." Two water waxes, available in England under trade names, are Gurr's Michrome Water Wax (A–27) and Hydrowax (A–26). We have used both the Hartman-Leddon wax and Carbowax with good results and understand that the media produced by Dow are equally satisfactory; several authors recommend the English waxes.

Since the waxes vary in hardness and hygroscopic properties, they are often mixed to produce a medium suitable for particular climatic conditions. Hale (*143*) made a careful study of these points and demonstrated that relatively high humidity interferes with sectioning and that the higher the temperature, the lower the atmospheric humidity must be for successful sectioning. The waxes may be used diluted as dehydrators; more often the washed tissue is placed directly in the molten wax for infiltration. Spreading and affixing to slides is more difficult than with paraffin sections; various means have been used to cope with this difficulty. It appears that the technician may have to try several of the methods recommended before finding one that is personally satisfactory.

If block staining is possible for the type of tissue under preparation, it simplifies treatment of the sections after spreading.

VI–29. WADE'S CARBOWAX METHOD (*321*) uses 2 grades of Carbowax (R–26). His technic was developed especially for making sections of leprosy skin lesions, but is satisfactory for normal skin and for other tissues. He uses mixtures of Carbowax 1540 and 4000 in the following proportions by weight: 1:9, 2:8, and 1.5:8.5. The last mixture is suitable for more variations in temperature and humidity than the others; the 2:8 mixture is best except in very hot and humid weather.

1. Put the waxes together in a beaker in the paraffin oven at 56°C where the mixture may be kept indefinitely.
2. Place washed specimens in the wax and infiltrate 1–3 hours; large specimens may require even longer. Agitate the tissues occasionally; one change of wax is desirable.
3. Block in boats (E–8), but do not place the boats in water; cool in a refrigerator. When well set, store in moistureproof containers, still in the boats and at room temperature.
4. Mount blocks and section as usual, taking particular pains to keep upper and lower edges of the block parallel with each other and with the knife edge. If there is difficulty in ribboning, apply with a brush a 25% solution of beeswax in chloroform to the upper and lower surfaces of the block in a uniform layer. When it is dull-dry, begin to section again; this method usually causes the sections to adhere to each other. If sections separate on cutting, it may be helpful to set the block aside, exposed to air, for a day or two; it then often sections well.
5. To spread the ribbons, use slides prepared by smearing on egg albumen very thinly and wiping off the excess. Dry these slides overnight at room temperature or dry them in the paraffin oven at 37°C for at least 3 hours. Place a few drops of distilled water containing 0.005% Tergitol 7 (R–187) on the albumenized slide and lay a segment of ribbon upon it. Manipulate with a needle

to orient properly and drain gently. The matrix will dissolve rapidly. Dry well.

6.   Stain the sections as usual. Since a small amount of wax usually remains on the slide, a preliminary washing in water is desirable.

Because spreading and affixing water-wax sections to slides is one of the most difficult parts of the whole technic, it seems desirable to give several alternative methods which have been found successful.

VI–30.   BLANK AND McCARTHY (39) float a section on their gelatin-dichromate mixture (F–33), place a slide beneath the section, lift it, arrange the specimen, and dry it. No heat is applied; the matrix of the section dissolves as the section is placed on the solution.

VI–31.   GIOVACCHINI'S METHOD (121) is to smear a slide thinly with his affixative (F–99), place a section on a slide, and leave it on a spreading table at 58–60°C for 15 minutes. It is transferred to an oven set at 58°C for 24 hours. An alternative to this method is to smear the slide with a very small amount of the gelatin mixture, float a section on water at room temperature, pick it up with the treated slide, orient, and dry in a dust-free place, 4 hours.

VI–32.   DOUBLE EMBEDDING IN CARBOWAX AND IN PAR-AFFIN is reported by Goland, Jason, and Berry (124) to be an improvement over single embedding in paraffin, with respect to tissue distortion. They used various grades of polyethylene glycols in their experiments; their blocks of tissue were 2 mm thick and fixed in either formalin or alcohol.

1.   Wash blocks in water and infiltrate in water wax at 61°C, 4 hours.
2.   Transfer to xylene at 61°C for 10 minutes and then to molten paraffin at 61°C for 30 minutes.
3.   Embed by the usual method for paraffin, including submersion in cold water.
4.   Mount on wooden blocks, chill in a refrigerator, and section at 6μ.
5.   Spread on a water bath (VI–23), mount on slides, and dry or spread on slides on a spreading table (VI–24). (No affixative is suggested by the authors, but the use of Mayer's albumen is a reasonable precaution.)
6.   Stain formalin-fixed material directly in Sudan III (1% solution in 70% alcohol) for demonstration of lipids. Mount in an aqueous mountant or
6a.   Stain alcohol-fixed material with Best's carmine for glycogen (XIII–5).
Results: The sections cut as readily as do good paraffin sections.

Glycogen is stained in the alcohol-fixed material; intracellular lipid particles are stained in formalin specimens. There is no apparent loss of lipid from sections of adrenals as a result of the 10-minute immersion in xylene.

The only materials for which this method is unsatisfactory are those which contain large amounts of adipose tissue.

NITROCELLULOSE METHODS

The term nitrocellulose is applied to two embedding media. The one which has been longest in use is called, in the United States, by a number of names including celloidin, collodion, and Parlodion; the last is a trade name. It is sold in dry strips and is relatively expensive. The low-viscosity nitrocellulose, R.S. 0.5 second (R–142), costs less and is more commonly used at present; its abbreviated designation is LVN.

Of the two varieties of LVN produced, one is made from wood and the other from cotton linters; the latter is preferred by most histologists. It is shipped, moistened by 30% of denatured ethanol, and should be handled strictly according to the manufacturer's directions (F–152), since it is very flammable and, under some conditions, explosive. Directions for making solutions of Parlodion and LVN are simple (F–153, 154). It is also possible to obtain commercial solutions of the latter (R–118); they are more expensive but are also time saving; they are safer for inexperienced technicians.

Nitrocellulose is an excellent embedding medium. Sections cut from nitrocellulose blocks usually show fewer artifacts than those embedded in paraffin. Large specimens can be more successfully sectioned in it than in other embedding media. Since, however, the sections are more difficult and more time-consuming to prepare than those made in paraffin, its use should be reserved for preparations which justify the extra time and effort. Routine preparations for ordinary histological purposes should be otherwise prepared.

The nitrocellulose preparation typically involves dehydration, passage into the nitrocellulose solvent, infiltration with the nitrocellulose solution, embedding, and then hardening of the block. Usually the sections are cut on a sliding microtome, although a rotary microtome is used under some circumstances.

The following method is satisfactory and not difficult. It is especially applicable to small specimens.

VI–33.   EMBEDDING IN PARLODION, Carothers (60).

1.   Dehydrate in the usual alcohol series to absolute ethanol; leave in the absolute alcohol 3–6 hours, 2 changes. The times may be altered for unusually large or small specimens.

2.   Transfer to absolute alcohol-ether, 1:1/vol, 1 hour.
3.   Place in a 2% Parlodion solution in ether-alcohol, 1:1/vol, in a container of appropriate size that can be tightly closed. Keep it closed during infiltration, several days to weeks, according to the size of the specimen.
4.   Loosen the cover enough to permit gradual evaporation of the solvent. When it is somewhat viscous, orient the tissue for cutting.
5.   Continue gradual evaporation until the Parlodion is firm; then loosen its edges and remove from the container.
6.   Trim the block, leaving about a millimeter of matrix on the top and sides of the specimen and several millimeters below it. Return it to the covered container, with a chloroform-saturated piece of cotton, for further hardening.
7.   When it is sufficiently firm, place the base of the block briefly in alcohol-ether to soften and press it firmly in a large drop of thick nitrocellulose on a fiber block (E–47). In about 10 minutes, return it to chloroform vapor to harden the fresh Parlodion; after a few hours, immerse the block in 70% alcohol. Leave in alcohol at least overnight before cutting; it may remain indefinitely.
8.   Cut sections on the sliding microtome (Fig. 6).

Some workers prefer to infiltrate by transferring the specimen to increasing concentrations of Parlodion up to 10%, instead of permitting evaporation of the solvent from a weak solution. For small specimens this is certainly not necessary. For larger ones it may be desirable.

VI–34. EMBEDDING IN LOW VISCOSITY NITROCELLULOSE (LVN). This reagent in amyl acetate is considered by many workers to be superior to ether-alcohol solutions of nitrocellulose as an embedding medium. Bennett (29) seems to have been the first person to employ this solvent with LVN, although its use with celloidin was proposed by Barron (22). The method below is essentially that described by Bennett. It is much more rapid than the VI–33 method, because of the superior penetrating power of amyl acetate and the low viscosity of the solutions.

1.   Have ready these solutions of LVN in amyl acetate: 10%, 20%, 30%, 40% (F–154).
2.   Dehydrate tissues in ethanol: 25%, 50%, 75%, and absolute, an hour or more in each depending on the size of the specimens; transfer to 30%, 50%, and 80% amyl acetate in absolute ethanol.
3.   Place in pure amyl acetate, 2 changes, 1 hour or more in each.
4.   Infiltrate in the solutions of LVN in amyl acetate, beginning with the 10% solution, 24 hours in each.
5.   Block specimens in glass dishes rubbed with a small amount of mineral oil, using fresh portions of the 40% solution. Place them

in a closed container with chloroform fumes until set; then immerse the blocks in chloroform, 2 changes, 12–24 hours each.

6. Mount the specimens on fiber blocks as in Carother's method (VI–33) and store in 80% alcohol or in a mixture of 95% alcohol and glycerol, 1:1/vol. The unmounted blocks may also be stored in either solution, but must be returned to 95% alcohol and be well dehydrated before being placed on fiber blocks.

7. Cut under 80% alcohol on a sliding microtome (VI–35).

Baird and Henson (*13*), who have used this method for decalcified heads of animals as large as *Erinaceus*, the European hedgehog, found that for specimens of this type and size it is better to have a longer series of LVN-amyl acetate solutions; they used the following percentages: 10, 15, 20, 25, 30, and 40. Increased time of immersion in each mixture was also necessary. Superior results were obtained by using negative pressure for the specimens in the 10% solution.

Nultsch (*238*) recommends the employment of tetrahydrofuran (THF) as a nitrocellulose solvent. Since it is also a tissue dehydrator, its use somewhat simplifies the preparation of nitrocellulose sections.

VI–35. CUTTING NITROCELLULOSE SECTIONS ON A SLIDING MICROTOME.

1. Study carefully both the microtome which will be used and the manufacturer's directions which accompany each instrument. Consult also Richard's manual (*265*) on microtomes. Examine Figure 6. Note particularly the devices for:
   a. attaching the block to the holder and adjusting the position of the block;
   b. regulating section thickness;
   c. attaching the knife and adjusting its angle;
   d. moving the knife to cut a section.

2. Make sure that the sliding surfaces are clean and well lubricated.

3. Fasten the knife in the knife holder. Place the block in the object carrier with its longest side parallel to the long axis of the microtome. Adjust the height of the block so that its upper surface is just level with the knife edge. Now swing the knife into such a position that it will slice through the specimen with a long, drawing cut for at least half the length of the blade.

4. Set the screw for regulating section thickness to cut at 15–20μ, if the microtome is not a familiar one. Otherwise set it as desired.

5. Flood both knife and block with 70% alcohol. Both should be kept wet while sections are being cut.

6. Draw the knife through the block with a straight, steady pull; avoid lifting or pulling down on the knife carrier.

7. Make a few preliminary sections; it is helpful if there is enough

Fɪɢ. 6.—Sliding microtome, designed for cutting nitrocellulose sections. By attaching a freezing head (see Fig. 3) in place of the object carrier, it may be used for making frozen sections. (Courtesy of the American Optical Company.)

celloidin over the specimen so that practice sections may be cut and all necessary adjustments made before the specimen is reached. Remove each section with a soft brush to a flat container of 70% alcohol. If they are to be kept in serial order, collect in a wide-mouth shallow jar and place filter paper, cut to proper size, between successive sections. When cutting is completed, remove the knife and dry it thoroughly. Empty the drip pan, if the microtome has one. Dry all smooth metal surfaces with especial care, and oil the slideway. Be sure to keep all other parts of the microtome well oiled.

VI–36. CUTTING NITROCELLULOSE SECTIONS ON A ROTARY MICROTOME may be accomplished by Walls' method (324), which we have found very satisfactory.

1.   After the specimen is blocked and the fresh nitrocellulose used in mounting has hardened (VI–34, step 6), transfer it to cedar oil

(R–145) and chloroform 1:1/vol, several hours, thence to pure cedar oil until it is completely clear.

2. Cut on a rotary microtome as if the block were of paraffin. The sections do not ribbon. If serial sections are needed each must be removed separately and stored in cedar oil, in order, between pieces of paper. Unless the tissue has been stained in block, it will be necessary to pass it to the solvent of the stain to be used and then to stain, dehydrate, and treat with oil of cloves as in VI–37, step 2.

VI–37. MOUNTING NITROCELLULOSE SECTIONS ON SLIDES, Carothers (60).

1. Transfer sections from 70% alcohol, either singly or in serial order, to a clean slide. Cover smoothly with a thin sheet of smooth hard tissue, such as cigarette paper, well moistened with alcohol; place several layers of bibulous paper on the tissue and roll lightly but firmly with a cylindrical object for about 10 seconds. The sections are thus pressed against the glass, and the alcohol is absorbed.
2. Peel off the paper and flood the sections at once with clove oil; leave it on the slide until the sections are translucent, usually 8–10 minutes. The oil dissolves enough of the nitrocellulose to affix the sections firmly.
3. Drain off the oil, and transfer the slide to 95% alcohol; after 15 minutes, replace with fresh alcohol of the same grade. When the clove oil has been completely removed, transfer to 70% alcohol.
4. Treat the slide, from this point, as if it carried paraffin sections which had been decerated.

An alternate method of affixing is to place the section(s) on a slide smeared with a thin layer of Mayer's albumen; follow the procedure in step 1 above and then immerse the slide quickly in 95% alcohol, at least 10 minutes before transferring to 70% alcohol.

VI–38. WILLIAMS' GELATIN METHOD FOR MOUNTING SERIAL NITROCELLULOSE SECTIONS (335).

1. Coat clean slides by dipping them into a warm solution of 1% gelatin; drain and dry in a nearly vertical position.
2. Cut sections; lay them in order on blotting paper which has been moistened well with 70% alcohol and placed in a flat, shallow dish with a cover.
3. Pick up each section with fine forceps, by the nitrocellulose edge; dip in 70% alcohol, and arrange in order on the coated slide.
4. Blot each completed slide with dry filter paper and press sections into firm contact with the gelatin. Place the slide in a covered

coplin jar containing 2–3 ml of undiluted formalin, 2–3 hours at room temperature. The formalin must not touch the sections. Transfer to 70% alcohol for storage; or stain after 20 minutes in the alcohol.

5. During these procedures do not allow the sections to dry out at any time; if they dry they will shrink.

VI–39. STAINING NITROCELLULOSE SECTIONS. Sections which have been embedded in nitrocellulose often stain more brilliantly than do sections in paraffin. It may, therefore, be necessary to use more dilute solutions than usual. The matrix stains rather deeply with many aniline dyes and, if this is a disadvantage, the nitrocellulose may be removed after the sections are on the slides, either before or after they are stained. The sections are stained either unmounted, in dishes, or mounted on the slide. The choice depends somewhat on the type and size of the sections as well as on the preference of the technician. In general, small serial sections are more easily handled if they are mounted before staining. If sections are to be stained in alum hematoxylin, time is saved by applying this stain in block before infiltration (XI–13). Mounted sections are stained in much the same way as paraffin sections.

VI–40. STAINING NITROCELLULOSE SECTIONS BEFORE MOUNTING. The general method is the same, whatever stain is used. The sections are cut, received in 70% alcohol, and kept in it until staining is begun. They are transferred to petri dishes and hydrated, if the stain is aqueous, or passed into the solvent of a nonaqueous stain. Each section may be treated separately or a dishful, all from the same block, may be stained at the same time. Sections are lifted from one dish to another with a glass rod, a brush, or a section lifter; or a container with a perforated bottom (E–79) may be lifted from one solution to the next. An example of the latter technic follows:

1. Hydrate sections from 70% alcohol in an alcohol series.
2. Transfer one section to Harris' hematoxylin (F–16) and examine it at intervals until the nuclei are overstained; time the staining period; transfer the section to tap water. With the time for these sections thus determined, stain the whole dishful accordingly; check each section briefly under the microscope to be sure that the timing was correct and transfer to tap water.
3. Dehydrate through 30 and 50 to 70% alcohol; transfer to acid alcohol (F–5) until the nitrocellulose is at least partly destained; be sure to avoid too much destaining of the nuclei.
4. Blue in 70% alcohol containing a few drops of sodium bicarbonate, sat sol; rinse in fresh 70% alcohol.

5. Transfer to eosin in 95% alcohol, 30–60 seconds; rinse out excess with one or more baths of 95% ethanol; then change to 99% isopropanol (R–107) to complete dehydration. Transfer to a slide and blot. Clear in beechwood creosote (R–13), oil of origanum (R–146), or carbol-xylol (F–49).

6. Rinse in xylene and mount in synthetic resin.

If the tissue has been stained with hematoxylin *in toto* before infiltration, sections should be examined for depth of staining; if overstained, dehydrate to 70% alcohol as in step 3, and differentiate with acid alcohol until the nuclei are clear and distinct. When the staining is correct, proceed with steps 4, 5, and 6.

Nitrocellulose sections, particularly thick ones, may be troublesome to mount after staining; they tend to curl or wrinkle. If this difficulty occurs, clear them in clove oil, which gradually dissolves the matrix, and rinse in xylene; then cover with xylene-resin and apply the cover glass. It may be helpful to place a weight on the cover (E–86).

Many other stains are suitable for nitrocellulose sections. The azan modification of Mallory's triple stain (VII–7) makes brilliant preparations.

VI–41. STAINING NITROCELLULOSE SECTIONS CUT FROM BLOCKS CLEARED IN CEDAR OIL (VI–36).

1. If the sections have been stored in cedar oil, transfer to 95% ethanol, several changes, to remove the oil.

2. Arrange sections on clean slides. Mount by method VI–37 or VI–38.

3. Run the mounted slides down to water.

4. Transfer to azocarmine solution (F–111A) diluted 1:10 with water; after 5 minutes, observe the process of staining microscopically until nuclei are deeply red.

5. Rinse in tap water; transfer to 1% phosphomolybdic acid until the cytoplasmic staining is reduced and the nuclei are still well stained.

6. Rinse in water, transfer to F–111B diluted 1:5 with water, 2–3 minutes or until the collagen in the section is well stained.

7. Rinse in water; transfer directly to 95% ethanol, absolute ethanol, 2 changes, absolute ethanol-xylene 1:1/vol, and pure xylene, 2 minutes in each reagent.

8. Mount in xylene-resin.

DOUBLE EMBEDDING METHODS

Specimens which are particularly difficult to section or which are irreplaceable are sometimes embedded first in nitrocellulose and then in paraffin, a process called double embedding. The sections ribbon and can thus be easily kept in serial order; they also have little tendency to wrinkle. The method is somewhat more laborious than embedding in either paraffin or nitrocellose alone. It should be used when it will produce superior results.

Double embedding in nitrocellulose and paraffin may be carried out in two ways. In one, the nitrocellulose block is prepared in the conventional fashion (VI–34) and, after chloroform hardening, it is trimmed closely, cleared, and embedded in paraffin. In the other, the specimen is well infiltrated with nitrocellulose but not embedded, and is transferred to chloroform, which both hardens the nitrocellulose and clears; it is then infiltrated with paraffin in the usual way.

VI–42. TO EMBED A BLOCKED CELLOIDIN SPECIMEN.
1.   Transfer the hardened block to chloroform, 2 or 3 changes. Remove, when transparent, to molten paraffin.
2.   Infiltrate, block, section, stain, and mount by the ordinary paraffin methods.

VI–43. BENNETT'S MODIFICATION OF PETERFI'S METHOD (29) is an example of the second method of double embedding.
1.   Dehydrate tissues through an alcohol series and 2 changes of absolute alcohol.
2.   Transfer to 2% LVN in methyl benzoate, 24 hours; then 10% LVN in the same solvent, 24 hours.
3.   Clear in benzene, 2 changes, 30 minutes each.
4.   Place in benzene saturated with paraffin, 30–60 minutes.
5.   Infiltrate in paraffin, and treat thereafter as usual for paraffin blocks.

EMBEDDING IN PLASTICS

Until recently, embedding in plastics that harden when polymerized has been a technic limited to electron microscopy. The hard, small blocks, cut on an ultramicrotome with a glass or diamond knife, yield excellent sections a fraction of a micron thick. It is, however, impossible with the casting mixtures used for electron microscope preparations to cut the larger and thicker sections usually needed for study with the light microscope.

Recently several modifications of the technics for electron microscopy have been proposed which permit the use of larger blocks of tissue and the cutting of sections ranging in thickness from 1–15μ. The methods are promising, not only for the preparation of tissues which are to be studied both with electron and light microscopes, but also for material difficult to cut in thin sections.

VI–44. CATHEY'S PLASTIC EMBEDDING METHOD (63).

Solutions: see F–52.

1. Fix blocks not more than 5 mm on a side in Zenker-formalin, Bouin's PFA, formalin-sublimate, neutral formalin, or Heidenhain's susa. Wash and, if necessary, remove deposits of mercury (III–20).
2. Dehydrate in 70% ethanol overnight; then in acetone, 3 changes, with 1 hour in each.
3. Place in solution I, 2 hours; solution II, 2 hours in a covered dish at room temperature.
4. Place tissues in McJunkin glass staining dishes (E–22). Fill completely with solution III; cover with a glass plate, and put in a 50°C oven overnight.
5. Remove the dishes from the oven and place in cold water; when cooled, remove from the dish with the point of a knife.
6. Cut out the blocks with a fine-tooth saw; trim excess plastic from the specimen; attach to block carriers with softened Carbowax 4000 (R–26), using a heated spatula.
7. Cut on a rotary microtome using a steel knife, at $1-15\mu$ as desired; Cathey uses a Leitz model no. 1212 and a no. 1234 C-profile knife; keep block and knife wet with 30% ethanol. Transfer the sections from the knife to 95% ethanol with a small brush, then to a mixture of 80% absolute ethanol, 16% butyl cellosolve, and 4% formalin.
8. Coat slides with a thin film of Mayer's albumen and heat briefly over a flame until the albumen begins to fume. Mount the sections with a fine sable brush and press flat with filter paper. Dry at 37°C, 3–4 hours.
9. Transfer to methyl Cellosolve acetate or to acetone, 2 changes, 10 minutes in each; this removes the plastic.
10. Stain as usual.

Results: There is relative freedom from shrinkage and compression artifacts.

CHAPTER VII

HISTOLOGICAL STAINS OF GENERAL APPLICATION AND A FEW SPECIAL METHODS

PARAFFIN SECTIONS: PREPARATION FOR STAINING AND TREATMENT AFTER STAINING

Spread slides must first have the paraffin removed—deceration or de-waxing—and then be carried to the fluid in which the stain is dissolved, which is generally water. Since the commonly used decerating reagents, xylene and benzene, are not miscible with water, some intermediate steps are necessary. Following staining, unless the slides are to be treated with an aqueous mountant, the water is removed and the slides are carried into the solvent of the mountant.

The removal of paraffin and transfer to water is called the deceration-hydration schedule; the preparation of the stained slide for mounting is called the dehydration-clearing schedule. Often the same reagents are used for both, but in reverse order. For example, one may decerate in xylene, hydrate through a graded series of alcohols, stain in an aqueous mixture and, after washing in water, dehydrate in the same grades of alcohol, clear in xylene, and mount in xylene-resin.

It is convenient to make up the reagents for these schedules in two series and to put them in labeled and numbered bottles; each label of the deceration-hydration schedule should be marked DOWN and each label of the dehydration-clearing schedule should be marked UP. The labels should also carry the name(s) of the reagent(s) and be numbered in order of use. Most of the reagents may be re-used many times unless they become much contaminated with stains or with water.

AN ALCOHOL-XYLENE SERIES may be made up with ethanol, methanol, or isopropanol. The following is a typical set.
DOWN: xylene (1), xylene (2), xylene-95% alcohol 1:1 (3), 95% alcohol (4), 70% alcohol (5), 50% alcohol (6), 30% alcohol (7). UP: 30%

alcohol (1), 50% alcohol (2), 70% alcohol (3), 95% alcohol (4), 95% alcohol containing 10 to 20% pure butanol (5), 95% alcohol-xylene 1:1 (6), xylene (7), xylene (8).

When xylene 7 in the UP series shows any sign of a whitish cloud, which indicates the presence of water, it should be poured into a bottle for used xylene and stored for various cleaning purposes; xylene 8 should be poured into the xylene 7 bottle after rinsing it with 95% alcohol-xylene 1:1/vol and draining well; fresh xylene from stock should be placed in the xylene 8 bottle.

A CELLOSOLVE-XYLENE SERIES may be made as follows:
DOWN: xylene (1); xylene (2); xylene-Cellosolve 1:1 (3); Cellosolve (4); Cellosolve (5); Cellosolve-water 1:1 (6) Up: Cellosolve-water 1:1 (1); Cellosolve (2); Cellosolve (3); Cellosolve-xylene 1:1 (4); xylene (5); xylene (6).

TRIETHYL PHOSPHATE may be substituted for Cellosolve in the above series with equally good results.
Benzene may be used in place of xylene in any series.

VII–1. APPLICATION OF THE REAGENTS TO THE SLIDES.
When a number of slides are stained at one time, the following is a suitable procedure for deceration-hydration and dehydration-clearing.
1. Place the reagent bottles on the laboratory bench in the order in which they will be used and then put in front of each bottle a staining box or jar (E–24). Put a permanent mark on the front of each box, using a glass scriber (E–60), or Labink (E–37) or similar material.
2. Arrange the spread slides in the staining tray of one of the boxes, always with the specimen side of each slide facing the front. If the tray is of glass or plastic, put the slides alternately straight across and obliquely; thus, each groove accommodates the ends of two slides and 19 slides can be carried in a tray with 10 grooves. This is a much better arrangement than putting them back to back, since it permits proper draining of the slides between one reagent and the next. Metal slide trays with narrower slots will take only 1 slide in each slot.
3. Pour solution 1 of the DOWN series into the first box and put the tray into the box with the specimen-bearing surfaces of the slides to the front. Leave 5 minutes. Pour solution 2 into the second box, pick up the tray from box 1, drain it well, first into the box and then on a paper towel, and set it in box 2 with specimens facing the front. Return the contents of box 1 to bottle 1, pouring the

reagent through a pleated filter paper in a funnel. Repeat this process through the entire DOWN series, placing the tray finally in a box of water, if this is the solvent of the stain to be used.

If only a few slides are to be stained at one time, proceed as above but use a coplin jar, with the front marked, arranging the slides as in the tray if there are more than 5. A coplin staining jar will hold 9 slides. Leave the slides in the jar; pour on each reagent in order and return it to the proper bottle; be sure to hold the cover of the jar part way across the jar opening to keep the slides in place.

In using the DOWN series the timing may be varied to suit the convenience of the worker; in the UP series timing may be much more critical; if so, this is usually indicated in the staining directions.

These same schedules may be applied to nitrocellulose sections mounted on slides. For unmounted sections, either nitrocellulose or frozen, that are to be mounted in resin, the same reagents are frequently used; however, the sections are placed in trays of glass or plastic (E–79, 80) with perforated bottoms and immersed in the proper order in dishes of reagents.

GENERAL STAINING METHODS

Staining methods range from the application of a single stain, through the use of two stains, to complex methods requiring a whole series of dyes. In these latter methods the stains may be applied one after another or, in some cases the staining solution will contain two or more dyes. For this chapter we have selected methods that will demonstrate the general character of the tissue, staining acceptably most of its elements. When more specific methods are needed, they may be found in appropriate chapters such as those on neurology or cytology.

Directions given in the first part of this chapter for the preparation of paraffin sections may be used with slight modifications for mounted frozen or nitrocellulose sections. The same staining formulae are used on mounted and unmounted sections.

One further type of staining is included in this section: the injection of a dye into a living animal, called vital staining. There seem to be an increasing number of useful technics for this purpose.

As an example of staining with a single dye we may cite the method for chlorazol black E.

VII–2.   DARROW'S CHLORAZOL BLACK E METHOD (82).
1.   Prepare tissue in paraffin following Zenker fixation. Davenport recommends Allen's PFA fixative (B–15), also.
2.   Decerate and hydrate sections. If necessary, remove mercuric chloride (p. 25).

3. Stain 5–10 minutes in a 1% solution of chlorazol black E (R–37) in 70% alcohol, freshly prepared and unfiltered.
4. Drain off excess and wash in 95% alcohol.
5. Dehydrate in absolute alcohol, clear in xylene, and mount in synthetic resin.

Results: Chromatin, dark; nucleoli, black; blood cells, light green to yellowish green; cytoplasm, greenish gray. Cell outlines and muscle fibers are black. Differentiation is sharp and clear.

Klatzo and McMillan (*172*) have used this method on a number of tissues and report that it may be used after various fixatives and, among other virtues, stains *Endamoeba* and fibrillar processes of cells in tumors particularly well.

Probably the most frequently used stain in histological laboratories is hematoxylin-eosin. For this, several of the alum hematoxylins are suitable. Eosin may be applied as an aqueous or an alcoholic solution; several types of eosin and erythrosin may be used. Edwards' modification of Ziegler's method is somewhat more time-consuming than other technics, but it produces excellent results.

VII–3. HEMATOXYLIN AND EOSIN; EDWARDS' MODIFICATION OF ZIEGLER'S METHOD (*164*, p. 242).

1. Decerate and hydrate paraffin sections from blocks fixed in any of the usual fixatives. If the fixative contained mercuric chloride which has not been removed, treat with iodine (F–132) or use the Cellosolve hydrating schedule.
2. Stain deeply in Harris' hematoxylin (F–16), 3–5 minutes. Check the stain microscopically and if necessary, return to the stain.
3. Wash in tap water.
4. Dip in and out of acid alcohol (F–5), about 5 seconds, until nuclear stain is correct; it should be a little heavy.
5. Wash in tap water.
6. Transfer to a 2% aq sol of phosphotungstic acid for 5 seconds; then to a 2% aq sol of sodium citrate, about 5 seconds, or until no hematoxylin runs from the sections; dip the sections in and out of the solution.
7. Wash, preferably in running tap water, 5–10 minutes.
8. Counterstain in 0.5% aq sol of eosin acidified with 0.5% glacial acetic acid, 35–40 seconds.
9. Remove excess eosin in tap water.
10. Differentiate in 95% ethanol or methanol, until no stain runs from the section.
11. Dehydrate in 3 changes of fresh absolute alcohol, acetone, or Cellosolve.
12. Clear in xylene and mount in synthetic resin.

Results: Nuclei, blue; collagen and amyloid, red; fibroglia fibers and elastic tissue, unstained.

There are numerous other good alum hematoxylin formulae (F–14 through F–18). They are used in essentially the same way. Counterstains are usually some type of eosin, although there are other suitable ones. The writer particularly likes Congo red, which is not often employed. It is applied in a 0.5% or 1.0% aq sol in step 8 of the foregoing method. After rinsing, the slide is dehydrated in 95% alcohol, cleared, and mounted as above. It stains cell membranes and spindle fibers particularly well.

VII–4. GREENSTEIN'S PHLOXINE-METHYLENE BLUE STAIN (*133*) brings out cytoplasmic detail and demonstrates well certain intercellular substances. He modifies the characteristics of phloxine by treatment with hydrochloric acid. The technic may be used on material fixed in 10% formalin, formalin-sublimate, acetic-alcohol-formol, Carnoy's, Bouin's PFA, and Orth's fluid.

1. Decerate sections and transfer to 95% alcohol or
1a. If sections contain mercuric chloride crystals, decerate and transfer to 3 successive baths of Cellosolve. See also III–20.
2. Transfer to 80% alcohol, 2 minutes.
3. Stain in dilute alcoholic phloxine (F–168), 3–4 minutes.
4. Rinse 30 seconds in 95% alcohol plus 0.5% sat aq sol of lithium carbonate.
5. Wash in water, several changes, 1 minute each.
6. Stain in azure-methylene blue (F–25) 5 minutes.
7. Differentiate in 2 changes of colophonium-alcohol (F–64), 2 minutes each, with constant agitation. Examine microscopically during differentiation. After PFA fixation the differentiation is rapid.
8. Pass through 2 changes of 95% alcohol, 2 changes of absolute alcohol and 1 change of absolute alcohol-xylene, 1:1, 3 minutes each.
9. Clear in 2 changes of xylene and mount in neutral synthetic resin.
Results: Nuclei, dark blue; cytoplasm, pale blue; basophilic granules of mast cells, leucocytes, and plasma cells stain metachromatically a lavender or red-violet; acidophilic secretion granules, erythrocytes, muscle cytoplasm, connective tissue fibers, colloid, amyloid, and fibrin, distinct shades of pink or rose. In our use of this method, chromosomes were dark blue and elastic tissue a deep pink.

VII–5. KLÜVER AND BARRERA'S TECHNIC WITH DARROW RED. Darrow red, Cert. No. CD-1, produces a stain much like that resulting from treatment with cresyl violet acetate (*255*). If it is applied for 10-15 minutes in place of the latter dye in the method of Klüver and Barrera (IX–13), to paraffin sections of non-nervous tissue or to sections of whole small animals, it makes a particularly good diagnostic stain; it demonstrates the various tissues very beautifully and characteristically.

1. Stain either frozen sections, or decerated and hydrated sections, by the method of Klüver and Barrera (IX–13, 1 to 10).
2. After rinsing, stain in Darrow red solution (F–71 and 72), 20–30 minutes.
3. Rinse in water; transfer fairly rapidly through 50, 70, and 95% ethanol. During this dehydration the differentiation of the Darrow red should be accomplished. Complete the dehydration in *n*-butanol.
4. Clear in xylene and mount in xylene-resin.

For celloidin sections, the staining time should be 20 minutes and in a weaker solution; the sections should be cleared overnight in terpineol-xylene 1:3.

There are a number of staining methods which are especially useful for demonstrating the intercellular substances of connective tissue. Several of them follow.

VII–6. LISON'S ALCIAN BLUE AND CHLORANTINE FAST RED TECHNIC (*197*).

1. Prepare paraffin sections of tissues fixed in Bouin's PFA, Bouin-Hollande, 10% formalin, Lillie's phosphate-buffered neutral formalin, or alcohol-formalin-acetic (85:10:5).
2. Decerate and hydrate.
3. Stain fairly deeply in Ehrlich's hemalum (F–15), 10–15 minutes.
4. Wash in tap water until blued.
5. Stain 10 minutes in alcian blue solution (F–8) and rinse in water.
6. Leave 10 minutes in 1% phosphomolybdic acid and rinse in water.
7. Stain 10-15 minutes in chlorantine fast red solution (F–55). The shorter time is often sufficient.
8. Rinse, dehydrate, clear, and mount in synthetic resin.

Results: Nuclei, purplish blue; mucin, granules of mast cells, matrix of cartilage, some types of connective tissue fibers, bluish green; collagen and ossein, cherry red; cytoplasm and muscle, pale yellow. Elastic tissue does not stain, nor do all reticulin fibers.

This method is particularly good for demonstration of developing bone, since the cartilage spicules remain brilliant green even when surrounded by cherry-red forming bone. We have used it on the hand of a human fetus of 14 weeks, fixed in PFA; the osteoblasts and osteoclasts stained diffusely and were more clearly demonstrated by Mallory's triple stain. In all other respects, the alcian blue–chloratine red technic seemed superior for demonstrating bone formation. We found that it is also a useful histological stain for nervous tissues; it colors neurons and their processes a dusty rose and Nissl substance a deeper shade of the same color. When the stain is applied to sections of entire small animals such as tadpoles, it produces beautiful and informative preparations. We prefer Harris' hematoxylin to Ehrlich's for staining nuclei.

VII–7.   MALLORY-HEIDENHAIN CONNECTIVE TISSUE STAIN, SCHLEICHER MODIFICATION, reported by Edwards (*164*, p. 247). In 1936 Mallory published a rather complex connective tissue stain which is excellent, except for its tendency to fade. This method had numerous modifications. One of them, often called Heidenhain's azan, has in its turn been altered in various ways by several workers. Some of these sub-modifications are difficult and time-consuming and unpredictably variable in results.

The best of them is Schleicher's (*283*), in the opinion of the writer; it is given here with a few changes.

1.   Use paraffin sections fixed in Helly's or Orth's fluid, or in 10% formalin with subsequent mordanting by the method of Peers (F–166).

2.   Decerate specimens; remove mercury deposits, if present, with Cellosolve in the Cellosolve-hydration schedule or with iodine solution (F–132). Rinse thoroughly.

3.   Stain in azocarmine solution (F–111A), either at room temperature or at about 55°C. Heat increases the intensity of the azocarmine stain. Rinse in water.

4.   Extract excess azocarmine in a 5% aq sol of phosphotungstic acid until the nuclei show red against pink cytoplasm; rinse in water.

5.   Stain in a diluted aniline blue-orange G solution (F–111B), 15–30 minutes; rinse briefly in water and pass at once to 95% alcohol.

6.   Differentiate in 95% alcohol under the microscope; continue the differentiation in absolute alcohol. It will usually take 5 to 10 minutes to remove enough stain so that the connective tissues are clearly defined unless a sufficiently dilute solution has been used.

7.   Clear in xylene and mount in xylene-resin.

Results: Collagen, reticulin, and matrix of cartilage and bone, blue; nuclei, red; cytoplasm, pink; mucin, blue; amyloid, fibrin, and axis cylinders, red. The cross striations of muscles are dark pink.

VII–8.   VAN GIESON'S STAIN is useful in distinguishing muscle from collagenous connective tissue.

1.   Decerate and hydrate paraffin sections made after almost any

type of fixation. If necessary, remove mercuric chloride crystals (VII–7).

2. Overstain with Harris' hematoxylin (F–16) to avoid too great differentiation in the next step; or use Weigert's iron hematoxylin (F–193), 5-20 minutes, without differentiation.
3. Wash in water.
4. Stain in picro-fuchsin (F–169), 5 minutes or until collagenous fibers are deeply pink.
5. Wash briefly in water.
6. Dehydrate in several changes of 95% alcohol made deep yellow with picric acid.
7. Clear in xylene and mount in xylene-resin.

Results: Nuclei, blue-black; collagen, red; muscle, yellow. This stain fades unless C.C. acid fuchsin is used.

Neither VII-5, -6, nor -7 demonstrate the elastic fibers of connective tissue. There are several stains which bring them out clearly; among them are resorcin-fuchsin, orcein, and Gomori's aldehyde fuchsin. Some of these stains for elastic tissue will be found in the following methods.

VII–9. FULLMER AND LILLIE (*114*) RECOMMEND ORCINOL-NEW FUCHSIN as an excellent stain for elastin since it does not react with any other tissue components.

1. Decerate sections and transfer to 95% alcohol.
2. Stain with orcinol-new fuchsin (F–159), 15 minutes at 37°C.
3. Differentiate in 70% alcohol, 15 minutes, 3 changes.
4. Dehydrate, clear, and mount.

Van Gieson's method (VII–8) may be applied between steps 3 and 4; or sections may be passed to water followed by pontacyl blue-black (F–171), 15 minutes.

Results: Elastic fibers are colored deep violet; collagen and other tissues remain unstained. If van Gieson's method is used, the smaller elastic fibers take up some of the acid fuchsin and may be difficult to see. With pontacyl blue-black, the nuclei are blue green.

One of the disadvantages in staining elastic tissue with Weigert's resorcin-fuchsin, which applies in some measure to the orcinol-new fuchsin technic, is that it is somewhat laborious to prepare the stain. Puchtler and Sweat have used a relatively new commercial resorcin-fuchsin (Chroma) which is quite satisfactory.

VII–10. RESORCIN-FUCHSIN METHOD, PUCHTLER AND SWEAT (*256*).

1. Decerate sections, remove mercury precipitates if necessary, and carry to 70% alcohol.

2.   Stain in 0.2% resorcin-fuchsin (R–174) in 70% ethanol, acidified with 1% hydrochloric acid, 4–5 hours.
3.   Rinse in water.
4.   Counterstain with van Gieson's picro-fuchsin (VII–8).
5.   Dehydrate, clear in xylene, and mount in synthetic resin.

Results: Elastic fibers of smaller arteries, lungs, and skin, black; those in the aorta and in the elastica interna of other large arteries, purplish black; collagen and other connective tissue intercellular substance, bright red; muscle, yellow.

A good trial tissue for this method is the mesentery of the opossum *Didelphis virginiana*. It is particularly rich in elastic tissue, and stains brilliantly with this technic. This method is also very successful in staining sections of elasmobranch rectal glands and whole sections of small animals.

Nitrocellulose sections are best mounted on slides before staining.

VII–11.   KORNHAUSER'S QUAD STAIN (*179*) may be used after fixation in Zenker's or Helly's fluid and after embedding in paraffin or nitrocellulose. The staining solutions are given in F–124.

1.   Decerate paraffin sections and transfer to 95%, then 85% alcohol. Remove deposits of mercury with 0.5–1.0% iodine solution in 85% alcohol. Remove the iodine with 85% alcohol.
2.   Stain 2 hours or longer in solution 1; determine the time by microscopic examination of the sections; they show the elastic fibers colored reddish brown to purple when they are well stained. Wash in 85% alcohol and hydrate.
3.   Stain 5–10 minutes in solution 2; rinse in water.
4.   Transfer to solution 3, 10–30 minutes or until the collagenous fibers are destained. Rinse very briefly in water.
5.   Stain 10 minutes in solution 4.
6.   Rinse in 50% alcohol several seconds; dehydrate in 95% alcohol, 2 changes, 2–3 minutes each; complete dehydration in absolute alcohol.
7.   Clear in xylene and mount in xylene-resin.

Results: Elastic fibers, reddish brown to purple; nuclei, blue; muscle and cytoplasm, violet to pink; collagen, reticulum, and basement membranes, green; red blood cells, myelin sheaths, and acidophile granules, orange.

VII–12   THE METHOD OF CARAMIA AND ANGELETTI (55) for differentiating serous and mucous components of salivary glands is simple and good. The directions apply to mouse tissue but should need little if any change for other animals.

1. Fix whole submaxillary glands in 95% alcohol, 9:1/vol, for 6–12 hours.
2. Transfer specimens directly to absolute alcohol, clear in cedar oil (use at least one change), rinse in xylene, and embed in paraffin.
3. Cut sections at 5–7μ, spread, decerate, and hydrate.
4. Stain 30 minutes in 0.1% alcian blue solution in 3% acetic acid, freshly filtered. Rinse in several changes of water.
5. Stain in 0.2% aq sol of acid fuchsin 4–6 minutes and rinse.
6. Dehydrate in 95% alcohol, 2 changes, and in absolute alcohol; clear in xylene and mount in xylene-resin.

Results: Serous cells show purple-red secretory granules; mucous cells have the mucus stained light blue. All nuclei are dark blue.

VII–13 SCOTT'S METHOD FOR BETA CELLS IN PANCREATIC ISLETS (285).

1. Fix in Bouin's PFA and prepare in paraffin.
2. Decerate and hydrate sections.
3. Oxidize in a mixture of equal parts of 0.5% aq sol of potassium permanganate and 0.5% aq sol of sulfuric acid, 2 minutes. Rinse in water.
4. Decolorize in 2% sodium bisulfite and wash in running tap water, 2 minutes.
5. Stain in aldehyde fuchsin (F–11 or F–12), 2 minutes.
6. Rinse in 3 changes of 95% alcohol.
7. Run sections down to water.
8. Stain in 0.5% phloxine, 2 minutes; rinse in water.
9. Place in 5% phosphotungstic acid 1 minute.
10. Rinse in running tap water 2–5 minutes.
11. Stain in 0.2% fast green FCF, 30 seconds.
12. Rinse in 95% alcohol 15 seconds, and in absolute alcohol 30 seconds; a second change of absolute alcohol may be necessary.
13. Clear in xylene; mount in xylene-resin.

Results: Beta-cell granules are deep purple, their cytoplasm light green; cytoplasm of duct cells, light green; red blood cells and nuclei of all cells, light red.

VII–14 ELFTMAN'S METHOD FOR ALDEHYDE-FUCHSIN AND PAS STAINING OF THE PITUITARY (98) gives good differentiation of the various cell types. The technic is not difficult. The directions apply to rat pituitaries.

1. Fix the pituitary in F–77, 12–48 hours at room temperature.
2. Transfer the tissue directly to 70% ethanol and prepare in paraffin. Section at 5μ.
3. Decerate and hydrate; remove the mercuric chloride with 1%

iodine, 10 minutes; then apply 5% sodium thiosulfate 3–5 minutes, and wash in running tap water, 5 minutes.

4. Transfer to 70% alcohol.

5. Stain in aldehyde-fuchsin (F–11), modifying the formula by changing the amount of paraldehyde to 0.75 ml and of hydrochloric acid to 1.25 ml. It takes 3 days to ripen at room temperature; 26 hours at 37°C; it should be stored at room temperature. Adjust the staining time to the age of the solution: 30 minutes, if it is just ripe, up to 60 minutes as it ages. It has a short useful life.

6. Transfer to 1% periodic acid, 15 minutes, and rinse in 2 changes of water, 2 minutes each.

7. Place in Schiff reagent (F–182) 20 minutes; a part of this staining solution should have been in use some time so that its strength is partially depleted.

8. Rinse in tap water.

9. Stain in 3% orange G acidified to pH 2.0 with hydrochloric acid, 10 minutes.

10. Rinse rapidly in water, dehydrate, clear, and mount.

Results: The nuclei are not stained. The thyrotrophs and Golgi bodies stain purple, gonadotrophs are red, and acidophils and red blood cells are orange.

Landing (*183*) has made a tabular summary of histological and histochemical procedures which are representative methods for preparation of the anterior pituitary glands. It will be helpful to consult this for the numerous other methods which are available. See also (*184*).

VITAL STAINING

Ratliff, Williams, and Mayberry (*261*) have demonstrated that elastic membranes of the aortae of mice are stained well by a series of 5 daily subcutaneous injections of 0.1 ml of a 1% aq sol of trypan blue. The stain is preserved by fixation in 10% formalin at pH 7-9, or in cold acetone and absolute ethanol.

VII–15. FOULKES AND BEHER (*107*) administered calcodur pink 2 BL, 0.25% solution in saline, to rats by subcutaneous injection. They adjusted the dose so that the animals received, each time, 20 mg of dye/kg of body weight. There were 3 injections at 48-hour intervals. The elastica interna of larger arteries was plainly demonstrated in paraffin sections after fixation in 80% alcohol.

Other kinds of intercellular substance of connective tissue stain with vital dyes by methods discussed in chapter X; see especially methods X–11, X–12, and X–13.

The phagocytic cells of connective tissue and of parts of the reticuloendothelial system also stain with vital dyes. The method of Foulkes and

Beher (VII–15) results in the storage of colored granules in Kupffer cells of the liver. Trypan blue in small doses, injected subcutaneously, is taken up and retained by the phagocytic cells near the site of the injection. When administered intraperitoneally, it is distributed throughout the body and picked up by the phagocytic cells of both the connective tissue proper and the reticuloendothelial system. Snook (*291*) gives directions for preserving the stain in whole mounts. He fixes in 10% formalin, 12–24 hours, rinses in water, dehydrates in 2 changes of dioxane and mounts, from the second change, in Diaphane. A similar method is useful for preparing injected tissues for sectioning. PFA like 10% formalin serves well as a fixative, followed by preparation in paraffin by the dioxane method.

CHAPTER VIII

HEMATOLOGY

The technics of hematology are not difficult since blood is easy to collect and to prepare. The small amounts usually needed may be drawn with little discomfort to the donor. Since it is a fluid tissue, it is easily spread into a single layer of cells for examination in the fresh or fixed condition. Many of the technical methods for staining or otherwise treating blood are relatively simple.

COLLECTION OF BLOOD SAMPLES

VIII–1. A FEW DROPS OF HUMAN CAPILLARY BLOOD are easily obtained by the prick of a lancet. The use of a spring lancet should be avoided since this instrument cannot be quickly sterilized between successive uses. This is an important matter in view of the prevalence of infectious hepatitis in the general population and the ease with which it is transmitted by instruments which cannot be sterilized merely by dipping in antiseptic solutions. A sterile, disposable lancet (E–38) with a sharp point and a shoulder to prevent too deep a cut is preferable. Such instruments are sold in individual sterile packets. They may be safely re-used after autoclaving; some laboratories consider that they are cheap enough to discard after a single use. Each student should have several; they may be re-used *on the same person* after washing and dipping in 70% alcohol.

VIII–2. TO OBTAIN BLOOD WITH A LANCET, wash well either a finger tip or an earlobe; then rub briskly with a piece of clean gauze moistened with 70% alcohol. The ear is the more suitable site for puncture since it is less sensitive, but its use is generally not popular. Prick the cleaned part, wipe away the first drop with dry gauze, and use the subsequent drops which should follow without pressure, wiping the skin after each has been removed. When the bleeding is completed, rub the area gently with 70% alcohol.

VIII–3. FOR LARGER QUANTITIES OF BLOOD than a lancet prick will provide, a number of methods are available, all of which permit repeated bleedings from the same animal at regular intervals. Human blood is easily obtained by venepuncture. This procedure should be carried out by an experienced person, with appropriate aseptic precautions; it should not be undertaken by students until they have been instructed and their competence demonstrated.

VIII–4. BLOODLETTING FROM THE EYE OF AN AMPHIBIAN, METHOD OF BERGER (33).

1. Make a pipet from a capillary tube about 1 mm in diameter; fire-polish the tip. Just before use wash in 0.1% solution of heparin (R–99).
2. Hold the frog to be exsanguinated securely with the left hand. Put the index finger of this hand into the mouth and press the eye upward to make it protrude.
3. Force open the nictitating membrane and insert the capillary tube gently at the inner angle of the eye, between the membrane and the eyeball; slide the tube along to the delicate, ophthalmic venous plexus which lies at the back of the orbit. Collect with the capillary tube the blood which flows freely into the orbit.
4. When the bleeding is finished, swab the eye clear with cotton wet with amphibian saline (F–180).

The same frog may be bled daily for long periods without noticeable ill effects, and will thus provide serial blood samples.

For other animals, the methods described in the following references are recommended: mice, Riley (267); hamsters, Turbyfill, Peterson, and Soderwall (313); rabbits, Nace and Spradlin (230).

TYPES OF HEMATOLOGICAL PREPARATIONS

A good approach to the study of blood is to examine it first in a living condition. Fixed and stained smears, although indispensable, nevertheless give little idea of the shape of the white cells. In a good living preparation many of them look much smaller than they do in smears where they are all somewhat flattened. Alive, the non-phagocytic leucocytes are usually almost spherical; the phagocytes may be spherical also, or they may assume various shapes as they attach to a surface and progress by ameboid movement or engulf particulate matter. The erythrocytes also are somewhat flattened in smears while in living preparations, in which they may be seen in both surface and edge views, their disc shape is apparent.

VIII–5. PREPARATIONS OF FRESH BLOOD. There are several simple methods of preparing living blood corpuscles for study. The directions below are for human blood. Place a drop of normal saline (F–180) on a slide, add a drop of blood, cover, and examine. A slide of this type will soon begin to dry at the edges but in the process will show very well both crenation and rouleau formation of red blood corpuscles. For a more permanent preparation, place a small drop each of normal saline and of blood on a thin cover glass and mix. Invert the cover over a deep depression slide (see Fig. 1); the diluted blood must remain in the center of the cover and must not touch the slide. Ring with melted Vaseline. Some of the white cells will usually come into contact with the undersurface of the cover and display considerable motility. They may be observed with a high dry objective or an immersion lens. These preparations should be kept as nearly as possible at body temperature. The microscope lamp or a warm stage will provide a suitable source of heat.

VIII–6. EFFECTS OF REAGENTS. To study the effects of reagents such as distilled water, hypertonic saline or 1% tannic acid on blood cells, place a drop of fresh blood on a slide; put the cover on, and irrigate with the reagent by placing a drop of it at one edge of the cover, to be drawn under by capillary action. The process may be hastened by applying a bit of blotting paper to the opposite edge of the cover.

VIII–7. DEMONSTRATION OF BLOOD PLATELETS. Place a small drop of 1% methyl violet in an equal quantity of normal saline on a well-cleaned finger tip or earlobe; prick the part with a lancet through the stain; mount a drop of the resulting mixture on a slide, cover, and examine with a 4-mm objective.
Results: Both platelets and white corpuscles are stained.

VIII–8. VAN HERWERDEN'S METHOD FOR FIXING WHITE BLOOD CELLS (*316*) preserves some of the cell shapes characteristic of living leucocytes.
1. Prepare one or more petri dishes fitted with two or three discs of thick filter paper in each half. Saturate the papers with water, drain, and warm the closed dishes in an oven set at 38°C, 20–30 minutes.
2. Put a small drop of warm Deetjen's (F–74) or Ringer's fluid (F–176) on each slide. Add a small drop of blood to the drop of fluid, place in the prepared petri dishes, and incubate in the 38° oven, 20–30 minutes.
3. Replace the filter paper in the lower dish with another, wet with full-strength formalin and return to the incubator, 30 minutes.
4. Remove slides and pour off excess fluid. The leucocytes and some red corpuscles will remain attached.
5. Stain in Giemsa's stain (VIII–16) 20–30 minutes or
5*a*. Air-dry and stain rather deeply with Wright's stain (VIII–15), or

5*b*.   Stain in Heidenhain's iron hematoxylin (XII–1) without preliminary drying, using 12–20 hours each for mordant and stain; differentiate to show mitochondria.

Results: With any of these stains, the pseudopods of leucocytes and
platelets show plainly. With Heidenhain's, the mitochondria also are
demonstrated.

ENUMERATION OF FORMED ELEMENTS OF THE BLOOD

To determine the total number of red corpuscles, white corpuscles, and
platelets in 1 mm^3 of blood, one uses a counting chamber and two
graduated diluting pipets, preferably certified by the Bureau of Standards (Fig. 7). The chambers have been modified in several ways since

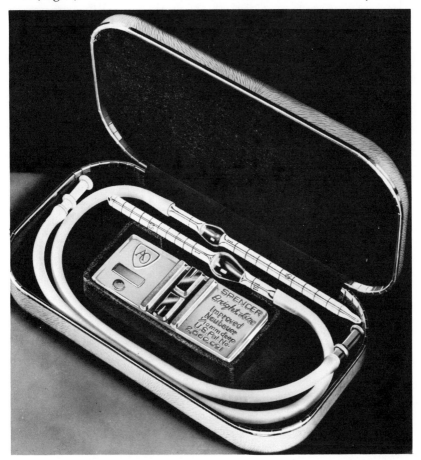

Fig. 7.—Hemocytometer equipment, including carrying case, diluting
pipets for red and white corpuscles, and counting chamber. (Courtesy of the
American Optical Company.)

they were first devised, both in respect to their basic method of construction and the rulings in the counting area. In this country the most
commonly used type is cast as one piece of glass with a central H-shaped
moat enclosing two plateaus, both of which are ruled by the improved
Neubauer method, to form counting areas. The cover glass is rectangular
and relatively thick. The Bright-Line counting chamber, made by the
American Optical Company, is particularly satisfactory because its lines
are clearly visible.

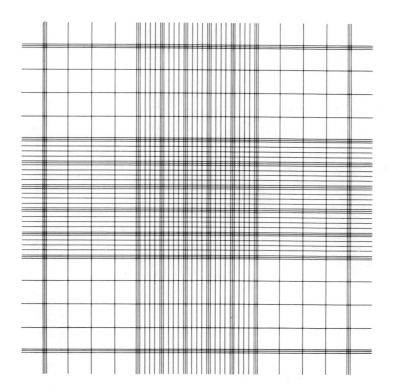

Fig. 8.—Diagram of the improved Neubauer ruling of the counting
chamber. (Courtesy of the American Optical Company.)

The markings of a chamber may be studied by using a diagram (Fig.
8) and a microscope with a 10× ocular and a 16-mm objective. Each
counting area is ruled into nine square blocks, each 1 mm². The four
corner blocks are subdivided by single lines into 16 smaller squares. The
central block is divided into 400 squares; these smallest units are combined into larger units of 16 squares, defined by triple lines. There are
25 of the 16-square units. The walls of the moat support the cover
glass; the depth of the chamber is 0.1 mm.

VIII–9. GENERAL DIRECTIONS. Whether red or white blood corpuscles or platelets are to be enumerated, the procedure is the same. Assemble the necessary equipment which includes the appropriate pipet, provided with a detachable rubber tube and mouth piece; appropriate diluting fluid; sterile lancet; and the counting chamber with its cover in place. Clean a finger or an earlobe with alcohol and prick with a lancet. Wipe off the first drop, leaving the skin dry. When the second drop is large enough, place the tip of the pipet just below its surface, and draw blood to the proper mark. Wipe the tip and plunge into the bottle of diluting fluid; draw the fluid by suction into the bulb and to the mark just above it. Rotate the pipet slowly during this process. Shake thoroughly for 3 minutes. Eject 2 or 3 drops from the pipet; wipe the tip and apply it to the edge of the cover glass, permitting the diluted blood to be drawn into the chamber by capillarity. Fill both counting areas, allowing no fluid to escape into the moat. Place the counting chamber on the microscope stage and adjust the light so that the cells or platelets may be seen clearly. Wait a few moments until the cells have settled before attempting to count them.

To avoid counting the same cells twice, adopt and follow consistently a standard path, such as from left to right to the end of a row; also count the cells that rest on the left and upper sides of a square disregarding those on the right and lower sides; or adopt the reverse procedure.

After use, wash the counting chamber with several changes of warm water; blot dry very gently with lens paper or soft linen. Clean the cover first in water and then in alcohol and wipe dry. Pipets are conveniently cleaned by a faucet suction pump (E–29). The pipet is attached to the pump by means of a rubber tube, and suction is produced when the faucet is turned on. Draw clean water through the pipet, then rinse with 95% alcohol and ether, successively, filling once with each. Continue the suction to draw air through the pipet until its interior is dry, as evidenced by free movement of the bead within the bulb.

VIII–10. TO COUNT RED BLOOD CORPUSCLES, use Toisson's diluting solution (F–189) and the pipet with the larger bulb and the mark 101 (Figs. 7 and 9). Draw the blood to the 0.5 mark and the diluting fluid to the 101 mark. After shaking, use the sample at once or store in the refrigerator, with the pipet tip protected; shake again thoroughly before using.

Use a 10× ocular and a 4-mm objective. Count the cells in 100 of the smallest squares in the middle block. Use a mechanical counter (E–17) if available. Cells of different shape and refractive index are white blood corpuscles, and should not be counted.

The number of red blood cells in 1 mm³ of blood may be derived by multiplying the number of cells in 100 of the smallest squares by 8,000. *Calculation:* Assume an enumeration of 500 cells in 100 squares.

500 cells in .25 mm² × 4 = 2,000 in 1 mm²

2,000 × 10 (the chamber depth is 0.1 mm) = 20,000 in 1 mm³

20,000 × 200 (the dilution factor) = 4,000,000

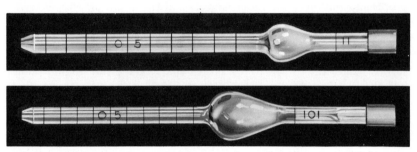

Fig. 9.—Red and white cell diluting pipets; the white pipet of this pair has the smaller bulb. (Courtesy of the American Optical Company.)

VIII–11. TO COUNT WHITE BLOOD CORPUSCLES, use 1% acetic acid for the diluting solution and a pipet with the smaller bulb and the mark 11 (Fig. 9). Draw the blood from a large drop to the 0.5 mark and fill with diluting fluid to 11. Use at once or store in a refrigerator. Proceed as for red cells, shaking the pipet and filling the counting chamber. Use the same lenses, and count the cells in the large corner blocks which are subdivided into 16 smaller squares. Count at least 4 blocks.

The number of white blood corpuscles in 1 mm³ of blood may be derived by averaging the numbers counted in each large block and multiplying by 200.

Calculation: Assume an average number of cells in 1 mm² = 35

35 × 10 (the chamber depth is 0.1 mm) = 350

350 × 20 (the dilution factor) = 7,000

VIII–12. TO COUNT BLOOD PLATELETS, use Wright and Kinnicutt's diluting solution (F–196) and the red blood cell pipet. Draw the blood to the 1.0 mark and the diluting solution to the 101 mark (see Fig. 9). Shake, and fill immediately the two counting areas. Place the counting chamber on the microscope stage, find the field, and wait 10 minutes before counting. Use the 10× ocular and a 4-mm objective. Count the number in 1 mm², the central block of 400 small squares. The number of platelets in 1 mm³ of blood may be derived by multiplying the number of platelets in 1 mm² by 1,000.

Calculation: Assume that the number of platelets in 1 mm² is 250.

250 × 10 (the chamber depth is 0.1 mm) = 2,500
2,500 × 100 (the dilution factor) = 250,000

MAKING BLOOD SMEARS

A satisfactory preparation for the study of fixed blood cells is a stained film one cell thick. The film is called a smear, and may be made on a slide or on a cover glass.

VIII–13. SMEARS ON SLIDES. Select slides with smooth edges; clean (E–66) and store in 70% alcohol in a jar until needed. Dry by light sweeping movements of a lint-free material (E–28). Obtain capillary blood (VIII–2) and after discarding the first drop and drying the skin, pick up the second drop with the smooth end of a slide. Transfer it quickly to either end of a second slide which is lying on the bench and is held in position by the left hand. Hold the first slide at an angle of 40–45°, in close contact with the second; the blood will spread quickly by capillarity. When it reaches the edges of the first slide, smear it quickly and evenly by pushing or pulling the upper slide, still held at the same angle, over the lower one. Prepare several smears from the same puncture. Label and store in a covered slide box.

The smearing must be done rapidly to prevent clotting, distortion, and uneven distribution of cells. A satisfactory smear has a grossly even appearance; its central area has a single layer of blood corpuscles. It is not at first easy to make a good smear. If much difficulty is experienced, it is desirable to practice with a colored stain rather than blood until the knack is acquired.

VIII–14. SMEARS ON COVER GLASSES.

Have ready several pairs of grease-free, clean, square cover glasses. Place a small drop of blood in the center of one cover; lay a second one over it with its corners approximately in the middle of each side of the lower one, making a star-shaped sandwich. When the fluid has spread by capillarity, quickly separate the covers by grasping two nearly opposite corners and sliding them apart; air-dry each with the smear side up, or place in fixative while still moist.

STAINING BLOOD SMEARS

In order to demonstrate the platelets, the nuclei, and the cytoplasmic granules of the various types of white blood cells as well as the sex chromatin mass present in the neutrophiles of certain female animals, smears are usually treated with one of the Romanowsky-type blood stains. Three commonly used formulae are those of Wright, Giemsa, and

Kingsley. A single slide or cover glass smear may be laid on a support on the table and the stain applied with a dropper; or it may be placed on supports in a petri dish or held in forceps (E–32). Many technicians find it more satisfactory to put slides in staining dishes (E–24), or covers in cover glass-staining dishes (E–23) that hold the necessary solutions.

VIII–15.   WRIGHT'S STAIN.

1.   Into a clean slide-staining jar pour enough Wright's stain to cover the smeared portions of the slides. For cover glass smears, put in the cover glass jars (E–23) enough stain so that no part of the cover glass is exposed. Into a second slide or cover-glass jar pour an equal amount of distilled water or buffer (F–47).

2.   Place a smeared slide in the stain for 1 minute; drain and transfer at once to the distilled water for 2 minutes.

3.   Rinse in running tap water until the smear shows a pink tint in the thinnest part. Drain in a vertical position, near gentle heat if possible.

4.   When the smear is dry, add a generous drop of oil (R–149) and study with an immersion objective; or mount a cover with immersion oil and study with a 4-mm objective and a 10× or a 15× ocular. A stain is satisfactory if the erythrocytes are pink; the nuclei of the white cells, purple or bluish purple; the granules of the neutrophiles, lavender, of basophils, dark blue and of eosinophiles, bright red; the cytoplasm of the agranulocytes, cerulean blue to purplish blue.

5.   If the staining is too pale, stain a second slide; increase the time to 1.5 minutes in stain and 3 minutes in water. If it is too dark, decrease the staining time. When the timing has been properly adjusted, several slides may be stained at one time.

6.   Mount satisfactory preparations in xylene-resin (F–145), using a No. 1 cover glass; or store uncovered, if immersion oil is to be applied directly to the smear. In the latter case, always remove the oil before storing by immersing the slide 5 minutes in xylene, then draining until dry.

7.   After staining a batch of slides, discard the water; filter the stain into a bottle with a ground-glass stopper, and store.

VIII–16.   GIEMSA'S STAIN.

1.   Fix smears by immersion in 95% methanol 2–5 minutes. Dry in a vertical position.

2.   Stain 20 minutes in dilute Giemsa: 1 volume of stock to 20 volumes of water or buffer (F–97). Rinse thoroughly in tap water and dry.

3.   Discard the dilute, used stain.

4.   Examine; the staining should be similar to that produced by

Wright's stain, but the neutrophile granules are usually somewhat more clearly seen. If necessary try other test slides, increasing or decreasing staining time.

5. Mount, study, and store as in step 6, VIII–15.

If large numbers of smears are to be stained, Giemsa's method is superior to Wright's, since many slides may be easily handled at one time.

VIII–17. IF PARASITES ARE PRESENT IN THE BLOOD, Melvin and Brooke (*219*) recommend adding Triton X–100 (A–43) to the diluent before mixing with Giemsa's stain. For thick smears they add 0.15% and for thin ones, 0.01%; the authors report that both background and parasites are clearer and brighter with this addition.

VIII–18. HAMRE'S METHOD (142, p. 121) slightly modified, for improving the stains of granules in leucocytes.

1. Stain 2 minutes in Wright's stain; transfer to water, 5–6 minutes.
2. Rinse in water; transfer to Giemsa's stain, 1 volume of stain/10 volumes of water, 15–20 minutes.
3. Rinse in tap water; air-dry.
4. Mount, study, and store as in VIII–15, step 6.

VIII–19. KINGSLEY'S STAIN (F–122) is one of the most precise in its results and is generally satisfactory. It has a rather complex formula, given in his 1935 paper (*170*). It may, however, be bought as two stock solutions (R–109) which, when mixed according to the directions of the manufacturer, make a working solution that is stable for more than 6 months. Results are beautifully consistent, and it is simple to use.

1. Fix the air-dried blood film with absolute methanol, 1 minute; dry.
2. Flood with working solution 5–7 minutes, or until a metallic scum forms on the surface of the fluid.
3. Wash with a stream of tap water; dry.
4. Study, mount, and store as in VIII–15, step 6.

VIII–20. BRECHER'S METHOD (*47*) FOR RETICULOCYTES stains the reticulum in the youngest of the red blood corpuscles circulating in normal mammalian blood and present in increased numbers in certain pathological conditions. Thompson (*310*) has observed that this same method also demonstrates Heinz bodies in dog blood.

1. Place 4 drops of staining solution (F–46) in a small test tube; add 5 drops of fresh or oxalated blood, and mix.
2. After 5–10 minutes, agitate the tube to obtain a uniform suspension of cells, draw up a sample in a capillary pipet, expel a drop on a slide, and smear.

3. Air-dry the smear; study in oil with an immersion lens.

Results: The cytoplasm of red cells is pale greenish blue; the reticulum of the reticulocytes is sharply outlined and deep blue. Heinz bodies are pale to deep blue and are in sharp contrast to the cytoplasm.

VIII–21. WATTS' METHOD (326) is useful if selective staining of eosinophiles is desired.
1. Fix a smear of human blood in 95% methanol, 15–60 seconds; dry.
2. Cover with filtered Harris' hematoxylin (F–16), 5 minutes.
3. Wash in tap water until blue.
4. Stain in Watts' solution (F–192) 30 minutes at 56°C.
5. Wash very thoroughly in running water.
6. Dehydrate in ethanol, clear in xylene, and mount in synthetic resin.

Results: Eosinophile granules, bright red; nuclei, blue-black; red blood corpuscles, faintly pink. Eosinophiles are much more easily seen when stained in this way than by Romanowsky stains.

VIII–22. RALPH'S METHOD (259), slightly modified, is satisfactory for identification of hemoglobin.
1. Cover a dried blood smear from a frog or tadpole with 1% solution of benzidene dihydrochloride in absolute methanol, 60 seconds.
2. Pour off and replace with 25% solution of Superoxol (R–102) in 70% ethanol, 90 seconds.
3. Wash briefly in water, dry, and mount in synthetic resin.

Results: The cytoplasm is dark brown and the nucleus colorless. Prints of spleen (V–5) stained by this method demonstrate clearly the distribution of red cells.

DEMONSTRATION OF NONCELLULAR COMPONENTS OF BLOOD

VIII–23. FIBRIN (142, p. 115).

1. Mount a drop of blood on a slide and cover.
2. Place in a moist chamber, 20–30 minutes at 35–38° to coagulate.
3. Loosen the cover with a few drops of water and thoroughly irrigate with water. Drain well.
4. Add immediately a drop of 1% aq sol of eosin and stain 3 minutes.
5. Drain, rinse in tap water, and stain 3 minutes with 1% aq sol of methyl violet or a 1% aq sol of brilliant cresyl blue.
6. Rinse in water, drain, air-dry, and mount in synthetic resin.

Results: A fine network of blue fibrin is distinguishable.

VIII–24. HEMIN OR TEICHMANN'S CRYSTALS (142, p. 115).

1.   Place on a slide a drop of blood, or a drop of the water in which
material, thought to contain blood, has been soaked. Add a few
crystals of sodium chloride, and heat over a flame until the residue
is dry.

2.   Apply a cover glass and run acetic acid under it, filling the space
between cover and slide. Heat to boiling, over a flame, until the
acid evaporates.

3.   Remove the cover. When the residue is thoroughly dry add synthetic resin and a fresh cover.

Results: If blood is present the preparation will show small brown
crystals, somewhat variable in size, in the form of narrow, rhombic
plates. They occur both singly and in groups that often have a stellate
form.

VIII–25. HEMOGLOBIN CRYSTALS (142, p. 115).   Allow a drop
of blood to dry on the slide without covering it. Long, red rhombic
prisms crystallize out. The blood of a rat is best for demonstration. A
more certain method is as follows: to 5 ml of blood in a test tube, add a
few drops of ether and shake the mixture vigorously until the blood
becomes laky. Place a drop or two of the laked blood on a slide and
allow it to dry in a refrigerator.

VIII–26. STUDY OF BLOOD IN SECTIONS (142, p. 119).   Ligate a
vessel, arranging the ligatures so that the part between them will be
distended with blood. Tie the ligatures tightly, cut distal to each and
transfer the piece of artery or vein to 10% formalin, Bouin's PFA
(F–40), or Zenker-formalin (F–198). Prepare and section in paraffin and
stain with phloxine-methylene blue (VII–4).

Many other tissue sections will also show blood cells in a suitable
condition for study if appropriate stains are applied. Giemsa's, Wright's,
and Kingsley's stains are good. The liver of *Necturus,* with its border of
hemapoietic tissue, is particularly recommended for such studies.

CHAPTER IX

NERVOUS SYSTEM

Some parts of the nervous system are not conspicuous in an ordinary histological preparation. Small branches of nerves are often difficult to find, and neuron cell bodies stain faintly and require practice for easy identification. More than any of the other organ systems it needs special technics for its successful preparation. There are many in the literature and most of them demand technical skill and practice; in fact, the most careful student must be prepared for a certain proportion of failures.

There seem to be no universal technics for preparation of the nervous system; different parts require different methods. Furthermore, several methods are often necessary to demonstrate all of the structural characteristics of any nervous element. It must, however, be noted that excellent preparations of the nervous system are possible and some technics produce slides of great beauty. Some of the more recent methods, such as those of Klüver and Barrera, demonstrate several elements.

It is difficult to choose a representative selection of methods from the extensive technical literature. The writer has included only some of those which are reliable and which, properly applied, produce results that can be considered a compensation for the effort involved. Many other excellent technics have not been described or cited because of limitations of space.

GRAY AND WHITE MATTER OF THE CENTRAL NERVOUS SYSTEM

IX–1.   DE LA PAVA AND PICKREN (86) use a simple technic which they apply especially to pathological brain stem and spinal cord. It is, however, useful for normal specimens. It does not make a permanent preparation.

1.   Cut slices of spinal cord or parts of the brain 5 mm thick; a slicing guide (E–64, 65) is useful.
2.   Transfer to iodine solution (F–133) about 1 minute; wash with gentle agitation in tap water 1–5 minutes.

3. Examine, covered with water, at a magnification of 5× to 10×, by reflected light.

Results: The white matter stains a very dark brown and the gray matter is faintly yellow. The color fades after several hours.

IX–2. LE MASURIER'S METHOD (*187*).

1. Fix the brain (and cord if desired) in 10% formalin or formol-saline (F–88), preferably by perfusion. Be sure that the specimens remain in the formalin long enough to become thoroughly hardened.
2. Cut slices, about 5 mm thick, in serial order if necessary, and wash first in running tap water overnight, then in 3 changes of distilled water, about 20 minutes each.
3. Transfer slices, 1 or 2 at a time, to about 500 ml of Mulligan's fluid (F–147) at 60–65°C, 2 minutes. Wash in a large amount of cold tap water, 1 minute.
4. Place in 1% aq sol of ferric chloride, 2 minutes, and wash in running water, 5 minutes.
5. Transfer to 1% solution of potassium ferrocyanide until the gray matter is bright blue, about 3 minutes. Wash in running water, 24 hours. Discard both the ferric chloride and potassium ferrocyanide solutions after they have been used for a brain and/or a spinal cord.
6. Store in 10% formalin or 70% alcohol.

Results: The gray and white matter may be clearly distinguished. The preparations are permanent.

NEURON CELL BODIES

Neuron cell bodies and some of their processes may be demonstrated by maceration and teasing, by squashes, and by Golgi methods.

IX–3. MACERATION AND STAINING OF CORD TISSUE.

1. Place small pieces no more than 2–3 mm in diameter, from the ventral horn of the spinal cord of an ox, in Gage's formaldehyde dissociator (F–94) or in 30% alcohol, 1–48 hours.
2. Wash well in water. Place in a 1% aq sol of methylene blue, C.I. No. (922) 52015, about 30 minutes.
3. Transfer the specimen and some fresh stain to a slide on a dissecting microscope and, using transmitted light, tease gently to free the neurons and as many of their processes as possible. The neurons are the largest and most deeply stained elements present.
4. Remove any obscuring debris from the slide, and most of the stain.

Cover the specimen with a cover glass, add water at one edge with a pipet, and remove it at the opposite side with bibulous paper until excess stain is removed.

5. Add Cellosolve with a pipet and remove it with bibulous paper as above. As soon as the material is in pure Cellosolve, begin to observe the color of the cells under the microscope. When the Cellosolve has differentiated the cells sufficiently, replace it with xylene; all trace of Cellosolve must be removed and the material well cleared.

6. When the cells are transparent, lift off the cover, add a drop of resin, and apply a fresh cover glass.

IX–4. SQUASH PREPARATIONS OF CORD. See V–3.

The nuclei of neuroglia are easily identifiable as are whole capillaries. Most neurons show one or more processes, some of considerable length. The preparations fade very little; some, in the writer's laboratory, which have had class use for over 30 years are still in excellent condition.

GOLGI METHODS

The Golgi technic demonstrates the shapes of neurons and their spatial relationships to each other in the central nervous system, when it has been successfully applied. It stains only a small number of neurons and their processes and shows nothing of their internal structure. The earlier forms of the method are capricious in the hands of most workers, and this is probably the reason that so many modifications of the original method have been proposed.

Golgi's technic, as first published, called for hardening the tissue in potassium dichromate solutions of gradually increasing strength for periods ranging from 15 to 50 days. When the hardening was completed the specimens were transferred to 0.75% silver nitrate solution, washed well in alcohol, and then prepared in paraffin. After sectioning, they were mounted in thick balsam without a cover glass. Of the very numerous modifications of the Golgi method, only a few are presented here.

IX–5. PORTER AND DAVENPORT'S MODIFICATION OF THE GOLGI METHOD (252).

This usually produces good results with the brains of small half-grown and adult rodents but is not satisfactory for fetal or neonatal specimens.

1. Cut thin slices of the brain of rats or guinea pigs, preferably with a slicing guide (E–64, 65). Fix in formalin-silver nitrate solution (F–103), 48 hours at about 25°C.

2. Rinse with water and transfer to 2.5% solution of potassium dichromate, 3–5 days.

3. Wash, dehydrate in an alcohol series, clear, and infiltrate in paraffin of a low melting point.
4. Section at 30–50μ, spread, dry, decerate, and mount under a cover glass in synthetic resin.

Results: Neurons and their processes are black against a yellow background. Some neuroglia stain also. Usually more neurons are stained with this method than with other Golgi modifications.

IX–6. THE COX-GOLGI METHOD (78) is Cox's modification of Golgi's dichromate and mercuric chloride method. Many variants of this have been published.
1. Cut pieces of brain 1 cm or less in thickness and immerse in Cox-Golgi solution A (F–102), using at least 30 times as much fluid as the volume of the tissue.
2. Leave the specimens in the solution several months at room temperature; change it once or more often if desired.
3. Wash, dehydrate, embed in paraffin, and cut sections 25–50μ thick. Treat paraffin sections on slides in the usual fashion, decerating and hydrating, then subjecting them to Cox-Golgi solution B (F–102) until the neurons are blackened.
4. Dehydrate and mount in xylene-resin, making very sure to remove all traces of water from the slide; or the section may be covered with mountant and dried thoroughly in a dust-free area and then covered after the addition of a little more resin.

Results: Cell bodies and processes are black or dark brown; the background is clear, often light yellow. Capillaries as well as neurons may be impregnated.

Bertram and Ihrig have studied the effects of various factors on the Golgi method. They recommend that fixation of the central nervous system be made by the pulsating-perfusion technic and that the pH of the perfusion fluid, fixative, and chromating solutions be carefully controlled. They use a glass electrode type of pH meter for this purpose. They also recommend the production of zinc chromate in the laboratory, since they have found some variation in commercial samples of this reagent (36).

IX–7. BERTRAM AND IHRIG'S CHROMATE–SILVER NITRATE METHOD (35) for adult dog, guinea pig, monkey, mouse, rat, and rabbit.
1. Perfuse the animal by the pulsating-perfusion technic (III–12), first with saline-acacia washing fluid, pH 7.0–7.2 (F–179), then with 10% formol-saline-acacia at the same pH (F–93).
2. When fixation is completed, remove the brain and cut into slices

2–3 mm thick, using a slicing guide (E–65); transfer the slices to 10% formalin at the same pH, 1–2 days.

3. Chromate the slices by transfer to a chromating solution, pH 3.1–3.2 (F–57) for 1 day.

4. Remove the slices, blot dry, and put in 1500 ml of a 0.75% silver nitrate solution for 2 days, keeping them in suspension by bubbling air through the mixture.

5. After silvering, follow the procedure below, as recommended by Fox *et al.* (108). Remove the silver crystals on the surface of the slices with water, absorbent paper, and soft camel-hair brushes. This cleaning may be continued if necessary in alcohol.

6. Prepare for sectioning by a modified paraffin method which encloses the specimen in paraffin but does not infiltrate it. This is practical because the tissue is firm and thick slices are cut.

   a. Put the slices through 2 changes of 95% and 100% alcohol (total time for the 4 changes, about 1 hour) and transfer to xylene for 10 minutes.

   b. Place in low melting point paraffin for 10 minutes and embed. With this treatment, the paraffin clings to the surface of the tissue and provides the requisite rigidity.

7. Mount specimens on blocks and cut sections at 90–100μ. The whole block should be cut at one time. Collect sections in serial order, in 95% alcohol, and mount as soon thereafter as possible.

8. Dehydrate sections in 100% alcohol and clear in xylene, using several changes of each. Since the silver chromate crystals separate from the surface at this stage, both alcohol and xylene should be filtered at intervals.

9. Place specimens on slides and cover with several successive layers of xylene-resin (Fisher's Permount was used by Fox and his colleagues). Let them harden in a dust-free place for several days. Moisten the surface of the mountant with toluene, apply the cover, weight it (E–86), and place the slide in a warming oven for a few hours. An alternative procedure would be to apply a thin solution of xylene-resin rather than toluene.

Results: Only a small number of neurons are stained in each section. Cells and processes usually difficult to demonstrate are beautifully clear, as are those which generally are well stained. The time of fixation may be extended to a year without loss of good staining capacity.

IX–8. THE MERCURIC NITRATE METHOD (Bertram and Ihrig, 37) is similar to IX–7.

1. Fix brains of kittens, rats, or mice by pulsating-perfusion (III–12) with 10% formol-saline-acacia solution, pH 7.0, after first washing out the blood with saline-acacia solution at the same pH.

2. Remove brains to 10% formalin, pH 7.0 and cut in 3-mm sections with a slicing guide (E–64, 65). Fix 2 days longer in 10% formalin, pH 7.0.
3. Chromate, for 1 day, in 200 ml of solution (F–57). This chromating step may be omitted and step 4 begun directly after fixation.
4. Remove slices from solution, blot dry, and suspend each slice by a cotton thread in 1000 ml of a sat aq sol of mercuric nitrate, Hg $(NO_3)_2$; the pH is adjusted to 5.8–6.0 with sodium acetate.
5. After 2 days, remove the slices from the mercury solution. Continue with the process described in IX-7, 5–9.

Results are beautiful in both chromated and nonchromated material when the mercuric chloride solution is used within a pH range of 5.8–6.0. The preparations show details of axons and dentrites very clearly, and the synapses with processes and cell bodies of other neurons are particularly plain. Some neuroglia are very clearly demonstrated. There is selective staining of different types of cells, such as the granule cells of the cerebellum and the Purkinje cells, according to the pH of the mercuric nitrate solutions.

NISSL SUBSTANCE

Nissl substance, often called Nissl's granules, chromophilic granules or tigroid substance, stains well with several dyes; among them are thionin, methylene blue, crystal violet, gallocyanin, and Darrow red. The Nissl granules are demonstrable in squashes and sections and are well stained in Klüver and Barrera preparations (*174*).

IX–9. SNIDER'S METHOD for bulk staining of Nissl substance in the brain (*289*).
1. Cut slices of brain 3–4 mm thick and fix in fixative-stain (F–183), 18 hours. If the blocks are thicker, they should remain in the solution longer: 10- to 15-mm blocks, 48–72 hours.
2. Transfer to dioxane, changing the fluid twice at 30 minute intervals.
3. Infiltrate and embed in paraffin.
4. Spread sections, dry and decerate in xylene.
5. Differentiate in 95% alcohol under the microscope; 5–10 minutes is usually sufficient. Complete dehydration in 100% alcohol. Clear in xylene and mount in xylene-resin.

Results: Nuclei are not well stained but Nissl substance is very clear. We find that suitable sections spread on 35-mm film and treated as directed on p. 75 are most useful, when projected, in demonstrating brain architecture.

NERVES AND NERVE FIBERS

Perpheral nerves, most of which are myelinated, are usually treated by various technics that stain myelin. Some of these methods also serve to demonstrate nerve terminations. One of the simplest is that of Bruesch, who applied it to the optic nerves of vertebrates.

IX–10. BRUESCH'S OSMIC ACID METHOD (*51*).

1. Select a stender dish about 50 × 30 mm. Make a frame which will fit into it, of glass rod or tubing, conforming in shape to the sides and bottom of the dish and with the ends about 10 mm below the lid.
2. Remove a piece of optic nerve, or peripheral nerve not more than 2–3 mm in diameter and about 1–2 cm long, from a freshly killed vertebrate. Attach it to the frame with a silk thread at each end, taking care to have it neither stretched nor sagging.
3. Place the nerve on the frame in the dish and pour in enough 2% osmic acid to cover the bottom, but not to touch the nerve; 5 mm will usually suffice. Fixation is by the osmic acid vapor, which is more effective than immersion in the fluid.
4. Cover the dish—the cover must fit tightly—and leave at room temperature 1–2 days; those nerves of the greater diameter should have longer treatment.
5. Remove the frame from the dish; the osmic acid may be kept for re-use unless it has darkened. Remove the specimen from the frame and wash it several hours in running tap water.
6. Prepare in paraffin, dehydrating with alcohol; section, spread, and mount.

Results: The myelin sheath of the nerve is blackened or colored dark gray.

IX–11. STILWELL'S SUDAN BLACK B METHOD (*302*) of preparing sections suitable for tracing the course of peripheral nerves in thick, frozen sections is simple and produces good results.

1. Immerse fresh specimens in McManus' fluid (F–139) for at least 2 days. Wash thoroughly in running tap water.
2. Decalcify, if necessary, in 50% formic acid, and 20% sodium citrate, 1:1/vol. Wash well in running tap water.
3. Infiltrate in gelatin, using 2, 5, and 10% solutions at 57°C, 2–3 days in each solution for a 3-cm specimen.
4. Block in 10% gelatin, chill several hours in a refrigerator, and trim well. Harden 24 hours in McManus' fluid, well chilled.
5. Cut serial frozen sections at 75μ. Orient on slides in a little 1%

gelatin. Allow excess fluid to evaporate and transfer to the re-frigerator. Immerse the slides in cold McManus' fluid to harden the gelatin used in mounting.

6. Wash the slides in cool, running tap water, then in distilled water, and pass to 70% alcohol.

7. Stain 15–30 minutes in a saturated, filtered solution of Sudan black B (F–185), in 70% alcohol; drain well.

8. Differentiate in 2 baths of 50% alcohol under microscopic obser-vation. The time required is usually not long.

9. Transfer slides to water; drain and mount them in glycerol-gelatin (F–101). Seal, if desired, with a non-aqueous cement.

Results: Myelin stains green to gray-green; large nerves and small myelinated axons are well stained. Some details of intrafusal endings and somatic motor terminations are visible. The finest detail in myelin may be seen, and there is little background staining in specimens in which there is little adipose tissue.

A more nearly permanent preparation might be made by using one of the hard-setting aqueous mountants.

A particularly satisfactory method for demonstrating nerve fibers is Bodian's. It calls for the staining of paraffin sections after they are spread. Davenport (*83*, p. 259) says that "its chief advantage is that direct impregnation of mounted paraffin sections . . . free of spurious precipitates can be made."

IX–12.   BODIAN'S PROTARGOL METHOD (*42*).

1. Perfuse the animal first with normal saline (F–180), then with formalin-acetic-alcohol (F–90). Remove the desired parts and fix at least 48 hours in the same mixture.

2. Prepare in paraffin, decerate sections, and bring to water.

3. Transfer to Protargol solution (F–172), 12–48 hours, at 37°C.

4. Rinse in water and reduce in hydroquinone solution (F–36), 2–10 minutes.

5. Wash thoroughly in running water.

6. Tone in 0.5–1% gold chloride solution, acidified with 3 drops of glacial acetic acid/100 ml, 5–10 minutes, until the sections are uniformly gray. Examine under the microscope. If the nerve fibers are deeply stained and the background is clear, continue to step 8. If the staining is light, intensify it by proceeding with step 7.

7. Place the slides in 0.5% aq sol of oxalic acid, observing the sec-tions microscopically. When they have darkened sufficiently, 30 seconds to 5 minutes, rinse in water.

8. Transfer to 5% aq sol of sodium thiosulfate, 5 minutes.

9. Wash thoroughly in running water, dehydrate, clear, and mount.

Results: The staining of nerve fibers, both myelinated and unmyelinated, is sharp and distinct. Neurofibrillae and end-feet are clearly shown, as are neuron cell bodies.

Johnels (*163*) recommends that reduction after gold toning be done with 50% alcohol to which 3–6 drops of aniline oil/100 ml are added. He finds that this suppresses co-staining of non-nervous tissue and makes the thick nerve fibers deep red or blue and the finer ones bluish black or black.

A method traditionally used for demonstration of fibers and fiber tracts in the central nervous system is Weigert's, in which the principal stain is hematoxylin. This has been modified by many workers. It is a good method but time-consuming, especially since it requires celloidin sections. A new technic which seems likely to replace it is that of Klüver and Barrera, which not only stains the myelin well but also the neurons. It is thus useful for cyto-architecture as well as tracts.

IX–13. THE KLÜVER AND BARRERA METHOD (*174*) is simple and effective; it may be applied to frozen, paraffin, or celloidin sections. The schedule presented here is for paraffin sections. The authors state that the method is most successful for frozen and paraffin sections.

1. Fix specimens in 10% formalin, prepare in paraffin, section at 15–20μ, and spread.
2. Decerate in xylene, transfer to absolute alcohol, and then to 95% alcohol, several changes.
3. Stain 16–24 hours in Luxol fast blue (F–123) at 57°C.
4. Wash off excess stain in 95% alcohol.
5. Wash in water.
6. Begin differentiation by quick immersion in 0.05% lithium carbonate.
7. Continue differentiation in several changes of 70% alcohol, which should be discarded when colored. Discontinue when gray and white matter can be distinguished. Do not overdifferentiate.
8. Wash in water.
9. Finish differentiation by rinsing 3–5 seconds in 0.5% lithium carbonate, then passing slides through several changes of 70% alcohol, which produces the most delicate differentiation, so that there is sharp contrast between the greenish-blue color of the white matter and the colorless gray matter.
10. Wash well in water.
11. Stain 6 minutes in cresyl violet solution (F–123) at 57°C.
12. Differentiate in several changes of 95% alcohol; discard the solutions when colored.

13. Clear in xylene-terpineol, 1:1/vol then in pure xylene, and mount in synthetic resin.

Results: Myelin sheaths, neurons and their Nissl bodies, glial nuclei, capillary endothelium, and the mesothelial lining of the arachnoid membrane are clearly stained; finer connective tissue fibers are not. This method stains well both peripheral nerves and the central nervous system in amphibians, birds, and mammals; various extra-neural tissues are also stained well. The stain is very useful as an oversight method.

Among the numerous modifications of this method which have appeared, several should be mentioned. Powers *et al.* (*255*) recommend counterstaining with Darrow red instead of cresyl violet. They proceed, after step 10 above, to:

11*a*. Stain frozen or paraffin sections 20–30 minutes in Darrow red (F–71, 72).

12*a*. Rinse in water, differentiate, and dehydrate through 50, 70, and 95% alcohol rapidly enough to prevent complete decolorization of sections but slowly enough to allow excess dye to leave the background. Complete the dehydration in butanol.

13*a*. Clear in xylene and mount in xylene-soluble synthetic resin.

Margolis and Pickett (*209*) have used the technic extensively, particularly on pathological specimens, and have suggested a number of substitutions for the non-myelin staining components of the formulae; the substitutions include periodic acid-Schiff and hematoxylin; phosphotungstic acid-hematoxylin; oil red O; or Holmes' silver nitrate.

Lockard and Reers (*199*) present a modification for combined staining of tissue elements in and adjoining the central nervous system as well as for demonstrating the cyto-architecture of the central nervous system.

Salthouse (*278*) uses Luxol fast blue ARN rather than MBSN, changes the duration of staining somewhat and, for certain purposes, changes the fixative. He reports that the former dye has a greater affinity for myelin than other Luxol fast blues that he has tried.

All of these modifications may be of use in special cases, and the authors cited should be consulted. However, the original method of Klüver and Barrera is a most excellent and beautiful technic.

DEGENERATING MYELINATED NERVE FIBERS may be prepared by numerous technics. Of these, two which are well-known are Marchi's method, as modified by Swank and Davenport, and the Nauta and Gygax technics and their numerous modifications. There are good descriptions of the former method by Davenport (*83*, pp.. 196–98) and in Conn *et al.* (*72*, pp.121–24). The latter method is described by Nauta and Gygax (*232*), and modifications of it have been offered by White

(*331*) and by Guillery *et al.* (*137*). The Klüver and Barrera technic, somewhat modified, may also be used to show degeneration according to Margolis and Pickett (*209*). Snodgrass *et al.* (*290*) describe another variation of the Klüver and Barrera technic.

NERVE ENDINGS

Nerve endings on muscle can be demonstrated by several technics. One which is usually successful uses gold chloride as the stain. Ranvier (*260*) proposed an early method for its use; IX–14 is one of its numerous modifications.

IX–14. THE METHOD OF ZINN AND MORIN (339) FOR STAINING NERVE ENDINGS ON SKELETAL MUSCLE. The authors used a wide variety of acids as fixatives and found that, of those tried, the most satisfactory were commercial lemon juice (R–111) diluted with water or 0.001M citric acid. Either may be used in step 1 below.

1. Place small pieces, about 4 mm², of guinea pig intercostal muscle in the commercial lemon juice or citric acid, 10 minutes or until they are translucent.
2. Wash in several changes of water, 5 minutes.
3. Transfer to a dish containing enough 1.0% aq sol of gold chloride to cover the specimens. When a definite golden color has spread uniformly over the specimens (5 minutes to more than 60) remove to water and rinse in several changes for 5 minutes. For steps 3 and 4, handle the specimens with glass instruments.
4. Immerse in a solution of 1 part of 90% formic acid in 2 parts of water and leave in the dark 24 hours.
5. Wash in several changes of water; tease the tissue apart gently on the slide. Select specimens which show suitable staining and mount in glycerol jelly. The writer has obtained more nearly permanent preparations by using a polyvinyl alcohol mountant (F–76).

Results: Successful preparations show black nerve fibers and nerve endings on light red or light purple muscle fibers. With polyvinyl alcohol mountants, the specimens were unchanged after 2 years.

Boyd (*45*) gives directions for a more precise technic which is particularly applicable to muscle spindles. Cole (*68*) lists modifications of the gold chloride method for cold-blooded animals and for various mammals.

IX–15. METHYLENE BLUE METHODS, involving perfusion or immersion of the tissue, produce well-stained nerve endings. The procedure below is based on the methods of Ehrlich (*96*).

1. Perfuse the whole animal with normal saline at body temperature to wash out the blood, then with methylene blue solution, medicinal grade, zinc-free, 0.001% in normal saline; 10–15 minutes after the initial perfusion, which should color the tissues, perfuse a second time. If the animal under study is large it may be convenient to perfuse only the part which is to be examined, using its principal artery.

2. About 20 minutes after the final perfusion, remove thin slices of the tissue to a slide moistened with the staining solution. Examine frequently under the microscope. When a deep color has developed in the nerve endings, transfer at once to a saturated solution of ammonium picrate.

3. If whole mounts of the tissue are to be made, tease to expose the nerve endings and transfer to a saturated solution of ammonium picrate and glycerol, 1:1/vol. Mount in the same mixture. It should be possible to make permanent preparations by mounting in one of the new hard aqueous mountants.

3a. For sectioned preparations transfer the tissues, after 10–15 minutes in the ammonium picrate, to Bethe's fluid (F–32) or preferably to Cole's fluid (F–63), 45–60 minutes. Wash in water 1–2 hours, changing it frequently. Dehydrate directly in absolute alcohol, several changes; clear in xylene and embed in paraffin.

1a. Instead of perfusing the whole animal, select small and thin portions and treat by moistening them at frequent intervals with 0.001% methylene blue; keep the tissue moist but not covered with the solution. When nerve endings are well stained, fix the pieces in ammonium picrate. From this point continue with step 3 above.

Larimer and Ashby (*185*) use leuco methylene blue for staining nerves in crustaceans. They reduce the stain with ascorbic acid or with sodium hydrosulfite and at times use hydrogen peroxide to attain deeper staining than is produced when tissues are merely exposed to the air. For fixation, they use 8% ammonium molybdate and for dehydration, butanol which preserves the color of the stain better than ethanol does.

Heller, Thomas, and Davenport (*151*) studied the staining of nerve fibers by immersing them in methylene blue. They concluded that the best staining is obtained when (1) there is continuous oxygenation of the staining fluid, (2) the staining solution is stabilized at pH 5.6 with a phosphate buffer, and (3) tissues of young animals are treated.

CHAPTER X

HARD TISSUES

Bone, cartilage, and teeth of vertebrates are the principal objects for consideration in this chapter. Scales of fishes and tests of certain invertebrates will also be treated briefly.

There are in current use several methods of preparing bone for study. Fresh, or cleaned and dried bone, is sawed into thin slices and ground down to an appropriate thickness with abrasives, then mounted in such a way as to demonstrate the architecture of the matrix. Fresh bone or tooth is sawed and ground in the same way and appropriately treated to show cellular detail or to demonstrate the location of an enzyme such as alkaline phosphatase.

Calcified tissue is fixed, decalcified, embedded, and treated by usual histological methods to show cellular components and matrix. In young animals the appropriate technics applied to such a part as a foot may, after decalcification of the skeletal elements, show not only the bone but its relation to surrounding soft tissues.

Teeth, bone, cartilage, tests, and scales of certain animals may be stained *in vivo* by ingestion or injection of dyes. Bones and scales are also colored by certain antibiotics. Whole skeletons or parts of skeletons of fixed specimens may be stained *in vitro* for demonstration of normal or abnormal structure or stages in development.

GRINDING

The traditional method of preparing compact bone for study of its architecture is to grind a thin section, usually on carborundum stones of increasing fineness, until a sufficiently thin section is produced and then to mount the section in very thick, heated balsam in such a way that the mountant does not enter the cavities in the matrix. Trapped air makes even the finest spaces black so that this procedure makes lacunae and even fine canaliculi beautifully plain. Disadvantages of this technic are the labor of producing the sections and the difficulties in mounting. Frost has devised a superior and rapid method for producing thin sections of ground bone. Although he applies it to fresh specimens, we have found it equally effective for dried material.

124

X-1. METHOD OF FROST (*110*) FOR RAPID MANUAL PREPA-
RATION OF THIN, UNDECALCIFIED BONE SECTIONS.

The following supplies and equipment are needed: carborundum abrasive paper with waterproof adhesive, grit 320, 360, or 400 (the lower numbers are coarser); a piece of flat plate glass about 25 × 30 cm; liquid household detergent, diluted about 1:500/vol; a fine-toothed hacksaw, 32 or more teeth to the inch.

1. Saw fresh, unfixed bone into slabs 1–2 mm thick and in any desired plane; work slowly to avoid heating and cracking the bone.

2. Moisten the back of a sheet of abrasive paper and place it on the glass, grit side up. Cover the surface with water and continue to use water liberally throughout the grinding process. With the fingers grasping the bone slab, move it over the paper with relatively light pressure and a circular motion that covers most of the width of the paper. Do this at the rate of 1 cycle/second. The bone grinds down quickly and saw marks should disappear in less than 1 minute. When they have been removed from one side, turn the piece over and repeat the process, preferably on an already used piece of paper. The second side is a little more difficult than the first. If the bone sticks, rub down the surface of the paper with an unused portion of the sheet or, if necessary, use a finer grit.

3. When the section is too thin to grind by holding with the fingers, wrap a strip of fresh carborundum paper wider than the piece of bone, grit side out, around the middle of a 25 × 75-mm glass slide. Press the partly ground bone upon the paper; it will adhere firmly to the carborundum points. Hold the ends of the paper between the thumb and forefinger or place the forefinger between its two ends and hold with thumb and second finger. Rub the bone with the same motion as before on a used carborundum sheet, which will grind less rapidly than a fresh one; grind the two sides alternately and keep their surfaces parallel. Continue grinding until the desired thinness is reached, avoiding too great pressure which may cause the section to crack. At about 75μ, the section will begin to be translucent and will be mottled with white. At about 50μ, it has the appearance of wet ground glass. If sections are to be stained by Frost's basic fuchsin technic, they should be about 75μ thick. If very thin sections are needed, continue the grinding on 400-grit paper, using generous quantities of water.

4. Place the section in a 50-ml flask with detergent solution and shake vigorously at least a minute to remove surface debris; rinse by shaking in several changes of water. Blot dry or transfer at once to stain.

STAINING THIN, GROUND BONE SECTIONS

Because of the difficulty of mounting sections in balsam, it has long been a common practice to apply stains to outline the cavities in bone. Basic fuchsin and silver nitrate have been so employed. Frost has modified the method, using both these and other stains. His treatment with fuchsin follows:

X–2. FROST'S METHOD (*111*).

1. Stain a section about 75μ thick with 1% basic fuchsin (R–87) in 30% alcohol, 48 hours at 22°C. Be sure that the stain covers the specimen and that the container is tightly stoppered; or
1a. Stain in 0.3% solution of basic fuchsin in 30% alcohol at 37–40°C, 8 hours; this is optional for adult bone, but essential for bones of infants, young children, or very immature animals; they are deeply and often opaquely stained by the more concentrated fuchsin.
2. At the end of the staining period transfer to tap water or to distilled water made slightly alkaline with ammonia; slight alkalinity prevents appreciable diffusion of the stain to the liquid.
3. Grind both surfaces of the stained bone in tap water or ammonia water, removing the stain completely from the side which will be in contact with the slide when mounted; stop the grinding of the cover-glass side when clear detail appears there, as determined by frequent checking under the microscope.
4. Wash in detergent and rinse as before.
5. Dry in air; mount in synthetic resin.

Results: In normal, fully mineralized bone the fuchsin stains the walls of all cavities in the matrix; there is no permeation of the fuchsin into the fully mineralized substance. In some pathological states there is a diffuse permeability of the affected areas. There is also diffuse permeation during early mineralization of new bone. The intensity of staining is directly related to the mineral density. The stain thus indicates the extent of mineralization as well as outlining the cavities.

MOUNTING UNSTAINED GROUND BONE SECTIONS

X–3. ENLOW'S PLASTIC-SEAL METHOD (*101*) for mounting unstained sections of bone is easily applied and produces excellent results.
1. Complete step 4 of Frost's grinding method, X–1, and air-dry bone sections thoroughly.
2. Submerge, one section at a time, in Parlodion solution (F–78). Agitate the section with an applicator stick to liberate air bubbles.

3. Transfer the section to a clean slide with a drop of the solution, just enough to flow around the specimen. Do not add more of the solution, since an excess will produce a lens effect and result in a distorted image.
4. Dry thoroughly.
5. Add several drops of a xylene-soluble resin and cover.

Result: The Parlodion solution prevents the access of mountant to lacunae and canaliculi in the bone so that, filled with air, they are black within the white calcified matrix. The sections may be studied, if desired, with a polarizing microscope.

PREPARATIONS OF UNDECALCIFIED TEETH AND BONES

It is possible to make a preparation of a jaw bone and teeth that shows both anatomical relationships and cellular detail. Brewer and Shellhamer have described a method for sectioning a jaw with teeth *in situ*. For making the sections, they used a 7/8-inch diamond disc attached to a dental hand piece and powered by a 1/10-hp motor.

X–4. THE METHOD OF BREWER AND SHELLHAMER (*49*).

1. Fix rat hemimandibles in 10% formalin, 24 hours. Wash in tap water, 8 hours.
2. Hold the specimen between thumb and forefinger and make a sagittal section through all of the molar teeth and a portion of an incisor by grinding away the alveolar bone alternately from the medial and lateral surfaces until the roots are visible. Grind by manipulating the disc, with the specimen held steady. The thickness at the end of this step should be 0.5 mm.
3. Separate the ground portion from the ramus of the mandible, and place it on a piece of moistened cork cut to a similar shape. Continue grinding as before until the section is about 80μ thick.
4. Transfer the section to water and remove debris by brushing; several changes of water are necessary.
5. Stain with hematoxylin and eosin (VI–11) or with periodic acid-Schiff (XIII–2). The complete process of grinding and staining requires less than 1 hour/section.
6. Dehydrate, clear, and mount in synthetic resin.

Results: These preparations demonstrate the calcified structures of the teeth and bone as well as their soft structure.

DECALCIFICATION

When bone is to be studied for cellular detail and in relation to other tissues, it is usually decalcified. With removal of its mineral constituents, it becomes easy to section and to stain. There are numerous methods of decalcification. The best ones do not alter the normal structure appreciably. All decalcification methods involve exposure of the bone to fluids that remove its minerals by solution.

GENERAL RULES AND PROCEDURES for the application of decalcifiers:
a. Decalcify, in most cases, after fixation.
b. When possible, saw large bones into thin slices before applying the decalcifier.
c. Use a strong decalcifier for large pieces of bone, or apply a weak one over a long period of time.
d. Use a generous amount of decalcifying fluid in a large container. Change it at frequent intervals. Suspend the specimen above the bottom of the dish.
e. Apply the decalcifier for the shortest period consistent with good results.
f. If desired, decalcify after embedding in celloidin.
g. Test the progress of decalcification.

METHODS FOR TESTING THE PROGRESS OF DECALCIFICATION:
a. Probe the specimen with a thin, sharp needle. Use this method only if a number of pieces of comparable size are being decalcified, some of which may be sacrificed to this process.
b. Test the used decalcifying fluid by the following method (*156*, p. 25): To 5 ml of the solution in which the tissue is being decalcified, add 1 ml of 5% sodium or ammonium oxalate. If a precipitate forms within 5 minutes, continue the decalcification. If the solution remains clear, the next step may be undertaken.
c. Examine the specimen by X-ray fluoroscopy (*322*) or by X-ray photography (*224*).

DECALCIFICATION BY FIXATIVES is one of the simplest and most satisfactory technics. The action of such a solution is gentle and takes some time to complete. If the piece is small enough or is larger but incompletely calcified, the writer considers this the method of choice. It is particularly applicable to specimens in which the relation of surrounding tissues to the bone is to be demonstrated.

X-5.   BOUIN'S PFA is used as follows:
1.   Place the specimen in freshly made PFA.
2.   Change the fluid at intervals of 2-4 days, according to size of specimen, until the decalcification is complete.

3. Wash well in running tap water, 15–30 minutes.
4. Prepare for sectioning, preferably in paraffin. A specimen such as the paw of a small young animal is informative if the sections are stained with Mallory's triple (VII–7) or Kornhauser's Quad stain (VII–11).

PERENYI'S FLUID (F–167) is recommended by Humason (*156*, p. 28) as a fixative-decalcifier for slightly calcified tissues.

X–6. DECALCIFICATION BY MAGNESIUM CITRATE, KRAMER AND SHIPLEY (*213*, p. 260). This method is satisfactory for specimens that are not too large. The bones are placed in a large quantity of fluid (F–135) which is changed every 3 days. The action is moderately rapid; a dog's rib takes about 15 days. The architecture of the soft tissues is well preserved.

X–7. DECALCIFICATION BY CHELATING AGENTS. These agents are satisfactory since they are efficient, cause little tissue distortion, and seem to have no adverse effect upon subsequent staining. The most commonly used compound is ethylene diamine tetracetic acid, often called EDTA and marketed under the trade names Versene (R–197) and Sequestrene (R–179). The results, in our laboratory, have been excellent.
A method described by Hillemann and Lee (*152*) for bones and teeth is as follows:
1. Perfuse adult guinea pigs, by artery, with 10% neutral formalin.
2. Remove the mandibles and fix 24 hours in 10% neutral formalin.
3. Transfer each specimen to 200 ml of 5.5% solution of either Sequestrene or Versene in 10% formalin; renew this fluid at the end of each week for 3 weeks.
4. Wash thoroughly and prepare for sectioning in paraffin.
5. Stain with hematoxylin and eosin; dehydrate and mount as usual.
Results: Fixation is good and staining is brilliant.

X–8. ENLOW'S RAPID DECALCIFICATION METHOD (*102*) is recommended by its originator as useful when large numbers of bone samples must be examined or screened in a minimum period of time. Finished mounts may be prepared from sizable pieces of bone in less than half a day.
1. Saw the fixed piece of bone into thin slices and grind down to 80–120μ by Frost's method (X–1) or by using a power-driven lap wheel.
2. Decalcify by any of the above methods or with Decal (R–60).
3. Wash in running tap water.

4.   Stain as desired, and mount sections; or affix sections to slides
      before staining. A weight on the cover glass for a few hours may
      be desirable.

Results: With hematoxylin and eosin, an eosinophilic collagenous matrix is evident, containing distinct basophilic resting, reversal, and
cementing lines. Cytoplasmic details are indistinct but nuclei are well
stained. Lamellar patterns are brilliant under polarized light.

X–9.   STAINING DECALCIFIED BONE *IN TOTO*.   Tappen (307)
recommends that for serial sections, decalcified bone be stained *in toto*
before embedding and sectioning. He uses undiluted Harris' hematoxylin and cuts sections on a freezing microtome after embedding in 15%
gelatin (F–95). We have found that paraffin, water wax, and LVN embedding are also satisfactory.

DEMONSTRATION OF FIBRILLAR GROUND SUBSTANCE OF THE MATRIX OF CARTILAGE, BONE, AND TEETH

Since the refractive index of the matrix of hard tissues in vertebrates is
so similar to that of the fibers which permeate it, the latter are often
difficult to demonstrate.

X–10.   RUTH'S METHOD OF DEMONSTRATION OF FIBRILLAE
(277) in these tissues is satisfactory. The method involves decalcification,
if necessary, partial dissociation, embedding in paraffin, and staining
for various types of fibers.

1.   Decalcify slabs of bone 5 mm in thickness which are preferably
      fresh and unfixed, but may be dried or fixed. If greasy, treat first
      with a fat solvent.
2.   Wash to remove decalcifier, then immerse in Mall's solution
      (F–136); the amount of potassium hydroxide in this solution should
      be adjusted to the size of the pieces. Treat very delicate specimens
      with a 1% solution and larger ones with 3%. If the latter pro-
      duces little dissociation, use 5% potassium hydroxide in Mall's
      solution. Change the solution as often as it appears cloudy; watch
      carefully for signs of dissociation, such as a fuzzy edge to the
      specimens or actual fragmentation. The process will take from a
      few days to 2 or 3 weeks.
3.   Wash overnight in gently running tap water to thoroughly remove
      alkali. If pieces are somewhat fragmented, they may be handled
      in tissue carriers.
4.   Embed in paraffin after dioxane dehydration. Cut sections 10–12μ
      thick.

5.   Stain with van Gieson's picro-fuchsin (VII–8) or with Korn-
     hauser's Quad stain (VII–11).
Result: The fibrillae of the matrix are characteristically colored according to the stain used.

STAINING OF HARD TISSUES *IN VIVO*

It is a useful characteristic of hard tissues that they may be stained with
vital dyes. Bone colors with madder ingested or injected while it is calcifying. Bone also stains with such madder derivatives as alizarin red S,
which is less toxic, and with some tetracycline antibiotics. Cartilage
stains *in vivo* with chlorazol fast pink and with trypan blue. The *in vivo*
staining of hard parts is not limited to endoskeletons. Fish scales from
injected specimens show rings of color. Certain invertebrates also take
up dyes in their calcareous tests.

X–11.   VITAL STAINING OF BONE WITH ALIZARIN RED S.

1.   Inject into the abdominal cavity of a young rat 0.2 ml of 2% aq sol
     of alizarin red S; for adult rats, use 0.5 to 1.0 ml.
2.   Repeat the dose at intervals, if desired, but in this case use a
     slightly smaller amount. Each successive dose will produce a layer
     of stained bone.
3.   Sacrifice the animal, and fix in 10% formalin. Treat the bones by
     any method which does not involve decalcification, i.e. prepara-
     tions of whole animals, whole bones, or ground sections of bones.
Results: The staining of bone begins within 2 minutes after administration of the dye and reaches a maximum in 12 hours. Only bone laid
down during dye administration takes the stain.

X–12.   THE METHOD OF MOSS (229).

1.   Inject young white mice, intraperitoneally, 3 times at intervals of
     30 minutes with 0.5 ml of either 5% aq sol of chlorazol fast pink,
     C.I. No. 353, or 2% aq sol of trypan blue, C.I. No. (477) 23850.
     Sacrifice 30 minutes after the last injection.
2.   Remove desired specimens and fix in 10% formalin at least 24
     hours; or fix the whole animal several days or longer.
After the above preparation, the entire skeleton may be cleared and
stored (X–16); individual bones may be cut and ground into sections,
or bones may be decalcified and cut in paraffin.
Results: Uncalcified matrix of forming bone, newly formed cartilage,
and collagenous and elastic fibers are differentially stained by both dyes.

X–13.   THE METHOD OF WEATHERALL AND HOBBS (327)

demonstrates that any uncalcified osteoid tissue and several types of dense connective tissue, as well as cartilage, stain *in vivo* with chlorazol fast pink. The reaction of the stain is determined by the extent of mineralization and does not necessarily correspond to the age of osteoid tissue.

1.   Inject adult rabbits with 10 ml of a 5% aq sol of chlorazol fast pink. Sacrifice within a few hours or up to 6–7 weeks later.
2.   Prepare the bone in any way desired. Decalcification does not affect the stain.

Results: Bone matrix not calcified at the time of injection, decalcified bone, cartilage, and collagen stain a deep pink.

X–14.   *IN VIVO* STAINING WITH ACHROMYCIN OR TERRA-MYCIN is another method of marking newly formed bone. Human bone obtained at autopsy or after amputation from a patient who had been given the antibiotic as medication has shown vital staining. This staining was described first by Frost, Villaneuva, and Roth (*112*).

When applied to fish, the tetracycline series of antibiotics has shown promising results. Weber and Ridgway (*328*) report a series of experiments in which they administered tetracycline, chlortetracycline, and oxytetracycline by adding the antibiotic to the culture water, by putting it in food, and by injection. Staining is detectable by a yellow-gold fluorescence when the parts are subjected to ultraviolet illumination.

D. W. Coble (personal communication) points out that it is easier to order these antibiotics by using their trade names: tetracycline is Achromycin; chlortetracycline is Aureomycin and oxytetracycline is Terramycin. Tetracycline is available in the veterinary grade as Polyotic (Lederle, Division of Cyanamid) at a lower cost. Coble uses this with good results by buffering the solutions with sodium bicarbonate ($NaHCO_3$), making the solutions a short time before use and refrigerating them.

Milch, Rall, and Tobie (*223*) report on the prolonged staining effect of a tetracycline in rabbits.

X–15.   THE METHOD OF FRY *ET AL.* (*113*) FOR MARKING FISH SCALES to determine rate of growth makes use of lead versenate.

1.   Inject fish with 5 or 7% lead disodium versenate (F–129), 50 mg/kg body weight.
2.   After allowing several weeks or months for growth, remove scales, place in tightly stoppered, well-filled small containers of 5% hydrochloric acid saturated with hydrogen sulfide while chilled in ice and water. Soak scales 4–8 hours at room temperature, agitating at intervals.
3.   Drain and refill containers with methanol; agitate at intervals, at least 12 hours.

4. Remove methanol and replace with 0.05% gold chloride. In 2 hours or less, the pinky-blue lead line generally develops. When it appears,
5. Remove the gold chloride solution and replace, for a short time, with 0.5% sodium thiosulfate. Rinse in water, dehydrate in alcohol, and mount in Euparal (R–82).

Results: The lead line is clearly apparent.

There are a number of unrelated methods for vitally staining hard parts of various marine animals. A representative account of such methods and a helpful literature list are given by Swan (*304*).

STAINING BONE AND CARTILAGE *IN VITRO*

Skeletons of animals which have been sacrificed make excellent preparations. They will show, according to the technic employed, the cartilaginous or the calcified portions. If a series of developing embryos is prepared, the growth of the skeleton and the progress of calcification may be traced. Skeletal defects are well demonstrated in this way. The earlier methods for staining skeletons of young animals to show both cartilage and bone seldom provided satisfactory results, in our laboratory. While bone stained well, the cartilage was seldom more than faintly tinted.

X–16.   BURDI'S METHOD (*54*) is a new and satisfactory technic. The directions apply to newborn rats and mice with maximum weights of 17.5 g and 4.5 g, respectively. The changes necessary for larger rats and mice (3–8 weeks of age) are indicated.

1. Sacrifice, skin, eviscerate, and remove fat and brain; rinse in water.
2. Fix in formol-acetic-alcohol (F–89) about 40 minutes (2 hours for older specimens).
3. Wash in water 30 minutes and drain well.
4. Stain in 0.06% filtered toluidine blue in 70% alcohol, 48 hours at room temperature, using 20 volumes of stain/specimen. For older animals use 0.12% toluidine blue.
5. Destain soft tissues in 35% alcohol, 20 hours; in 50% alcohol, 28 hours; and in 70%, 8 hours.
6. Blot specimens well and immerse in 1% aq sol of potassium hydroxide containing 2–3 drops of 0.1% alizarin red S/100 ml; use 20 volumes of fluid for each specimen. Transfer daily for 3 days to a fresh solution of the potassium hydroxide and alizarin red or until the calcified parts of the bones are the desired color and the soft tissues are cleared. For older specimens, use 3% potassium hydroxide in the clearing-staining solution for about 4 days.

7.   Rinse in water and blot.
8.   Transfer to glycerol-alcohol, 1:1/vol, 1–2 hours, then to the same
     fluid for storage and final clearing. Older animals require an inter-
     mediate fluid of 2 parts glycerol, 1 part benzyl alcohol, and 2 parts
     70% ethanol by volume, 1 day. From this fluid, transfer them to
     the clearing solution in step 8.

Results: The toluidine blue stains rib cartilages, cranial base synchon-
droses, epiphyseal cartilages, and limb joints a brilliant blue, while the
bone is a deep red.

CHAPTER XI

EMBRYOLOGY

CLEAVAGE IN LIVING EGGS

Although it is possible to follow the process of cleavage in fixed preparations that show a graded series of stages, it is probably more valuable, or at least more interesting, to see the zygote dividing *in vitro*. There are several sources of eggs, in suitable stages, which may be procured without too much trouble.

In most aquaria containing snails it is possible to find egg masses deposited on the walls. If these are removed shortly after laying, a number of the stages in spiral cleavage may be seen in each egg mass. Frog's eggs either collected after laying or inseminated in the laboratory, are valuable specimens for following stages in cleavage. Eggs of echinoderms are less commonly available, since they are difficult to procure except at the seashore and the ripening of gametes is seasonal. It is probably best to make observations on nematode eggs, since they are very easily procured and available at any time of the year.

XI–1. EGGS OF *Blatticola blattae* are recommended by Schell (*281*) for the study of cleavage to early morula stages. He finds that *Blatta germanica* is almost always infested with this parasite. *Periplaneta australasiae* and *P. americana* usually harbor nematodes belonging to the genus *Leidynema*, and these also produce eggs suitable for study, although they are smaller.
1.   Behead the cockroach and withdraw the digestive tract through the caudal end of the insect, placing it on a slide in a few drops of water. Open the colon with dissecting needles and transfer the emerging nematodes to water on a fresh slide.
2.   Puncture female specimens with a needle and take up with a fine pipet the eggs which escape, collecting them in water in a small glass dish.
3.   Transfer a drop of the egg-water suspension to a 22-mm cover glass. Invert it over the well of a depression slide and seal the edges with Vaseline. Study with a compound microscope at a magnification of about 100.
If desired, the rate of cleavage may be hastened by the use of a micro-

scope lamp adjusted to increase the temperature of the mount. At 34–36°C, cleavage will progress from 1–16 cells in 4–5 hours. Temperatures above 50°C are usually lethal.

The eggs of other nematodes will furnish suitable material for cleavage and maturation studies, and any species of nematodes that are abundant locally should be investigated for their suitability. Frogs' lungs are usually infested with nemas, and soil nematodes are often abundant and easy to collect if one buries small pieces of raw meat in the ground. Some of the nematodes that are present in the soil will be found on the meat within 24–48 hours.

The large worms *Ascaris megalocephala* (*Parascaris equorum*) from horses, and *A. lumbricoides* from pigs are both obtainable in some localities. The former species may be had from zoos where horses are killed to provide food for the carnivores. The latter may be collected from abattoirs. Both species should be dropped into normal saline at the host's body temperature and transported in vacuum jars to the laboratory; otherwise, they will die. It is most important to remember, in handling these specimens that they produce a substance which has been called ascaric acid, and which is intensely irritating to the eye if introduced by rubbing with a contaminated hand. Careful washing of the hands after the handling of the specimens is essential.

In both of these large ascarids, the eggs are contained in two uteri which fuse posteriorly to form the vagina and which are continuous anteriorly with the slender, very long and much convoluted ovaries. The developmental stages are located serially within the uterus; the range is usually from sperm entrance at the anterior end to cleavages near the vagina. Occasionally the last stage found is the fusion of pronuclei. Eggs in this stage will cleave if they are incubated at host temperature.

XI–2. EGGS FROM LARGE ASCARIDS.

1. Remove a female from the vacuum jar; it is distinguished from a male by its straight posterior end. Pin it out in a dissecting dish in 0.9% saline and open by longitudinal incision.

2. Cut the uteri at both the vaginal and ovarian ends and place in a finger bowl containing the saline solution kept at proper temperature.

3. If all stages from sperm entrance through mitosis are to be studied, cut the uteri in pieces approximately 1 inch long and place each piece in a watch glass of warm saline, preferably in an incubator where the proper temperature may be maintained. The serial order of each piece should be marked on its container.

4. Mount the desired stages in saline on slides; support the covers and ring with Vaseline; or mount the eggs on covers and invert over the wells of depression slides. If necessary, incubate the pro-

nucleus stages and examine from time to time until cleavage begins; then observe the process under the microscope.

Permanent whole mounts of suitable stages may be made by fixing the eggs in Carnoy II (F–50) and staining with Feulgen's stain (XIII–1).

If it is desired to fix portions of uteri for sectioning, see XII–1.

AVIAN EMBRYOS

For obtaining the embryos of birds either for study alive, or for fixation, the equipment needed and the preliminary steps are the same. The following directions are for hens' eggs but may be applied, with slight modifications, to the eggs of other birds.

Equipment and materials: Incubator (E–36), stabilized at 38°C and provided with a dish of water; incandescent electric lamp, with a 50-watt bulb and, preferably, with a gooseneck; warming table or electric stove or infrared lamp to keep fluid at about incubating temperature; devices to hold eggs in the desired positions, such as syracuse watch glasses or petri dishes with a ring of Plasticene on which an egg may rest, or egg cartons; two 1-liter flasks; several 250-ml flasks; medicine droppers; several petri dishes; syracuse watch glasses; finger bowls and a large container for egg yolks and shells; forceps, curved and straight; scissors; section lifters of various sizes; a thermometer; 1 liter of 0.9% salt solution at 38°C; several 1-liter flasks of tap water at 38°C and, for each, a packet containing 9 g of sodium chloride to be added to the warm tap water when needed.

XI–3. INCUBATION. Mark each egg with the date and hour of the start of incubation. Turn all eggs twice each 24 hours. Keep the container of water that provides moisture for the atmosphere within the incubator well filled; replenish with water warmed to the temperature of the incubator. In calculating stages, allow 4–5 hours for the eggs to become warmed. For example, if eggs of about 24 hours' development are needed, incubate 28–29 hours.

XI–4. OPENING EGGS. Begin by filling a 250-ml flask with saline at 38°C. Place it on a warming table or stove where it will maintain this temperature. Select an egg of the desired stage; hold it with the pointed end down and, with forceps or other pointed tool, make an opening in the blunt end a little to one side of its center. Insert curved scissors in the opening and cut out and remove a piece of shell about an inch in diameter. Gently pick up and cut away the inner layer of the shell membrane, avoiding injury to the embryo beneath it. Place the egg in its supporting device.

This method of opening is preferred by the writer, becàuse it is unlikely to result in injury to the embryo. However, if the technician does not find it satisfactory, or if embryos of more than 72 hours' incubation are to be dealt with, use the following technic:

Hold the egg horizontally in the left hand. Make an initial small hole with forceps near the middle of its upper surface. Cut out a piece of shell as directed above. Place the egg on its support near the lamp and very gently withdraw, by medicine dropper, some of the thinner albumen. If some of the thicker albumen begins to escape, cut off the protruding portion quickly with scissors. Remove more shell and more albumen until the embryo is well exposed and accessible for operation. If the yolk rotates and the embryo changes position, manipulate it gently with finger and/or section lifter to return it to its proper position.

XI-5. TO STUDY IN THE LIVING CONDITION.

1. Drop on saline and after adjusting the light to provide both heat and illumination, begin observation of the embryo. If the embryo is as old as 48 hours, this type of observation will be fruitful for some time, although the opacity of the yolk as a background conceals some morphological features.

2. When it becomes desirable to study the embryo with transmitted light, put warmed saline in each of 3 finger bowls and in a syracuse watch glass. Remove more shell from the egg if it is necessary to provide more space for manipulations.

3. Pour warm saline into a 250-ml flask and place a medicine dropper nearby. Drop saline on the embryo and keep it covered with this fluid at all times.

4. Cut completely around the sinus terminalis with curved scissors, freeing the blastodisc. Insert a section lifter of appropriate size beneath the embryo, lift it and transfer it to a petri dish or finger bowl containing warm saline. Move the lifter gently under the surface of the fluid to dislodge the blastodisc. Transfer the embryo to a bowl of fresh saline and with a medicine dropper and gentle agitation remove the yolk. If necessary, transfer to a third container of saline to clean the specimen completely. If these operations have not dislodged the vitelline membrane, grasp its edge and twitch it off.

5. Change the specimen to a syracuse watch glass of saline. Remove most of the fluid and then flatten the embryo with jets of liquid from the medicine dropper. Leave only enough saline to keep the embryo moist. Arrange most specimens yolk side down, but place one or more with the yolk side up for better observation of digestive and circulatory systems.

6. Place the living preparation on the stage of a dissecting microscope, using transmitted light for study. A substage lamp will usually furnish about the right amount of heat. If necessary, it may be supplemented with the gooseneck lamp. Add saline in small

amounts as needed. If all manipulations have been successfully carried out, an embryo may remain alive for several hours. Cover and return to an incubator if observation must be interrupted.

XI–6. TO FOLLOW DEVELOPMENT FOR SEVERAL DAYS the egg should not be removed from its shell. Instead, it should be opened with aseptic precautions and a window provided for observation.
1.   Rub the egg shell with 70% alcohol.
2.   Remove a piece of shell not more than an inch in diameter from the blunt end of the egg, using sterilized instruments.
3.   Wrap the egg in a 6-inch square of Saran Wrap (E–58) or similar material, smoothing the portion over its opening to make it wrinkle-free. Press the remainder of the material together at the pointed end of the egg to complete the seal.
4.   Incubate with the opened end up. Remove from the incubator at desired intervals for observation.

Embryos Prepared for Study of the Circulatory System

It is difficult to follow all details of the circulatory system unless embryos have been especially prepared for this purpose. There are two good methods: injection with India ink and treatments with reagents that stain selectively the hemoglobin in the red blood corpuscles.

XI–7. DEMONSTRATION OF THE CIRCULATORY SYSTEM in greater detail than is possible in a living specimen may be made by a modification of Knox's method, XIV–7, using steps 1, 2, and 3.
1.   Prepare an embryo as in XI–4.
2.   Treat with benzidine dihydrochloride (F–29) and hydrogen peroxide (R–102), XIV–7, step 1, while the egg is in the shell. When the vessels have become a deep blue, remove the stained embryo to water, free it of yolk and vitelline membrane, flatten it in a clean syracuse watch glass, and proceed with steps 2 and 3 of Knox's method.
Results: The circulatory channels containing blood will remain a bright blue for a while and then become a deep reddish brown. With either color, they may be seen very plainly. The color begins to fade within 24 hours; thus, the preparations are not permanent.

Another method of demonstrating the circulatory system is to inject it with India ink. When the injections are successful the embryos make beautiful preparations.

XI–8. INJECTION OF EMBRYOS WITH INDIA INK is done while the heart is still beating strongly, so that it forces the injection fluid

around. Some technicians use medicine droppers with rubber bulbs.
Others favor cannulae made of soft glass tubing, 1/8-inch inside diameter, with the tip turned at a right angle to the stem. The cannula is
connected by rubber tubing of appropriate size to a glass or plastic
mouthpiece. Medicine droppers and cannulae must both have tips fine
enough to enter the larger blood vessels of the chick. Some workers
decant the yolk, floating it in warm water, and inject the embryo before
removal of the blastodisc. Others prepare it as in XI–5, turning the yolk
side up and injecting at the end of step 5. This is probably an easier
method and will be used in the following directions.

1.   Partially fill several cannulae, from the larger end, with Higgins'
      India ink diluted 1:1 with normal saline. If possible, provide a
      rubber tube for each.
2.   Place the embryo under a dissecting microscope or a magnifying
      glass of suitable power, adjusting the light so as to both warm
      and illuminate it. Select the largest available afferent vessel; the
      sinus terminalis is often good, although a fork of one of the large
      vitelline veins is excellent. Be sure that the ink is in the tip of the
      cannula so that introduction of air may be avoided.
3.   Pierce the blood vessel carefully and inject a small amount of ink;
      if this is insufficient, add more, watching to see that all of the ves-
      sels are filled. Place a drop of fixative where the cannula has en-
      tered to avoid loss of blood and ink; withdraw the tip and flood
      the specimen with formol-nitric, 10 minutes.
4.   Place a slip of paper under the specimen; lift it carefully, removing
      wrinkles with drops of fixative from a pipet. Transfer the speci-
      men, on the paper, to Gilson's fluid. (See XI–10, step 3.)
5.   Complete by following XI–11; make the stain very pale.

Results: A number of embryos may be ruined in learning this procedure,
but when the knack has been acquired it is possible to produce embryos
in which the whole circulatory system is clearly demonstrated and the
finest capillaries filled.

The following method, like the India ink injection technic, makes
permanent preparations.

XI–9. O'BRIEN'S METHOD (240) for staining hemoglobin in embryonic blood cells is a catalase reaction with peroxide and *o*-dianisidine.

1.   Remove an embryo of the desired age from the egg and prepare,
      washing in saline until the yolk is removed and flattening in a
      syracuse watch glass. Cover with the staining solution (F–75) and
      leave until a clear and distinct orange stain forms in the blood
      cells.
2.   Remove staining solution by pipet and add water, 5 minutes.
3.   Remove water and add a 50% aq sol of dioxane.

4. Transfer to pure dioxane, 30 minutes, 2 baths.
5. Clear in xylene, 30 minutes, 2 baths.
6. Mount in synthetic xylene-soluble resin.

Results: The blood vessels are clearly indicated by the orange erythrocytes. The stain is permanent.

XI–10. FIXATION OF EMBRYOS for whole mounts or sections.

1. When the egg has been prepared (XI–4) and the embryo is in the desired position, flood with formol-nitric (F–92). Fix 15–30 minutes, according to the size of the embryo, adding more fixative as needed to keep the embryo covered.
2. Cut around the outside of the sinus terminalis with curved scissors, if the specimen is not more than 48 hours old. For larger embryos, cut through the area vasculosa, making a circle about 2 cm in diameter. Insert a section lifter of appropriate size beneath the embryo and transfer it to a petri dish or finger bowl containing 38° saline. Move the lifter gently to dislodge the blastodisc. Transfer the specimen to a second bowl of warm saline and, with medicine dropper and gentle agitation, remove the yolk. If necessary, transfer to a third container of saline to clean the specimen completely. If these operations have not dislodged the vitelline membrane, grasp its edge and twitch it off. When no yolk remains and the vitelline membrane is removed, orient the embryo with yolk side down and insert beneath it a slip of smooth, thin cardboard, a little wider than the specimen. Remove wrinkles by dipping in and out of the water and with jets from the medicine dropper.
3. Transfer embryo on the paper to Gilson's fluid (F–98), floating it first on the surface, then carefully submerging it. Fix from a few hours to several days.

XI–11. PREPARATION OF WHOLE MOUNTS ON SLIDES.

1. Remove the embryo on its paper from the fixative to water made deep yellow with Lugol's solution (F–132). Change the solution several times within 30 minutes; rinse well.
2. Stain in alum cochineal (F–13) until the specimen is pink, 30–60 minutes. Rinse in tap water.
3. Dehydrate to 70% alcohol through the usual series, 15–30 minutes in each dilution.
4. Differentiate in 70% acid alcohol (F–5) until the embryo is a bright pink. Rinse in 3 changes of 70% alcohol.
5. Place the embryo on a piece of smooth bibulous paper; cut around the outer edge of the specimen with curved scissors; the cut edge usually adheres firmly to the paper.

6.   Transfer to Cellosolve, dioxane, or triethyl phosphate, 3 changes; leave at least 1 hour in each; they may be left here indefinitely.
7.   Clear in xylene; detach the embryo from its paper with a needle or very thin blade.
8.   Mount in xylene-resin under a supported cover glass.

Instead of mounting embryos on slides it is better to embed them in plastic. They are more easily visible in this medium and much less easily broken. They can be prepared through the 72-hour stage by the following method. Larger embryos should be embedded in glass boxes rather than in rings.

XI-12.   PLASTIC MOUNTS OF EMBRYOS.

Roudabush's article (271) is the basis of the following method:

Equipment and materials: A sheet of plate glass; plastic or metal rings (E–55) with an inside diameter of ¾ inch and a depth of ⅛ inch, cut from tubing and with cut surfaces smoothed; an oven which can be heated to 55°C or higher; 18-mm square cover glasses; Ward's Micromount holder (E–41) or 1 × 3-inch glass slides; Selectron plastic monomer (R–178); catalyzer.

1.   Transfer stained and differentiated embryos from dehydrator to absolute alcohol for 1 hour with 2 changes, then to anhydrous ether for no more than 30 minutes.
2.   Place in a small amount of monomer, under vacuum if air bubbles are present; leave the embryos until they sink. They may remain in the monomer overnight without injury.
3.   Mix well 5 to 10 ml of monomer with 2–4 drops of catalyst (the larger quantity is used for more specimens). Place the rings on the glass plate and drop the mixture with a medicine dropper into each ring until it is about one-fourth to one-third full. Remove any persistent bubbles with a thin wooden applicator.
4.   When the plastic has set to a gel, remove the embryos from the monomer and place them upon the gelled layer, yolk side uppermost and one to each ring.
5.   Mix a second lot of plastic with catalyzer in the same proportions as above; when the bubbles have disappeared add more plastic to the molds until each is quite full.
6.   Lower an 18-mm square cover on the preparation, without trapping a bubble, and leave overnight at room temperature to gel.
7.   Put in a cold oven and raise the temperature slowly to 80°C in the course of an hour; hold it there 30 minutes. If the oven will heat only to 55°C, polymerize for 8 hours.
8.   When the plastic is cool, remove the covers and the rings from the glass and push the plastic discs out of the rings. Take off, by gentle rubbing with a cloth, any irregularities at the edges.

9*a*.   Insert the completed discs, yolk side down, in Ward's Micromounts, securing them at the rim of the depression with small dots of cement or

9*b*.   Mount the discs, yolk side down, in synthetic resin on an ordinary 3 × 1-inch glass slide.

XI–13. PREPARATION FOR SECTIONING.

1.   Remove the embryo, on its paper, from the fixative and transfer it to water.

2.   Stain in alum cochineal (F–13) until deep red, 6–12 hours, or in Harris' hematoxylin (F–16) until deep blue.

3.   Rinse specimens stained in alum cochineal in tap water, 5 minutes, with several changes; rinse those stained in hematoxylin 1 hour, several changes.

4.   Dehydrate in Cellosolve to remove mercuric chloride crystals.

5.   Clear in toluene or xylene, several changes, 2 hours.

6.   Infiltrate in paraffin, 2–3 hours.

7.   Embed with the orientation of the embryo indicated. This may be done by marking on a piece of paper with a soft pencil two lines exactly at right angles to each other, like a reversed capital L. Place the paper in the bottom of the embedding dish, marked side up. Arrange specimens, which have not begun to rotate, with that part of the head which is to be sectioned first parallel with the short arm of the L, the dorsal surface up, and the neural tube parallel with the long arm of the L. For specimens of 48 hours or more of incubation, arrange the embryo with the head as above and with the dorsal surface of the turned portion nearest the long arm of the L; if any part of the neural tube has not yet rotated, it should be parallel with the long arm. When the specimen is removed from the embedding dish, the pencil marks will be found transferred to the paraffin and can be used as guides for trimming. For reconstruction work other guides, which are more precise, may be tried.

8.   Place the embryo on the object carrier according to the plane in which the section is to be cut (see step 9). Trim with special care in order to produce an even ribbon. Leave only enough paraffin beyond the sides of the specimen to allow cutting the ribbon into segments without injury to a section.

9.   In order to have the embryo conventionally placed when sections are studied with a compound microscope, use the following rules:

    a.   For cross sections, always mount the embryo on the object carrier with the posterior end next to the object carrier. Place the mounted block in the object clamp with the yolk surface of the blastodisc next to the knife edge. In chicks that have not begun rotation this will mean that all of the ventral surface of the chick is nearest to the knife edge. But when, as at 55 hours, the anterior part of the specimen has completed rotation, the left side of the rotated portion will be next to the knife.

b. For sagittal sections, mount the embryo with the left side next to the object carrier and the neural tube parallel to the plane of section. Put the object carrier in the microtome with the ventral side next to the knife; the right side will then be sectioned first.

c. For frontal sections, mount the specimen on the block with the blastodisc side next to the object carrier. Place it in the object clamp with the right side next to the knife. The dorsal surface will be sectioned first.

Cut all sections serially at 10–15μ.

10. Spread sections, taking particular care to keep the rows even and straight as possible; dry overnight.

11. Decerate and mount in cellulose caprate (F–53); this dries overnight and protects the fragile sections from damage by careless handling. They may be mounted less safely in xylene-resin, or

10*a*. Spread ribbons on a 35-mm film (E–30) in one continuous row. Dry overnight.

11*a*. Decerate and, while still moist, cover with a plastic spray.

AMPHIBIAN EMBRYOS

Developmental stages of frogs and other amphibia are important in the study of embryology. The collection of material was formerly limited to the natural breeding season; now, at least for the frog, it is possible to obtain eggs and embryos at almost any season of the year, thanks to the researches of Rugh. These have been reported in a series of articles and in a number of laboratory manuals. The methods are summarized by Rugh (*276*, pp. 30–31).

XI–14. RUGH'S METHOD OF INDUCING OVULATION in *Rana pipiens* (*272–76*). Collect or buy several females more than 75 mm long and two males at least 70 mm long. The number of females needed will depend on the time of year. In most northern states seven will be required from early fall until January; five in January and February; still smaller numbers as the breeding season approaches. In areas where egg laying may occur in January or February, smaller numbers will be sufficient. Of seven females, one is for injection and the others furnish pituitaries. If enough females are not at hand for pituitaries, use twice as many males.

The Carolina Biological Supply Co. (E–33) sells sets of frogs for inducing ovulation from late October through March for a reasonable price.

1. Use the frogs as soon as possible after they are caught or are received. If they must be kept for a few days, maintain them at a temperature not higher than 10° C.
2. Place the largest female in a covered glass jar with a little water.
3. Remove the pituitaries of the other female frogs by the following procedure:

   a. With scissors, begin a cut in the angle of the jaw, directed first posteromedially, then directly across the occipital region, and finally forward and lateral to the angle of the other jaw. This separates the cranium from the rest of the head. Note, on the cranial floor, the cross formed by bones. The optic chiasma is just dorsal to the cross and the pituitary is posterior to the chiasma.

   b. Hold the cranial floor uppermost and, beginning at its posterior end, make 2 parallel cuts with scissors through the floor, lateral to the brain and as far anterior as the eye. Lift the flap of bone thus formed and find the pituitary gland which will be attached to the brain at the chiasma or adhering to the cranial floor. It is small and pinkish in color.
4. Remove the gland to a small quantity of water (about 1.5 ml) in a small dish. Secure the other pituitaries in the same way.

   When all of the glands have been removed, draw them into a 2-ml luer syringe without a needle attached; then add an 18-gauge needle.
5. Hold the large female by the legs, head down, and with the needle pointed downward and almost parallel to the ventral body wall inject the glands into the posterolateral part of the abdominal cavity; avoid injury to large blood vessels and viscera. Place the injected female in about 1 inch of water in a gauze-covered glass jar at room temperature if the eggs are to be used within the next 3 days. If their use is to be delayed as much as 5 days, the jar should be kept at 10°C.
6. In 24 hours determine whether ovulation has occurred by bending the frog's body at the pelvis with the legs at right angles to the body and squeezing the abdomen from anterior to posterior by closing the hand around it gently. If the eggs emerge in numbers, the oviducts are full and the eggs are ready for insemination; if they do not appear, repeat the process in 24 hours.
7. Before stripping the female, prepare a sperm suspension by removing testes from the 2 male frogs; mince them with clean scissors in 20 ml of pond, spring, or non-toxic tap water. After 20 minutes, at room temperature, place the sperm suspension in 2 clean finger bowls.
8. Strip the eggs into the bowls of sperm suspension, dividing them evenly. Rotate the bowls so that all eggs will come into contact with sperm and let them stand 3 minutes. Flood them with the

same kind of water used to make the sperm suspension and leave undisturbed until the eggs have rotated.

9.   When the dark poles are uppermost, lift the egg mass from the bottom of the bowl with a clean section lifter, so that it floats in the water. Cut it into small clusters of eggs, less than 15 in each. Distribute the eggs into finger bowls containing about 50 ml of non-toxic water (see 7), 2 clusters to each bowl.

10.   If several stages of development are needed at one time, keep the bowls at various temperatures ranging from 13–28°C. Within this range lower temperatures retard, and higher temperatures hasten, development.

Modifications of this technic for other amphibians are given by Rugh (275, pp. 30–32).

SECTION METHODS

Preparation of the eggs and embryos of amphibians for sectioning is difficult for a number of reasons. One of the main ones is the heavy content of yolk. It is particularly difficult to infiltrate with paraffin, which, after certain fixing and dehydrating procedures, does not penetrate well; the yolk shatters or drops out frequently and as it does so, distorts or tears the tissues around it. Such troublesome effects occur not only in eggs but in the cells of young embryos that contain yolk. They may occur, also, in sections of some ovaries. Another source of trouble is the jelly which surrounds the egg. Many remedies for these difficulties have been proposed, and there are now available several technics which are satisfactory. Some of these combine the results of several workers, while others are new approaches to the problem.

The fixative to be used is one critical point in the technic. There are several containing dioxane that are satisfactory. Slater and Dornfeld (286) advise the use of Puckett's mixture (F–43). For *Triturus* embryos, these authors fixed 6 hours or longer, washed and dehydrated with dioxane, cleared 5 minutes, and infiltrated and embedded in paraffin, 56–58°. The embryos did not shrink or harden and sectioned well. The fixative of Gregg and Puckett (F–105) was formulated especially for frog eggs and is a good one, and Smith's modification of Tellyesnicky's fluid is generally considered satisfactory.

XI–15.   FIXATION IN TELLYESNICKY, SMITH'S MODIFICA-TION (F–187) and preparation in paraffin. This method is applicable to frog eggs and to tadpoles up to 10 mm long. The fixative usually dissolves the jelly around the eggs.

1.   Mix the fixative immediately before use; immerse the egg clusters in a generous quantity, changing it once in the 24-hour fixation period.

2. Wash 6 hours in slowly running tap water and store in 3% formalin or
2a. Transfer directly to 3% formalin and renew the solution as it becomes colored.
3. Remove the eggs to tap water; if the jelly has not disappeared by this time, place the eggs in 1% sodium hypochlorite (R–181) solution. Rinse well and if any vitelline membranes still remain, dissect them off.
4. Dehydrate in dioxane, several changes, transfer to dioxane and paraffin 1:1/vol, at a temperature which just keeps the mixture liquid, 3–4 hours.
5. Remove the specimens from dioxane-paraffin to molten paraffin, 55°C, 3–4 hours and embed, orienting carefully, or
5a. Remove the jar of paraffin-dioxane from the heat and leave the eggs in the mixture until it is convenient to infiltrate them.

XI–16. THE METHOD OF GREGG AND PUCKETT (*134*), modified.

1. Place eggs in a volume of fixative (F–105) fifty times greater than the volume of the egg mass, leaving them 24 hours with occasional agitation.
2. Wash in finger bowls of tap water with frequent changes, 1 hour.
3. Remove a number of eggs from the mass, put them in a test tube with tap water, and shake well. Pour off the water, which should contain some of the jelly; add more and shake again. Repeat until most of the jelly is removed.
4. Transfer to a 1% solution of sodium hypochlorite and shake again more gently. If the operation is carefully performed, the eggs will be freed of the remaining jelly and the vitelline membranes. If the latter remains on any egg, dissect it off carefully with dissecting needles.
5. Wash several hours in 8–10 changes of water; remove all trace of the hypochlorite solution.
6. Place in Cellosolve to remove the mercuric chloride, several changes. Transfer to dioxane to complete dehydration, 1 or more changes.
7. Rinse briefly in benzene, infiltrate 3–4 hours in 55° paraffin, and embed in 55° paraffin with careful orientation.

Orientation: Amphibian embryos are oriented, in embedding and sectioning, by the method in XI–13, steps 7, 8, and 9.

The method of Slifer and King (*287*) for grasshopper eggs is excellent and may be applied to the eggs of other insects.

XI–17. BARRON'S PARAFFIN METHOD (*22*) for embryos of certain amphibians and fishes permits easy sectioning of the yolky ma-

terial and uses a fixative which is generally not satisfactory unless this particular technic follows it.

1. Dehydrate Zenker-fixed specimens in the usual alcohol series from 30% to 95%, 1 hour in each; finish in 2 changes of absolute alcohol, 1 hour for each change.
2. Transfer to absolute alcohol-amyl acetate 1:1, 2 hours, then to pure amyl acetate 24 hours.
3. Put in paraffin and amyl acetate, about 1:1/vol, and keep at the melting point of paraffin 2 hours.
4. Transfer to pure molten paraffin, 1 hour, 3 changes.
5. Embed as usual.

XI–18. GRIFFITHS AND CARTER (*135*) use a dioxane–picric acid fixative and soak the embedded block in a mixture of ethanedial and some surface-active agent, in the preparation of heavily yolked eggs for sectioning. Their schedule is:

1. Fix 24 hours in dioxane–picric acid fixative (F–106).
2. Wash in several changes of dioxane until excess picric acid is removed.
3. Dehydrate in three to five 3-hour baths of Cellosolve, according to size of the specimens.
4. Transfer to 2% celloidin in Cellosolve. Leave 12 hours at 30°C to insure good penetration.
5. Clear in three 4-hour baths of benzene.
6. Embed in wax-ceresin or other paraffin mixture having a melting point of about 54°C.
7. Block, trim to expose tissue on the leading edge, and immerse in 5% solution of Tergitol (R–187) in pure ethanedial (R–74) 12 hours to a few days according to size.
8. Wipe block to remove excess fluid, cut and spread sections.

During immersion in fluids, and in wax infiltration, keep the specimens at a subatmospheric pressure of 700 mm Hg.

Results: Griffiths and Carter have used this method for ovaries and developing eggs of *Eleutherodactylus* sp. and *Sphenophryne* sp.; both are frogs which lay eggs with a large quantity of yolk and which undergo direct development. They have also used it for various reptile eggs and refractory tissues of adult animals, which section well and stain normally after this treatment.

STAINING

The staining of sections of yolk-rich tissues offers some difficulty since it is necessary to avoid dyes which color the yolk deeply and thus obscure cellular detail. Rugh (*275*) recommends alum hematoxylin and Heidenhain's hematoxylin as well as Feulgen's technic; of these, the writer prefers Feulgen's. There are two others which should be mentioned, those of Piatt (XI–19) and of Slater and Dornfeld (XI–20).

XI–19. JANUS GREEN–NEUTRAL RED STAIN FOR AMPHIBIAN EMBRYOS, Piatt's modification (*251*). Sections are best cut at 5μ.

1. Place hydrated sections for 2 minutes in 0.1% aq sol of ammonium tungstate containing 3 drops of hydrochloric acid/250 ml of solution for prefeeding stages, or 5 drops/250 ml for feeding larvae.
2. Stain prefeeding stages in 0.1% aq sol of Janus green, 30 seconds and 0.1% aq sol of neutral red, 60 seconds. For feeding larvae, use these stains in 0.05% aq sol, 30 seconds in each, and if staining is too deep, reduce time to 20 seconds.
3. Dehydrate rapidly through the usual alcohol series; leave in absolute alcohol 1 minute.
4. Clear in xylene or toluene and mount in synthetic resin.

Results: There is little staining of yolk. Cell membranes and fibrils are deep blue to black; ends of nerve fibers and neurofibrillae, green. Muscle striations are clearly shown.

XI–20. METHOD OF SLATER AND DORNFELD for staining amphibian embryos (*286*). This was used by the authors on *Triturus* embryos but does well for other amphibians.

1. Stain hydrated sections in Harris' hematoxylin (F–16), 5 minutes. Wash in water, differentiate in 35% acid alcohol; blue in tap water.
2. Stain in 1% safranin O in aniline water (F–21), 5 minutes and wash in tap water.
3. Stain in 0.5% fast green FCF in 95% alcohol 1–2 minutes. Check under the microscope; the yolk granules should remain bright red and the ground cytoplasm should be green.
4. Wash in absolute alcohol and complete dehydration in it.
5. Clear in xylene and mount in xylene-resin.

WHOLE PREPARATIONS

Both cleaving eggs and embryos make useful whole preparations. They are fixed in Smith's modification of Tellyesnicky's fluid (F–187), washed well and bleached in 3% hydrogen peroxide or by Mayer's chlorine method (F–137). It is practical to keep the specimens in vials from which they can be decanted into watch glasses for study. In Smith's method for teleost embryos, they are placed in small glass tubes. Useful preparations of developmental stages including larvae are made by cutting the specimens into halves in any desired plane. These and all other types of specimens make good preparation when embedded well in plastic.

XI–21. GENERAL DIRECTIONS FOR WHOLE PREPARATIONS OF EGGS, EMBRYOS, AND LARVAE OF AMPHIBIANS.

1. Stain bleached specimens in alum cochineal (F–13) diluted with water to a pale rose color, 12–24 hours.
2. Wash.
3. Dehydrate, preferably in dioxane, using at least 3 changes in 24 hours. Specimens may be left several weeks in dioxane without harm.
4. Prepare in plastic. Transfer from dioxane to absolute alcohol, 2 changes, 1 hour each; then to absolute alcohol–ether 1:1/vol, 2 changes, 30 minutes each. From this point follow XI–12, beginning with step 2. For most specimens, it may be best to cast in small glass molds rather than rings.
4a. Prepare in diethyl phthalate, Nelson's method, (*164*, p. 160). Transfer from dioxane to diethyl phthalate (R–66), changing the solution at least once. Preserve in vials or bottles of suitable size and transfer for study to syracuse watch glasses. The specimens may be used many times if handled with reasonable care, and may be seen from all sides. A thin brush is a good instrument for moving them. After study, return them to the clearing solution.

TELEOST EMBRYOS

The eggs and embryos of fishes are treated much like those of amphibians. The following method is a good one.

XI–22. SMITH'S METHOD FOR TELEOST EGGS (*288*).

1. Cut ⅛-inch glass tubing into pieces less than 80 mm long and heat-seal one end; for larger specimens, use tubing of greater diameter.
2. Fix teleost eggs which have deeply colored yolk in desired stages of development in corrosive-acetic (F–67) and transfer to 10% formalin.
3. Place several eggs in each piece of tubing and stopper with cotton. The preparation may be studied by rotating the tubes; or
3a. Place eggs with transparent yolk such as those of the cunner (*Ctenolabris*) in formalin in the well of a depression slide; seal edges of the cover with cement (R–33). The upper or lower surface of the egg may be seen simply by changing the focus.

CHAPTER XII

CYTOLOGICAL METHODS

This chapter will be concerned particularly with nuclear material: chromosomes, nucleoli, and sex chromatin, and with some of the technical methods for demonstrating them. We shall consider briefly methods for mitochondria, Golgi apparatus, and other cytoplasmic structures. Many technics which deal with purely cellular structures have been discussed in chapters VII, VIII, IX, and XI.

In general, cytological methods have altered strikingly in recent years. These changes reflect improvements in microscopes, the introduction of more histochemical methods, and the increased need for karyotype analysis, as well as the appearance of new reagents and the discovery of such structures as the sex chromatin mass.

SECTIONS FOR NUCLEI AND CHROMOSOMES

In much of the early cytological work the chief reliance was placed on section methods. In the hands of good technicians, these provided material for study which led to numerous important discoveries, although they also imposed limitations. The chromosomes of a single cell were often divided among several successive sections, necessitating laborious reconstruction. With many types of fixation, the chromosomes were so close together that details of their structure were difficult to determine. However, sections have the unique advantage of showing the normal interrelationship of parts and are still, for some purposes, to be preferred to other types of preparations. As an example of sectioned cytological preparations for chromosome study, the following will serve. It is a composite of the methods of numerous workers, some of them from the zoological laboratory of the University of Pennsylvania. It involves the use of one important cytological stain, Heidenhain's hematoxylin.

XII–1.   ASCARIS EGGS prepared for the study of sperm entrance, egg maturation, and early embryogeny
1.   Fix uteri removed from *Parascaris equorum (Ascaris megalo-*

cephala) in an extended condition in Carnoy II (F–50) 3–4 hours; avoid overfixation.

2. Wash uteri well in 95% alcohol and store in 70 to 80% alcohol.
3. Cut each horn of the uterus in pieces not more than 1 inch long and number them in order beginning with the anterior end. Number 1 almost invariably shows sperm entrance; 2, 3, and sometimes also 4 and 5 are maturation stages. Beyond these are the formation and fusion of pronuclei (fertilization); then usually early cleavage and finally, stages in embryogenesis. Numbering the pieces thus facilitates finding the desired stages.
4. Prepare in paraffin by the dioxane or Cellosolve method (VI–14 and VI–16); section at 10μ.
5. Spread, dry, decerate, and hydrate the sections.
6. Stain with Heidenhain's iron hematoxylin.

A. Mordant in iron alum, 4% aq sol (F–115), 2–4 hours or longer; filter mordant back into the stock bottle.

B. Rinse well; there should be no iron alum in the water over the slides but some must be left in the sections.

C. Transfer to the hematoxylin solution (F–115) 2–4 or more hours. Leave slides in the mordant and the stain approximately the same length of time. Filter the stain back into the stock bottle.

D. Rinse 5–15 minutes in running tap water.

E. Differentiate in 2% iron alum solution. Place the slides in this solution until excess stain disappears leaving the sections still grossly dark. Several slides may be done at one time in a staining dish. Rinse thoroughly for several minutes in tap water. Now take each slide separately, dip it in the iron alum for a minute or two, and examine at a magnification of about 100 diameters. If the chromosomes are not clear, dip in clean tap water and return to the differentiator. Repeat the destaining and rinsing until the chromosomes are still deeply stained and the cytoplasm is light. When this stage has been reached, rinse well; place in a staining dish in running tap water.

F. Rinse in running water one to several hours. Be sure this water contains no iron for it will remove more hematoxylin and make the stain too light. If iron-free tap water is not available, rinse in a number of changes of distilled water, using fresh baths at 15-minute intervals.

G. Dehydrate, clear, and mount in xylene-resin.

Result: The chromatin, nucleoli, and centrosomes are black. The achromatic figure is gray and the cytoplasm, a faint blue-gray.

A method in which the tissues are stained in bulk rather than after sectioning is ingenious and satisfactory. This uses the valuable Feulgen reaction.

XII–2. NEWCOMER'S BULK FEULGEN STAINING METHOD (235).

1. Fix slices of fowl testis, not more than 5 mm thick, in Newcomer's fluid (F–149) several hours to several years.
2. Remove from the fixative; blot lightly; transfer to 1 N hydrochloric acid at 60°C for 10 minutes.
3. Blot again lightly and transfer to Schiff's reagent (F–182), 30–60 minutes.
4. Blot, transfer to isopropanol, 2 changes, 3 hours each.
5. Place in a small evaporating dish containing equal quantities of paraffin and isopropanol. Put the dish in an oven overnight at 53°C.
6. Transfer to fresh melted paraffin, infiltrate for an hour, and embed.
7. Cut sections at 4μ; spread on slides flooded with 4% formalin after treatment with Haupt's affixative (F–110); dry.
8. Decerate in toluene, transfer to fresh toluene, and mount in synthetic resin dissolved in toluene.

Results: The preparations are as good as those stained after sectioning. There is considerable economy in time and materials.

SQUASHES FOR CHROMOSOMES

Of the cytological methods for chromosomes presently in common use the most popular and most generally useful are the squashes. The newer methods make it possible to attain good separation of chromosomes, excellent staining, and collection of cells in the most suitable stages for study. They have the further advantage of relative simplicity.

A squash is a preparation made from a small bit of tissue reduced still further in size by manipulations such as teasing or repeated aspiration and ejection through the tip of a fine syringe needle or pipet. The small bits are then placed on a slide under a cover in an appropriate fluid; enough pressure is exerted upon the cover to flatten the cells without rupturing the cell membrane.

There are several variations of this basic procedure. To insure that there will be numerous division figures, the number of mitoses may be increased by various means; these include the collection of mitoses over a period of 12–24 hours by treatment with colchicine or a similar drug that halts the divisions at metaphase; injury to the tissue in such a way that the rate of cell division is increased; or the use of embryonic or other tissues which normally divide rapidly.

In some cells, chromosomes may be separated simply by judicious pressure. Others are successfully treated before squashing by subject-ing them to hypotonic solutions which cause the cell to swell and thus allow the chromosomes to move farther apart. If a mitotic poison such as colchicine is also used, the spindle will be broken and the chromosomes still more widely separated. The chromosomes themselves are also somewhat condensed by this treatment and their details made plainer. Another method of separation and of cell flattening is air-drying. The cells are spread out in a thin layer, usually after some initial treatment, and the fluid in which they were suspended is allowed to evaporate.

The choice of means of applying pressure for squashing is governed to a considerable extent by individual preference since there are several methods which will, in experienced hands, produce equally good results. The student should experiment with several and, finding one which is satisfactory, continue to use only that one, at least for similar kinds of tissue. The most common technic is to place bibulous paper over the covered specimen and apply pressure with the thumb. The users of this method find that it soon becomes easy to judge the amount of pres-sure needed. At the opposite extreme is the method of Carr and Walker (61) who leave the slide with cover glass in place for 30 seconds under the flat end of an upright copper rod which weighs 2.5 kg. Still other methods are tapping the cover with the wooden handle of a needle or with the eraser of a pencil, rubbing a blunt needle over the surface of the cover glass, and exerting pressure with a screw type of hose clamp (E–35), with a modified spring-type pinchcock, or with an ordinary spring type of wooden clothespin.

Fixation of squashes is usually in an acetic acid solution or a mixture of acetic acid and alcohol. Frequently the solvent of the stain is a solu-tion of acetic acid and water, so that a single mixture both stains and fixes. Stains commonly used are aceto-orcein or aceto-carmine. The strength of the orcein solutions varies according to the material; to some formulae, phenol is added. Feulgen's stain is also often applied. Most methods are for temporary preparations which may be studied for a few days to a few weeks if the edges of the cover are sealed to the slide, preferably with Dentist's Sticky Wax (R–61). Many such prep-arations may be made permanent (XII–6).

XII–3. DILLER'S METHOD for mamalian tissues and tumors (90) is an example of one of the earlier, very good technics in which only pres-sure is used to separate the chromosomes.

1.   With fine needles, tease bits of tumor or other tissue into minute fragments in a drop of aceto-orcein (F–2). This may be done im-mediately after excision, or the tissue may be stored indefinitely under refrigeration in the fixative-stain.

2.   Press a cover glass firmly upon the tissue and tap sharply on the

cover with a blunt instrument. Examine by microscope and dissociate further if necesary.

3. Dehydrate by Bridges' method (XII–4, steps 1–4).
4. Counterstain in fast green.
5. Rinse in 2 changes of alcohol and mount in Diaphane (R-65).

Results: Chromosomes and nuclei are well stained, not only in tumors but in kidney, liver, spleen, and gonad cells. The cytoplasmic details are not well preserved.

For better cytoplasmic preservation, Diller recommends the following variation: Tease tissue in isotonic saline on a cover glass; squash, slip apart horizontally, and float on any fixative suitable for preservation of nuclear, cytosomic, or archoplasmic structure. Stain as desired.

XII–4. BRIDGES' VAPOR METHOD of changing reagents and dehydration (50) is useful for squashes and requires little equipment.

1. Make a vapor chamber of a jar 4–6 inches deep and of a circumference suitable to the number of slides to be treated at one time. Line the wall, bottom, and cover with paper towels or filter paper. The bottom should have the thickest covering. Soak this wick material with a slight excess of 95% alcohol.
2. Stand aceto-carmine or aceto-orcein squashes, with cover glasses in place but with the edges not sealed, against the wall; cover the jar tightly. The squashes should be covered with a minimum of stain.
3. Leave the slides in the vapor jar 24 hours or more; the alcohol vapor gradually replaces the excess stain.
4. Immerse slides, with their covers in place, in 95% alcohol in a staining jar, several hours to several days.
5. Lay each slide, cover glass side up, in 95% alcohol in a shallow petri dish. Slip a needle under one corner or edge of the cover, holding the opposite corner in place with the fingers to prevent slipping, and slowly remove the cover from the slide.
6. Lift the slide from the alcohol, drain, add 2 or 3 drops of thinned Euparal, and cover.

One of the earlier papers which records effects of hypotonic solutions was by Makino and Nishimura (207). They used distilled water and applied it for various periods to the testis tissue of 16 vertebrates and 32 invertebrates, with fixation following directly; except for fish material, they found it satisfactory. A more commonly used hypotonic solution is weak sodium citrate. It is employed in the following technic.

XII–5. TJIO AND WHANG'S TECHNICS FOR BONE MARROW (312). Their directions are for mammals, birds, and amphibians. The

methods given below apply to mammals, including man, and to birds.
Method A:
1. Aspirate about 0.5 ml of bone marrow from the sternum, iliac crest, or tibia and drop at once into the colchicine solution (F–62). Transfer to a fresh solution, freeing the marrow as far as possible from blood clots. Leave in the second bath, 1–2 hours at 20–30°C.
2. Transfer to a 1% aq sol of sodium citrate, 20 minutes.
3. Place the material in a watch glass containing an orcein–hydrochloric acid mixture (F–4). Heat, but do not boil, over a small flame to effect rapid fixing, staining, and softening.
4. Transfer a bit of marrow to a slide, add a drop of 2% aceto-orcein (F–3), and cover with a 22-mm cover glass. Squash by tapping the cover gently with a blunt pencil or needle. Remove excess fluid from the edges of the cover; express the remainder by pressure applied to the cover through blotting paper.
5. Seal with a waterproof cement such as Krönig's (R–33).
6. Store in a cold place; the slides keep for about 3 months. If desired, make them permanent by the dry ice freezing method (XII–6).

METHOD B: To prepare the bone marrow by air-drying instead of squashing, proceed as follows.
1. Obtain bone marrow and prepare in colchicine solution as in method A.
2. Centrifuge at room temperature at 400 rev/min., 4–5 minutes. Remove supernatant and add 2–3 ml of a 1% aq sol of sodium citrate. Mix by shaking and leave 30 minutes.
3. Centrifuge and remove the supernatant. Add 5 ml of alcohol–acetic 3:1/vol (F–9). Resuspend and leave 2–5 minutes; repeat.
4. Centrifuge, remove all supernatant, add a drop of fresh fixative, and agitate to resuspend the cells.
5. Deliver a droplet of the cell suspension, 1–2 mm in diameter, from a fine-tip pipet on each of several chemically clean slides. Blow gently on each droplet as soon as it is in place to assist spreading and drying. Dry thoroughly.
6. Stain in 2% acetic-orcein, in a staining jar.
7. Dehydrate in the alcohol series; pass through 2 changes of absolute alcohol–xylene 1:1/vol; clear in 2 baths of xylene and mount in synthetic resin.

These preparations may also be stained with Feulgen's, Wright's, or Giemsa's stain or with crystal violet.

Results: The number of reliable metaphase plates from each aspirate varies from 10 to more than 100. The technic is rapid as well as simple; slides can be ready for study 3 hours after aspiration. With air-drying, ruptured cells are rare.

XII–6.　MAKING SQUASHES PERMANENT: the quick-freeze method of Conger and Fairchild (*70*).
1.　Flatten the top of a block of dry ice by inverting it on a plane surface.
2.　Place temporary preparations stained with aceto-carmine, aceto-orcein, or Feulgen's on the flattened surface of the block, cover glass side up, and press them down on the dry ice until thoroughly frozen; this usually takes about 30 seconds, but longer freezing does no harm.
3.　Without removing the preparation from the ice, pry up the cover with a razor blade or needle slipped under one edge. With the same instruments, remove the sealing mixture from the slide and/ or cover glass.
4.　Immediately place the still-frozen slide, or the cover if it carries the material, in 95% or absolute ethanol,[1] 5 minutes. Transfer to a fresh bath of the same alcohol for a few minutes to several hours. If aceto-carmine preparations are old and have become over-stained, clear and differentiate them by adding 5–20% acetic acid to the first alcohol bath.
5.　Remove slides from the last alcohol bath without draining. Place a very large drop of Euparal or Diaphane at an end of the slide, draw it up to the alcohol-covered cells with the edge of the cover glass, and lower the cover gently. This makes an untidy slide but prevents collapse of the cells. Do not press out the excess of the mountant until after a day or two of drying.
Results: The cells adhere firmly to the glass and there is little loss of material. If the cover or the slide has been smeared with an affixative before squashing, all of the cells will adhere to the treated surface. The preparations are always better than those conventionally dehydrated.

Bowen (*44*) suggests a modification of this method. He uses the standard freezing-microtome specimen holder, slightly altered, and freezes the slide with small releases of carbon dioxide gas.

XII–7.　THE METHOD OF FORD AND WOOLLAM FOR FETAL MAMMALIAN CHROMOSOMES (*106*). The times and quantities are for mice in day 14 of pregnancy. For other animals and stages, slight adjustments may be necessary. The procedures combine the technics of Ford and Hamerton (*105*), of Tjio and Whang (*312*), and of Rothfels and Siminovitch (*270*), with modifications.
1.　Inject the dam intraperitoneally with 0.3 ml of 0.025% solution of Colcemid (Ciba). Sacrifice an hour later.

---

[1] Celarier (*64*) finds that tertiary butanol is also a good dehydrator for squashes.

2. Remove the fetuses and decapitate them. Dissect out the livers and place each in 5 ml of 0.1% Colcemid in 0.85% sodium chloride solution buffered with 0.0066 M phosphate at pH 7.0. Break up the liver by repeated slow aspiration and expulsion with a fine-tip pipet.

3. After 85–90 minutes, centrifuge the cell suspension 5 minutes, 400 rev/min and remove the supernatant.

4. Add 5 ml of 1% sodium citrate shake to suspend the cells; after not more than 15–20 minutes, spin down at the same rate.

5. Add 1–2 ml of freshly mixed acetic-alcohol 1:3/vol without disturbing the cells; refrigerate during fixation 30 minutes at 4°C.

6. Centrifuge as before, remove the supernatant, and add 1–2 ml of 45% aq sol of acetic acid.

7. Spin down, remove the supernatant, and add about 0.5 ml of 45% acetic acid for each 6 slides to be prepared; suspend the cells.

8. With a fine pipet, which will retain large aggregations of cells, dispense the suspension on chemically clean slides arranged on a hot plate set at 54°C. On each slide make 2 rows of 4 drops each of the suspension. The drops will dry rapidly, producing a series of concentric rings where the mitotic figures are concentrated.

9. Stain when dry in lactic-acetic-orcein (F–125) at least 30 minutes. Wash off excess stain with 3 changes of 45% acetic acid and air-dry. Without mounting, examine under oil with an immersion lens.

10. Mount suitable slides in Euparal or similar mountant after removing oil with xylene and drying the slide.

Results: The chromosomes are well separated, the slides are better, and the figures larger and more numerous than those of adult mouse marrow prepared similarly.

Numerous other good methods for making squashes could be cited. Sparano (*294*) describes a technic in which regeneration following partial hepatectomy provided abundant mitoses. Ford and Hamerton's method (*105*) for preparing squashes of bone marrow cells after colchicine injections is also excellent. Welshons, Gibson, and Scandlyn (*329*) have devised a method for rapid production of semi-permanent preparations suitable for study of translocations in mouse chromosomes. Carr and Walker (*61*) stain with carbol-fuchsin (F–48) with good results.

METHODS FOR CHROMOSOMES IN SMALL YOLK-RICH EGGS

The study of chromosomes in the yolk-filled eggs of small insects, during maturation and young embryo stages, is difficult. Most stains color yolk globules so deeply that nuclear detail is obscured. A. R. Whiting (*332*) proposed a technic, using Feulgen staining, which shows chromosomes well in whole *Habrobracon* eggs. She enclosed the eggs in a sac of lens paper for their processing and removed them only when cleared. This method permits the mounting of a single egg on a slide; it can be moved, if necessary, by pressure on the cover.

Von Borstel and Lindsley have modified this method in two ways. They attach several eggs to a slide or to a cover glass at fixation and extract with methanol-chloroform to avoid the plasmal reaction which may color the yolk in Feulgen staining.

XII–8. METHOD OF VON BORSTEL AND LINDSLEY (319).

Reagents: Kahle's fixative or its modification (F–121); 5% solution of sodium hypochlorite or of Chlorox (R–41); Feulgen's leuco-basic fuchsin (F–83) or sulfonated azure A (F–24); saturated solution of sulfurous acid in water; 1 N hydrochloric acid; an alcohol dehydrating series including absolute; xylene; Labink (E–37); and methanol-chloroform 1:1/vol.

1. Assemble cover-glass rack or cover-glass staining dishes and reagents. Put identifying marks on covers with Labink.
2. Soak *Drosophila* eggs in the hypochlorite solution, 2–5 minutes, retaining them in a small sieve (E–78). Rinse with distilled water, pipetting it on the eggs in the sieve which has been placed on bibulous paper. For *Habrobracon* and *Sciara* eggs, omit this step.
3. Arrange the eggs with a dissecting needle, in rows on the covers, and puncture each one; the exudate serves to attach the egg to the glass, and the puncture permits proper fixation. Place the covers in their racks.
4. Fix by immersing racks and covers in the fixative at least 30 minutes for *Sciara* and 30 minutes to several days for *Habrobracon* and *Drosophila*.
5. Transfer to 70%, 95%, and absolute alcohol, 2–5 minutes each.
6. Extract in methanol-chloroform at 37°C, 1–16 hours to prevent plasmal reaction.
7. Hydrate through the alcohol series, 2–5 minutes in each concentration.
8. Hydrolyze in 1 N hydrochloric acid at 60°C, 14–16 minutes; rinse in water.
9. Stain in leuco-basic fuchsin, 30–120 minutes or
9a. Stain in sulfonated azure A, 30–120 minutes.
10. Rinse three times in sulfurous acid baths, 3–5 minutes in each, or
10a. Rinse 5 times in water, 2–3 minutes in each bath.
11. Dehydrate in the alcohol series, 2–5 minutes in each grade.
12. Transfer to absolute alcohol-xylene 1:1/vol then to xylene.
13. Mount in xylene-soluble synthetic resin.

Results: The chromosomes of the embryo are clearly demonstrated without the troublesome background staining caused by the plasmal reaction.

XII-9. CATHER'S METHOD FOR MOLLUSK EGGS (62). Some mollusks, such as *Illyanassa obsoleta,* produce small yolky eggs which also offer staining difficulties. Cather proposed the following method which uses Gomori's hematoxylin and produces clear results.

1. Rub a thin film of albumen on a slide. Place eggs on the slide in a small drop of water.
2. Drop on Nissenbaum's fixative (F–151) from a height of about 1 cm. Tilt the slide back and forth; drain off excess fluid. This affixes the eggs to the slide. Flood the slide again with fixative, drain, and place in a jar of fixative, 2–12 hours.
3. Hydrate through 70% and 50% alcohol to water, 10 minutes in each.
4. Hydrolyze at room temperature in:
   a. 1 N hydrochloric acid, 5 minutes;
   b. 5 N hydrochloric acid, 15 minutes;
   c. 1 N hydrochloric acid, 3–5 minutes.
5. Stain in Gomori's chromalum hematoxylin (F–114) diluted 1:1/vol with water, transferring the slide directly from the last hydrolysis bath. Place the jar in a 60° incubator, 25–30 minutes; return to room temperature.
6. Differentiate in 1 N hydrochloric acid 3–5 minutes, removing the cytoplasmic stain.
7. Wash in tap water 10 minutes; dehydrate in alcohol beginning with 35% and ending with absolute.
8. Clear in xylene and mount in xylene-resin.

Results: The chromosomes are blue-black and the cytoplasm clear or nearly so; if it is gray, the achromatic apparatus is visible and the chromosomes are not obscured.

SEX CHROMATIN METHODS

Barr and Bertram (21) first demonstrated the presence of the sex chromatin mass in neuron nuclei of the female cat. Since their initial report it has been found in a number of mammals in the intermitotic cells of various tissues. Barr (20) reports a study of 24 species of mammals including the rat, mouse, hamster, and guinea pig; of these, there were 6 which did not have it in a clearly rescognizable condition: the rabbit and all of the rodents studied.

The mass is probably easiest to demonstrate in neurons, since there it occupies a characteristic position with respect to the nucleolus and stains with several routine stains. It has been demonstrated, in laboratory animals, in many other tissues. In man it is practical to demonstrate it and to study it for clinical purposes in cells which are most easily obtained, such as neutrophiles, epithelial cells from oral and vaginal mucosa, skin biopsies, and such embryonic membranes as the amnion.

Barr (20) describes the sex chromatin mass in epithelia as usually "adherent to the inner surface of the nuclear membrane and so closely related to the membrane as to have a plano-convex outline. It is about a micron in diameter and can be resolved frequently into 2 components of equal size."

XII–10. STUDY OF SEX CHROMATIN IN BLOOD SMEARS. Female human blood smears, conventionally made and stained, may be used. These are entirely satisfactory for providing clear pictures of the neutrophile nuclei, but they are somewhat laborious to study. Humason (156, p. 363) recommends making the smear from the buffy coat of a tube of oxalated blood which has stood several hours or has been centrifuged at low speed. This coat lies directly upon the red blood cell layer; smears from it will contain an abundance of neutrophiles.

1. Make blood smears and stain with a Romanowsky type of stain; Wright's stain is satisfactory.
2. Study 500 neutrophiles, examining each for a small drumstick-shaped mass attached to one lobe of the nucleus; this is the sex chromatin mass. Record all cells with this distinguishing characteristic and calculate the percentage. Barr finds that the range in blood smears is from 1% to 10%, with 3% as an average. Smears from males may show, infrequently, a projection resembling the sex chromatin drumstick.

Klinger and Ludwig (173) report a series of studies on the preparations of human material for the diagnosis of genetic sex. Their method for sections of epithelium, oral smear, and amniotic membrane are given below.

XII–11. KLINGER AND LUDWIG'S METHODS FOR SEX CHROMATIN BODIES.

A. *For biopsy specimens of epidermis:*
1. Fix in Davidson's solution (F–73) 3–24 hours. Transfer directly to 95% alcohol, 3 changes, to wash out the fixative.
2. Prepare in paraffin and section at 12μ. Spread the slides; decerate and transfer to absolute alcohol.
3. Immerse the slides in 1% celloidin in alcohol-ether, 5 minutes; transfer to 70% alcohol until the celloidin is hard.

4. Carry down to water; hydrolyze in 5 N hydrochloric acid at room temperature, 30 minutes.
5. Rinse well in several changes of water; transfer to buffered thionin solution (F–188) 15–60 minutes. Use the shortest time consistent with adequate staining.
6. Rinse in water; pass to 50% and to 70% alcohol. When heavy clouds of stain are no longer given off from the sections, complete the differentiation in 80% and 95% alcohol.
7. Dehydrate in absolute alcohol, clear in xylene, and mount in xylene-soluble synthetic resin.
B. *For oral muscosa smears:*
1. Make epithelial smears in the usual way (V–2); fix in 95% alcohol, 15 minutes. To complete, follow method A, beginning with step 3.
C. *For amnion stretches:*
1. Fix the amnion in 95% alcohol, 30 minutes. Stretching between pairs of rings (E–57) is a good precaution against wrinkling.
2. Dehydrate well in absolute alcohol.
3. Cut the membrane in square 5-mm pieces. Impregnate them in 2% ether-alcohol-celloidin, 5 minutes and float onto slides previously coated with egg albumen. If specimens are wrinkled, stretch and flatten with dissecting needles.
4. When the celloidin is firm, place the slides in 70% alcohol, 5 minutes.
5. Hydrolyze in 1 N hydrochloric acid at 58°C, 20 minutes. To complete, follow method A, beginning with step 5.

Results for A, B, and C: The sex chromatin is deep blue-violet, in sharp contrast to the lightly colored particulate chromatin of the nucleus. The cytoplasm is colorless. It is an essential characteristic of this method that the sex chromatin stains more deeply than any other chromatic part of the nucleus. If nucleus or chromatin granules show much color, it is difficult to be certain of the identity of the sex chromatin mass. Good results may be obtained in each of these methods by using Schiff reagent instead of thionin, otherwise following exactly the same procedures. The authors used Barger and DeLamater's formula for Schiff's (F–181).

GOLGI BODIES AND MITOCHONDRIA

The cytoplasmic organelles are rather discouraging to treat technically; they have always offered difficulties because of their relatively small dimensions and their modifications in shape and position. Since such beautiful images of both have been produced by electron micrographs, slides made for study with light microscopes seem less valuable than they were previously. It is, however, still necessary to study these structures with conventional microscopes. The methods given below will produce suitable preparations for the purpose.

XII–12.   METHOD OF BENSLEY (*31*), somewhat modified by Cowdry (*77*), for supravital staining of mitochondria.
1.   Prepare a liter of 0.0001% solution of Janus green B in 0.85% sodium chloride, using a 1% aq sol as a stock. Place it in a perfusing bottle about 4–5 feet above the animal.
2.   Bleed an anesthetized guinea pig or rat from the throat and dissect it enough to put a cannula, connected by a clamped tube to the perfusing bottle, into the thoracic aorta. Open the right auricle and begin perfusion.
3.   After a minute, open the abdomen and momentarily compress the superior vena cava. Expose the pancreas.
4.   When the pancreas is slightly swollen and of uniform dark bluish green color, the perfusion is completed; 10 minutes is about the usual time required. Remove the pancreas to salt solution.
5.   Cut out 1-mm pieces of the pancreas, mount in salt solution, and cover. Compress slightly and study the acinous tissue, which is lighter in color than the islets. Find the greenish blue mitochondria in the proximal parts of the cells.
Results: The mitochondria can be seen well until they bleach to a leuco base. Thereafter they recolor to a pinkish tinge.

XII–13.   ALTMANN'S ANILIN-FUCHSIN-PICRIC ACID METHOD for mitochondia, slightly modified (*7*).
1.   Fix very small pieces of tissue, not more than 2 mm thick, in equal parts of 5% potassium dichromate and 2% osmic acid, 24 hours.
2.   Wash in tap water, 1 hour.
3.   Dehydrate in the usual alcohol series, 12–24 hours in each mixture (3–6 hours has been found to be adequate).
4.   Transfer to equal quantities of absolute alcohol and xylene, 30 minutes.
5.   Clear in xylene 2–3 hours; infiltrate in 60° paraffin 3 hours; embed and section at 3 or 4μ; spread and dry.
6.   Decerate and hydrate to distilled water.
7.   Stain in a 20% solution of fuchsin in aniline water (F–20); pour the stain on the slide and heat gently 6 minutes.
8.   Blot and differentiate by flooding the slide with 1 part of saturated aqueous solution of picric acid diluted with 2 parts of water. Observe the color against a white background.
9.   Rinse rapidly in 95% alcohol; finish dehydration in absolute alcohol; clear in xylene, and mount in cedar oil of immersion viscosity, or in synthetic resin.

Results: Mitochondria are crimson against bright yellow cytoplasm. The color fades, and the slides should be kept in a dark, cool, dry place. This method gives good results with both adult and embryonic tissues.

Technics which demonstrate mitochondria incidentally are given in chapter VIII.

XII–14. ELFTMAN'S DIRECT SILVER METHOD FOR GOLGI BODIES (97).

1. Immerse fresh tissue in 2% silver nitrate solution in 15% commercial formalin at pH 4, 2 hours, or in 0.7% silver acetate in acetate buffer, 5 hours.
2. Develop in 2% hydroquinone in 15% formalin from 2 hours to overnight.
3. Return to 15% formalin until fixation is complete.
4. Prepare by the paraffin method for sectioning and cut at 2–5μ.
5. Spread, dry, decerate, and hydrate.
6. Bleach with 0.1% ferric ammonium alum until the desired depth of color in the Golgi bodies is obtained, using a microscope; this will take from one to several minutes.
7. Stain if desired, in phloxine, aniline blue, or methylene blue which have little effect upon the silver impregnation or
7a. Replace the silver with gold (IX–12) before applying other stains, especially any which use the Schiff reagent.
8. Dehydrate, clear, and mount in synthetic resin.

Results: Golgi bodies are deeply black; with counterstains, other structures will be demonstrated.

CHAPTER XIII

HISTOCHEMISTRY

The histochemical methods now available are so numerous that it is not possible, in a limited space, to make a representative selection. The methods discussed here are only a sampling. Students and other interested workers are advised to consult manuals which contain extensive information, such as Lillie's *Histopathologic Technic and Practical Histochemistry (193)*, and Pearse's *Histochemistry (247)*. Davenport, in *Histological and Histochemical Technics (83)*, gives a considerable number of methods admirably chosen and presented for the less experienced worker. Other titles will be found in the Bibliography.

There are many journals devoted wholly or in part to the methods of histochemistry. In the latter group are *Stain Technology, Science, Anatomical Record,* and the *Journal of the Royal Microscopical Society.* The *Journal of Histochemistry and Cytochemistry* is concerned almost exclusively with the subjects indicated by the title.

SPECIAL PRECAUTIONS. There are a number of difficulties peculiar to histochemical work that must be noted. In methods for enzymes that are heat labile, the use of technics which take account of this condition is essential; frozen sections are therefore frequently employed. Certain cell constituents, such as fats, are destroyed by reagents in some of the preparation schedules and these schedules must of course be avoided. Water-wax methods may be helpful in these cases. The greatest problem is the migration of materials to be demonstrated, during the preparation procedures, and when this occurs the finished slides will give entirely false impressions of localization. The migration may take place during almost any stage of the technic, from fixation until after the section is mounted. Freeze-drying and some of its substitutes are helpful in preventing this difficulty. The freeze-drying method involves the use of rather complicated apparatus. There is an excellent discussion of this method in the second edition of Pearse's *Histochemistry (247,* pp. 25–48). Since a method which requires less expensive apparatus and still produces good results is desirable, the process called most commonly either ice-solvent drying or freeze-substitution is often employed. This also is discussed by Pearse (*247,* pp.

48–51). The articles by Blank, McCarthy, and DeLamater (*40*) and by Woods and Pollister (*336*) are also recommended.

The first histochemical method to find widespread use was Feulgen's reaction, which uses the Schiff reagent as its staining solution. The original paper describing the reaction was published by Feulgen and Rossenbeck (*104*). Its title indicates that it demonstrates a nucleic acid of the thymonucleic acid type. It was often called, at first, Feulgen's thymonucleic acid technic; it is also referred to as Feulgen's and Rossenbeck's nucleal reaction. It demonstrates the presence of DNA (desoxyribonucleic acid) by two successive procedures. The first is the release of aldehydes from DNA by acid hydrolysis, and the second is the coloration of the aldehydes by the Schiff reagent.

There have been many slight modifications of the technic as first published. The one cited below is an excellent one.

XIII–1. THE NUCLEAL REACTION OF FEULGEN AND ROSS-ENBECK (*104*), MODIFIED BY DE TOMASI (*89*). For formulae see (F–83).

1. Fix small pieces of tissue in sublimate-acetic (F–184) not more than 6 hours. Several other fixatives are suitable, but most authors prefer one which contains mercuric chloride.
2. Wash thoroughly in water; prepare in paraffin, preferably removing the mercury crystals during dehydration (III–20).
3. Rinse hydrated sections in cold 1 N hydrochloric acid; hydrolyze at 60°C in 1 N hydrochloric for 4–5 minutes and rinse in the cold 1 N hydrochloric.
4. Stain in solution A (F–83) 3–5 hours; drain.
5. Transfer to 3 baths, 10 minutes each, of solution B (F–83) in closed staining jars.
6. Rinse in water.
7. Counterstain, if desired, in 1% aq sol of orange G, 3–5 minutes. Wipe off excess dye and transfer to 95% alcohol. Complete the dehydration in absolute alcohol, clear in xylene, and mount in xylene-resin.

To make control slides, omit the hydrolysis procedure, step 3; treat the controls like the other slides in all other respects. Another control method, that of Jackson and Dessau (*159*), depends on the removal of DNA from slides fixed in Carnoy by the use of Varidase (streptokinase-streptodornase), Lederle. The enzyme preparation is made to provide a solution containing 100 units of Varidase/1 ml; it is dissolved in 0.025 M Veronal buffer at pH 7.5, containing 0.003 M magnesium sulfate and is applied to the slides at 37°C for 1 hour by dropping on a fresh supply each 15 minutes.

Results: Chromosomes and chromatin in nuclei are stained violet to purple. In the controls, made by either method, they show no coloration.

The Feulgen reaction is specific, in most cases, for DNA. Another reaction which makes use also of the Schiff reagent demonstrates chiefly polysaccharides of several kinds. It is accordingly less specific, although still a dependable histochemical reaction. It has two principal parts: oxidation, usually with periodic acid which releases aldehydes at the site of polysaccharides, and the coloration of the aldehydes with the Schiff reagent. Since the oxidation is most often carried out with periodic acid, the process is called the periodic acid-Schiff reaction, or PAS. Other commonly used oxidizing agents are chromic acid, perchloric acid, and lead tetraacetate. See also *79, 122*. The method was first described by three workers: McManus, 1946; Lillie, 1947; and Hotchkiss, 1948.

XIII–2. PERIODIC ACID—SCHIFF STAINING REACTION. The material is prepared in paraffin after fixation in formalin-alcohol-acetic, Carnoy's fluid II, or Gendre's fluid. Several other fixatives will also serve.

1. Transfer mounted and decerated slides to absolute alcohol, then to a 1% solution of nitrocellulose in absolute alcohol-ether, 1:1/ vol 2–3 minutes. Drain, allow to almost dry, and place in 80% alcohol for 5 minutes.
2. Oxidize 10 minutes in a 0.5% aq sol of periodic acid; wash well in running tap water.
3. Transfer to Schiff's reagent prepared by Lillie's cold method (F–182), 10 minutes.
4. Expose to 0.5% aq sol of sodium metabisulfite ($Na_2S_2O_5$), 3 changes, 2 minutes each; wash thoroughly in running tap water, about 10 minutes.
5. Counterstain, if desired, in Harris' hematoxylin (VII–3) after transfer to distilled water.
6. Dehydrate, clear, and mount.

Results: Strongly PAS-positive tissue components stain deep red, including gastric mucin, muscle glycogen, basement membranes, and reticulum in some locations.

XIII–3. E. E. MEYER (*222*) reports an interesting and valuable use of the PAS technic. He applies it to whole chick embryos of various ages. He found that the embryos treated *in toto* and subsequently sectioned gave a stronger reaction than embryos sectioned and spread before treatment. By this method, glycogen is very clearly demonstrated in ectoderm, endoderm, skeletal muscle, epimyocardium, and in primordial germ cells. PAS-positive membranes around the neural tube and notocord are made plainly evident.

The PAS method may be made specific for glycogen by applying an agent to the sections which eventually blocks the staining of all PAS-positive materials, but does not block glycogen staining for a long time. Bulmer's method for this follows. See XIII–7 for a good test material.

METHODS FOR GLYCOGEN

XIII–4. BULMER'S GLYCOGEN METHOD (53) is based on the fact that dimedone will block most staining with Schiff's reagent in a relatively short time and will block glycogen staining only after long treatment.

1.   Fix in 10% formalin, acetic-alcohol-formalin, Rossman's fluid, PFA, or by the method of Lison and Vokaer (198).
2.   Prepare in paraffin; treat spread sections with nitrocellulose as in XIII–2, step 1.
3.   Oxidize in 0.5% aq sol of periodic acid, 10 minutes; wash in running tap water.
4.   Expose to a 5% solution of dimedone (R–67) in absolute alcohol, 3 hours at 60°C.
5.   Wash; treat with Schiff's reagent (F–182) 10 minutes.
6.   Rinse in sodium bisulfite solution and leave in running water 10 minutes.
7.   Dehydrate, clear, and mount.

Results: Glycogen alone will show the characteristic red stain.

XIII–5.   BEST'S CARMINE STAIN FOR GLYCOGEN (38) is a cytological rather than a chemical method. It is included here because preparations made by this technic are often used for comparisons of presence and location of glycogen demonstrated by histochemical methods. See 23 and 30.

1.   Fix small blocks of glycogen-rich tissue such as liver or pigeon breast muscle (see XIII–7) in very cold Rossman's fluid (F–178), 10% formalin or Gendre's fluid (F–96).
2.   Prepare in paraffin, dehydrating from the rinsing water if 10% formalin was the fixative; if Rossman's or Gendre's fluid was used, transfer the specimens directly to 95% alcohol, several changes, then to normal butanol, several changes, and to paraffin.
3.   Section, spread, decerate, and hydrate as usual.
4.   Stain in Harris' hematoxylin, 5 minutes or until the nuclei are well colored; blue in tap water.
5.   Stain in Best's carmine stain (F–31), 5 minutes.

6. Differentiate in a solution of 40 ml of 95% ethanol, 18 ml of absolute methanol, and 45 ml of water until the differentiating fluid remains clear.
7. Dehydrate, clear, and mount in xylene-resin.

Results: Globules of glycogen are bright red and nuclei are blue.

XIII–6. TEST FOR SPECIFICITY OF GLYCOGEN STAINING.

To be sure that the reactions produced by Best's carmine stain really demonstrate glycogen, follow this procedure. Spread adjacent sections from a ribbon, one on a slide and one on a cover glass, leaving a space on the slide for the subsequent addition of the preparation which has been made on the cover. Treat the slide with Best's carmine; dehydrate, clear, and mount it. Apply to the cover-glass specimen an enzyme preparation that digests glycogen; follow this by staining with Best's carmine. The steps are:

1. Spread a section on a cover glass (VI–27).
2. Decerate and hydrate as usual; treat with 1% malt diastase in 0.02 M phosphate buffer, pH 6.0, 30–60 minutes at 37–40°C.
3. Rinse well, dehydrate to absolute alcohol, dip in 1% nitrocellulose in ether-alcohol, 2–3 minutes; allow the section to become nearly dry, and transfer it to 80% alcohol to harden.
4. Follow steps 4–7 of XIII–5, mounting the control section as close as possible to the untreated one.

Results: If the material stained by Best's carmine is glycogen, there will be none demonstrable in the control section.

This same method can be followed with XIII–3 and XIII–4 to indicate whether or not the substance reacting is glycogen.

XIII–7. NAIK'S USE OF PIGEON BREAST MUSCLE (231) as a

test material for solutions and for the methods used in the demonstration of glycogen is excellent. He points out that it has these advantages. In the pigeon, the breast muscle has both red and white fibers. The large white fibers, about 70μ in diameter, are very rich in glycogen; the red fibers, containing about one-fifth as much glycogen as the white ones, are about 30μ in diameter. The two types of fibers are well defined and are arranged in a characteristic pattern with the white fibers on the outer borders of a fasciculus. They are therefore very easy to locate and to study.

Naik fixes the muscle as soon after death as possible in thin strips, cutting them with a sharp scalpel or razor blade and handling the material as gently as possible, since the reaction to each cut is the loss of some glycogen. The muscle of pigeons 10 days old is less irritable than that of adults. He uses Rossman's fluid at -10°C and keeps the tissue in the fixative at that temperature for a few days.

FAT AND LIPID STAINING

The staining of fat has been done, in the past, principally with Sudan III or Sudan IV. Although these stains give, under proper treatment, distinctive coloration, they should be superseded by some of the dyes mentioned below which produce more brilliant coloration. Most fat stains are oil soluble and work by solution in the fat itself which thereupon takes their color. Fat preparations must be mounted in aqueous media, since otherwise the contents of fat cells disappear during dehydration and clearing processes. See also 26 and F–81.

XIII–8. LILLIE AND ASHBURN'S METHOD FOR STAINING FAT with oil-soluble dyes (194). The staining solution is a freshly made dilution of a saturated solution of the dye in 99% isopropanol. This makes a supersaturated working solution. The authors use Sudan brown, oil red 4B, or oil red O.

1. Dilute 6 ml of stock (the isopropanol solution of stain) with 4 ml of water. After 5–10 minutes, filter the fluid; it may be used for several hours.
2. Stain thin frozen sections 10 minutes; then wash in water.
3. Stain 5 minutes in an acid alum hematoxylin.
4. Blue in tap water.
5. Carry each section from water to a slide; drain and mount in gum syrup (F–22) or in an aqueous mountant which solidifies quickly and preserves fats.

Results: With oil red O, fat stains deep scarlet. This is probably the most satisfactory of the three stains; with oil red 4B, fat is similarly stained; with Sudan brown, fat is deep brownish red and nuclei are blue. Other oil-soluble dyes which may be similarly used are oil blue N or NA carcinel red, and coccinel red.

XIII–9. LILLIE'S METHOD[1] FOR STAINING NEUTRAL FATS WITH OIL BLUE N may be applied to thin frozen sections, preferably cut after gelatin embedding. The stock solution is stain made in 60% isopropanol.

1. Stain sections 5–10 minutes in working solution of oil blue N, 6 ml of stock/3 ml water. Wash in water.
2. Counterstain 5 minutes in 0.001% aq sol of Janus green B (R–108). Differentiate 1 minute in 1% acetic acid. Wash well in water.
3. Float onto slides.
4. Remove excess water and mount in Apáthy's gum syrup.

[1] Lillie, *Histopathologic Technic,* Blakiston 1948, p. 159.

Results: Fats are deep blue, cytoplasm pale green, and nuclei grayish green. BELL (26) recommends oil red O as a fat stain and uses as a solvent a 1% solution of Tween 40 in 30% alcohol, making a dye concentration of 0.25%. He finds that sections mounted in Farrant's medium have not faded in the two years since he prepared them and that there is no crystallization of the stain.

XIII–10. PHOSPHOLIPIDS, METHOD OF MENSCHIK (220).

This method is based on these facts: Nile blue sulfate (R–141) stains phospholipids blue; all lipids other than phospholipids can be removed by treatment with acetone. Thus, after acetone extraction has been accomplished any material stained with Nile blue can be considered a phospholipid.

1. Fix in Baker's calcium-formalin (F–27) 6–12 hours. Rinse in water.
2. Embed in gelatin and cut frozen sections, avoiding storage in water more than 10–15 minutes. Carbowax sections may also be used.
3. Stain in Nile blue solution (F–150) 90 minutes at 60°C. Rinse in water.
3a. If counterstaining is desired, stain 5 minutes in 1% aq sol of safranin plus a few drops of aniline oil; rinse in distilled water. Do this after step 2.
4. Place sections in acetone at 50°C; heat this on a water bath and remove the dish from the heat; leave 30 minutes. If the sections are thick, place in a second bath of warm acetone for 30 minutes more.
5. Transfer to 5% acetic acid, 30 minutes, for preliminary differentiation; rinse in water.
6. Complete differentiation in 0.5% hydrochloric acid, 3 minutes.
7. Wash in water, several baths.
8. Mount in glycerol jelly (F–101).

Results: Without counterstaining, phospholipids are blue or bluish green; everything else is colorless. With counterstaining, nuclei are red and phospholipids, blue.

Enzymes are usually demonstrated histochemically by subjecting thin slices of tissue to a substrate containing the compound on which this enzyme acts; the product of the reaction between the compound and the enzyme is then deposited at the site of the enzyme location within the cell. If the reaction product is colored, it can be easily localized. If it is not colored, it can often be changed into visible form. This process may be beset with a host of difficulties but there are, nevertheless, various relatively simple and dependable methods a few of which will be given below.

ENZYME DEMONSTRATION METHODS

XIII–11   THE METHOD OF ELLIS (*100*) FOR DEMONSTRATION
OF ENDOGENOUS DEHYDROGENASE SYSTEMS is a good ex-
ample of a simple and elegant procedure. It makes use of the fact that
endogenous dehydrogenase systems reduce water-soluble, colorless
tetrazolium salts to their insoluble, colored formazans. It also avoids
the loss of these enzymes which is caused by freezing. The technic may
be applied to whole animals, but it is better to begin with a single organ
in which the circulatory system is fully preserved. The directions are for
the kidney of a rat.

1.   Inject a rat intravenously with an aqueous solution of heparin,
     using 1.5 mg of heparin/100 g body weight.
2.   Anesthetize or kill the animal and remove a kidney, keeping the
     artery intact.
3.   Prepare a 10-ml luer syringe by attaching to it a 22-gauge hypo-
     dermic needle and inserting the needle in one end of an 8 to 10-
     inch piece of PE–50 polyethylene tubing (Intramedic). Fill the
     syringe with 37°C, M/20 phosphate buffer at pH 7.6; be sure that
     there are no air bubbles in the system. Insert the tubing into the
     artery and secure it with a ligature.
4.   Place the kidney in a dish of 37°C physiological saline (0.85%);
     the dish should be in a water bath that will keep the fluids at this
     temperature. Submerge the syringe in the water bath.
5.   Perfuse the kidney gently with the buffer until the blood is washed
     out of the vessels.
6.   Unlock the syringe from the needle while both are submerged
     and empty it. Refill with M/20 phosphate buffer containing
     0.25% neotetrazolium chloride or blue tetrazolium and, after
     expelling any air, reattach the needle.
7.   Perfuse the kidney for 6–10 minutes, delivering the tetrazolium
     solution at the rate of 1 ml/minute.
8.   Disconnect and empty the syringe and refill with warm M/20
     phosphate buffer containing 10% formalin; attach the needle as
     before and perfuse for several minutes.
9.   Transfer the kidney to 10% formalin for a longer period of fixa-
     tion or section at once on the freezing microtome; rinse the sec-
     tions in distilled water and mount in glycerol jelly.

Results: Fine, colored formazan crystals, predominantly of the blue (di-
formazan) type are deposited at the sites of enzyme activity. The times
of perfusion of the neotetrazolium may need to be increased for organs
with a lower dehydrogenase activity.

It is possible to combine a demonstration of enzyme with PAS staining. The following method uses the Schiff reaction as a histological rather than a histochemical reaction.

XIII–12 MOFFAT'S METHOD FOR ALKALINE PHOSPHATASE AND PAS-POSITIVE MATERIAL in the same section (226). This technic uses the 1939 method of Gomori as modified by Martin and Jacoby (211). It does not specify the method of preparation in paraffin. A suitable routine is fixation of small slices of material in 80% alcohol at 4°C or lower; dehydration in absolute alcohol, several changes in 24 hours at the same temperature; clearing in benzene, several changes; and infiltration in 52–56° paraffin, using as short a period as is consistent with proper infiltration, not more than 2 hours.

1. Decerate and hydrate sections.
2. Incubate in sodium glycerophosphate–sodium barbitone substrate (F–142), 2–14 hours; wash well in water.
3. Transfer to 0.5% silver nitrate, 5 minutes and wash thoroughly in water.
4. Reduce in solution F–141.
5. Wash in running tap water; rinse in distilled water.
6. Tone in 0.25% aq sol of gold chloride, 5 minutes. Rinse in water.
7. Treat with 5% solution of sodium thiosulfate. Wash in running tap water and rinse in distilled water.
8. Place in 0.5% periodic acid, 5 minutes.
9. Rinse in water.
10. Stain in Schiff's reagent (F–182), 15 minutes.
11. Wash thoroughly in running tap water, dehydrate, clear, and mount.

Results: A silver deposit, gold toned, is produced at sites of enzyme activity. This is not lessened by the PAS treatment. The PAS-positive elements are well stained, but the PAS treatment should be considered, as used here, a histological and not a histochemical method.

ACID PHOSPHATASE METHODS have, in the past, given more trouble than those for alkaline phophatase. A number of the difficulties have now been overcome, and this enzyme may be reliably demonstrated. Some precautions, however, need to be observed. Sams (279) points out that preparation of material in paraffin leads to loss of enzyme and unreliable results. She also finds that calcified tissues give good results after decalcification and that infiltration either in celloidin or in gelatin is satisfactory. She fixes in 10% neutral formalin at 4°C. Schajowicz and Cabrini (280) also find that paraffin embedding has a deleterious effect on acid phosphatase demonstration, and that the 10% neutral formalin is a suitable fixative. They emphasize particularly that hard tissues must be completely decalcified to obtain reliable results; they use 20% sodium citrate and 5% formic acid in equal parts as a decalcifier. Mineralized tissues, prostate, spleen, and liver are rich in this enzyme.

XIII–13 GOMORI'S ACID PHOSPHATASE METHOD (*128*) with some modifications is applied to frozen sections.

1. Fix thin slices of cold tissue in 10% formalin at 4°C.
2. Cut 6 to 10-μ frozen sections; mount them on slides, using an affixative. Dry well at room temperature, about 30 minutes.
3. Incubate at 37°C in the working solution F-104, 30 minutes to 12 hours. The average time required is 4–5 hours, and it should be kept as short as possible. Rinse well.
4. Immerse in a weak (2.5%) aqueous solution of yellow ammonium sulfide, 1–2 minutes.
5. Wash well in water.
6. Mount in glycerol jelly or in any aqueous mountant which preserves lead sulfide.

Results: A black precipitate of lead sulfide appears at sites of acid phosphatase activity, and localization is relatively precise. Schajowicz and Cabrini, *loc. cit.*, report finding the precipitate in osteoclasts and chondroclasts and in the walls of vessels in areas of active erosion.

Gomori's directions call for a rinse in 2–3% acetic acid between steps 3 and 4. Desmet points out (*88*) that this rinse, which was intended to remove nonspecifically precipitated lead deposits, may instead remove all traces of a true positive reaction and should by all means be omitted, as it is in many reports of this method.

Adenosine triphosphatase occurs in many locations in animals and is particularly abundant in secretory capillaries and blood capillary walls.

XIII–14. SECRETORY CAPILLARIES, BARRADI AND QUINTON-COX (*17*). Secretory capillaries may be demonstrated by the Wachstein-Meisel ATPase technic (*320*) on sections of the parotid glands of rabbits, rats, and guinea pigs; on the eccrine sweat glands and on the parietal cells of gastric glands of the same animals. The same method can be applied to demonstrate the walls of blood capillaries in non-secretory tissue.

1. Make thin slices of tissue from any of these parts: the parotid glands, the skin of foot pads, the mucous membrane of the body of the stomach.
2. Fix the slices 18 hours in cold formol-calcium (F–91). Transfer to 0.88 M sucrose solution, with 1% gum acacia, for several hours.
3. Make frozen (cryostat) sections at 10μ, mount on cover glasses, and dry at room temperature, 3 hours.

4. Incubate at 37°C in the Wachstein-Meisel substrate mixture (F–191), using the following time schedule. Parotid glands: rabbit, 15 minutes; rat, 2.5 hours; guinea pig, 2 hours. Eccrine sweat glands: rabbit and guinea pig, 15 minutes; rat, 30 minutes. Parietal cells of gastric glands: all animals, 3 hours.

5. Wash thoroughly in running water, then immerse in a dilute aqueous solution of ammonium polysulfide, 2 minutes.

6. Wash in tap water; mount in Apáthy's gum syrup.

Results: Sites of enzymatic activity show brown to black deposits of lead sulfide appearing as solid cylindrical structures or hollow tubules with opposed cellular membranes of neighboring secretory cells clearly demarcated. Staining of blood capillaries tends to interfere with staining of the secretory capillaries. The rabbit parotid provides the best demonstration of secretory capillaries; the rat preparations are best for eccrine sweat glands; and guinea pig sections show best the intracellular secretory capillaries of the parietal cells of the stomach.

This method has been used by other workers to demonstrate bile canaliculi.

CHAPTER XIV

INJECTION METHODS

The demonstration of circulatory arrangements, of ducts of glands, of ureters, and of air passages in lungs is of value for both gross and microscopic studies. Whole mounts of embryos with injected circulatory systems are very useful, both for seeing the systems as a whole and for reference in studying sections. Minute details of blood vessel arrangements may be studied with less trouble in thick sections of injected specimens than by reconstructing them from thin sections of uninjected specimens.

In this chapter, the term injection methods is used in reference to a much wider range of technics than are commonly included under this designation. Instead of limiting the discussion to the filling of vessels and ducts with an injection mass, it seems practical to include also methods in which these parts are made particularly plain by other physical means. For instance, it is simple to allow the blood vessels of an organ or a living mammalian embryo to be well filled by ligating first the efferent(s) and then the afferent(s) before fixation and later to stain the whole mount, or sections, with a dye which makes red blood cells particularly conspicuous. This technic is less difficult than injection and gives excellent results. By using histochemical methods it is possible to demonstrate inter- and intra-cellular secretory tubules in several glands. This also may be called an extension of injection methods. Another atypical technic is to demonstrate lymph vessels by injecting India ink into the abdominal cavity of rats or mice. The lymphatics selectively absorb the carbon and stand out clearly. The often-used method for demonstrating lymphatics in the mesentery of the gut by feeding an animal cream a short time before sacrifice may also be considered an injection method, in this broader sense.

For injections of animals to be dissected, the most suitable material devised to date is latex which has the excellent properties of remaining in a liquid state until the injected animal is treated with a preserving fluid and thereafter remaining flexible. For corrosion preparations in which the tissue surrounding the injected part is removed by chemical means, vinyl acetate is suitable. For material which is to be sectioned, a well-colored gelatin injection mass is usually a good choice, although in some cases India ink is superior; or latex may be used.

INJECTION FOR DISSECTION

To inject animals for dissection, the student is referred to the instructions from supply houses which are sent on request with the injection medium (325). Colored latex and a suitable syringe and needles (E–71) should be ordered for this purpose.

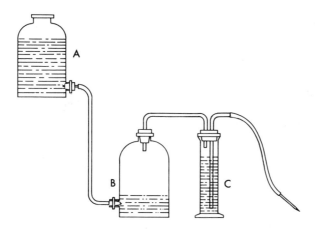

Fig. 10.—Apparatus for continuous air-pressure injections. *A* is a large container of water elevated to a height of 7 or 8 feet; *B* is a tightly corked carboy in which compressed air collects and from which the air is transmitted to *C*, the container holding the injection mass. A mercury manometer may be added to *B* to register the air pressure.

INJECTION FOR CORROSION PREPARATIONS

Corrosion preparations of entire circulatory systems may be made with vinyl acetate (R–198). It is probably best to begin with a small animal or organ and with a single color put into either the arteries or the veins. When experience has been gained, several systems may be injected in the same specimen.

The resin solution is sold by several supply houses, and directions accompany the reagent if requested. The following outline should serve as an introduction to the technic. It is for the kidney of a cat or dog.

XIV–1. CORROSION PREPARATION OF AN ORGAN.

Equipment and materials: Ligatures; normal saline; vinyl acetate solution; a luer syringe and 18-gauge needle for the saline; a metal syringe and needles 16- and 18-gauge, for the vinyl acetate (R–198); a deep jar of water and one of strong hydrochloric acid, technical grade.

1. Insert a needle into the artery and hold in place with a ligature. Attach a 10-ml luer syringe to the needle and wash out the blood with water, refilling the syringe which may be detached from the needle, several times if necessary, until the washing fluid emerges from the veins free of blood.
2. Remove the needle from the artery and tie in a dry needle for the metal syringe. Rinse the syringe and needle with acetone, then fill, or partially fill, with the vinyl acetate before attaching.
3. Force the injecting material slowly into the kidney. When the color of the injection mass appears at the periphery of the organ, it may be assumed that the injection is complete. Tie off the artery, remove the needle, and place the specimen in water until the mass hardens.
4. Wash the instruments in acetone as soon as the injection is completed.
5. When the vinyl acetate has hardened, place the injected specimen in the container of hydrochloric acid until the tissue dissolves; this should take less than 24 hours for a small kidney. Wash the cast of the arteries well, dry, and mount in liquid in a museum jar or embed in plastic. See the method of Puckett and Neumann (258) for injection of a whole animal.

Corrosion preparations of the air passages in lungs are also instructive and not difficult to make. Essentially the same method is used; the injection is made through the trachea.

INJECTIONS FOR WHOLE MOUNTS

Whole preparations of injected specimens are useful. The circulatory systems of chick embryos are particularly well demonstrated by such preparations. Directions will be found in the section on embryology (XI–7).

West and Gorham (330) have published an account of an injection method for such small animals as mice. They describe the use of a cannula that is unlikely to puncture the thin wall of the aorta, which is entered through the tip of the left ventricle. They used, as injection media latex, latex-thorotrast, and vinyl acetate. Animals injected with latex were dissected and parts, such as the intestine and limbs, were cleared in oil of wintergreen to show the course of the arteries. They point out that the latex-injected material sections well and that since latex-thorotrast is radiopaque, whole preparations made with this material may be studied by X-ray.

INJECTIONS FOLLOWED BY SECTIONING

XIV–2. AUGULO, HESSERT, AND KOWNACKI (9) have formulated a carbon-gelatin injection mass that fills the coronary arteries and the smallest arterioles (less than 10μ) but does not enter the capillaries. Although the method was devised for dogs, it should be useful for other laboratory animals.

1. Anesthetize a dog with ether. Inject a 20% solution of magnesium sulphate through the left femoral vein until cardiac arrest occurs.
2. Remove heart, lungs, and trachea together through a left thoracotomy incision. Isolate the heart by dividing the pulmonary vessels; dissect out and discard nonessential tissue. Wash in water.
3. Identify the coronary vessels and surround them proximally with purse string ligatures. Insert and fix polyethylene catheters of suitable diameter.
4. Place the heart in distilled water heated to 37°C and perfuse with physiological saline of the same temperature. When the heart is free of blood, clamp the catheters to insure a filled vascular system.
5. Remove the clamps and perfuse with 250–300 ml of the carbon-gelatin mass (F–118) under 15–20 mm Hg pressure. Reclamp the catheters and place the heart in ice water for 2 hours.
6. Transfer to 10% neutral formalin, one to several days.
7. Prepare blocks of heart tissue in celloidin and section at $50–120\mu$; mount the sections in the usual way.

Results: The smallest injected arterioles, of diameter less than 10μ, are well demonstrated, and the communicating capillaries are not filled. Normal morphology is unaltered. If respiratory passages of the lungs are injected through the bronchi with this medium, the fine passages are filled and no material passes from alveoli to vascular channels.

Jee and Arnold (*161*) have furnished another formula (F–119) for a gelatin-India ink injection mass which is well suited for the preparation of sections following injection.

METHODS FOR LYMPHATICS

XIV–3. DEMONSTRATION, IN THE MESENTERY OF A MAMMAL. For this, almost any laboratory animal will serve but the cat is an easy subject because of its appetite for cream.

1. Offer a hungry cat a cup of cream.
2. Thirty minutes after the meal has been ingested, anesthetize the animal with ether; be sure not to give a lethal dose of anesthetic.

3.   Open the abdomen and examine the mesentery of the intestine. If
      cream-colored vessels cannot be seen, cover the gut with cheese-
      cloth moistened with normal saline and examine again in a few
      minutes. Eventually all of the mesenteric lymphatics will be full
      of fat globules and will appear as white lines converging to the
      lymph nodes near the attachment of the mesentery.

XIV–4. DEMONSTRATION, IN THE DIAPHRAGM AND MEDI-
ASTINUM OF RATS.   This method may be used as a classroom demonstration and the preparation discarded after use; or the material may
be preserved for microscopic study.
Equipment and materials: Dissecting tools and a dissecting board,
several pairs of rings for making stretches (E–57); a luer syringe, 5-ml
capacity with a fine needle; jars of 10% neutral formalin and normal
saline; Higgins' India ink.
1.   Inject a rat intraperitoneally with 2–3 ml of Higgins' ink diluted
      1:1 with distilled water, just before use. After 30 minutes, anesthe-
      tize with ether.
2.   When anesthesia is deep, make a long incision in the ventral body
      wall. Examine the diaphragm and the gut mesentery. The former
      almost always shows deeply colored lymphatic vessels; the mesen-
      tery may show them also.
3.   Make one or more stretches of the diaphragm and, if the staining
      is good, of the mesentery. Rinse in saline before fixation. Transfer
      to a jar of 10% formalin. Label the specimens and cover the jars.
3a.   If the specimens are to be used for classwork, they may be studied
      on the rings in normal saline.
4.   Dissect the mediastinum, noting the deeply colored lymph nodes
      and their connecting lymphatic vessels. Fix *in situ* with 10%
      formalin, and when the tissue is somewhat hardened remove it as
      a whole if possible. Fix further with formalin, and prepare as a
      whole mount in plastic (V–32).
5.   Stain the stretches lightly with alum cochineal or Grenacher's
      borax-carmine. Prepare as whole mounts in xylene-resin (V–20).

The injection methods for lymphatics differ from those applied to arteries and veins for several reasons. The vessel walls are so thin that it is
difficult to enter them with needle or cannula without tearing, so that a
direct injection through an afferent or efferent vessel is rarely successful. The valves also offer a serious obstacle to injections in a centrifugal
(peripheral) direction. It is, however, possible to take advantage of the
fact that the capillaries of the lymphatic system are much more perme-
able than those connecting arteries and veins; this was demonstrated in
XIV–4. If the parenchyma of such an organ as the ovary is injected

with a suitable material, it will pass into the lymphatics which will then be clearly visible. This type of injection is called indirect, and is usually used for the lymphatic system.

XIV–5. THE PAPAMILTIADES METHOD (242) produces specimens suitable for preparation in paraffin or for dissection. The injection formula gives selective penetration of the lymphatics unless, by mistake, the needle penetrates a blood vessel.

Solutions and materials: A luer syringe of 5-ml capacity and a fine needle, 25-gauge; a bath of water warmed to 50–60°C and containing the fresh specimen to be injected; the injecting mass (F–120); the fixative. The directions which follow are for injection of the ovary of a dog.

1. Warm the ovary thoroughly in the water bath.
2. Inject the mass directly into the medulla of the specimen; massage the ovary gently after injection to facilitate the distribution of the injection mass. For very small specimens, running warm water provides enough agitation to cause the mass to enter the lymphatics.
3. Fix in F–161, 5 or more days if the specimen is to be prepared for sectioning; in 10% formalin if it is to be dissected.
4. For specimens to be sectioned use the dioxane-paraffin technic (VI–14). Cut sections at 10–20μ; stain with alum hematoxylin and counterstain with picro-fuchsin, van Gieson's modified formula (VII–8); dehydrate and mount as usual.

Results: The fine details of the lymphatics are clearly indicated as well as their relation to surrounding tissues.

DEMONSTRATION OF BLOOD VESSELS BY STAINING

XIV–6. CROSSMAN'S STAIN (80) depends for its excellent results upon the strong affinity of red blood cells for chromotrope 2 R. It is applicable to both embryonic and adult tissue.

1. Fix specimens in 10% neutral formalin in 0.85% sodium chloride, 24–48 hours. Wash in 70% alcohol.
2. Dehydrate thoroughly; infiltrate in paraffin or celloidin. Cut sections at 6–10μ and mount on slides.
3. Stain in chromotrope 2 R (F–58), 1–5 minutes.
4. Rinse sections in several changes of water; the last one should show no dye.
5. Transfer to 5% phosphotungstic acid in 95% ethanol, moving the slides at intervals. Examine microscopically and continue until all basophilic elements are decolorized. The less strongly acidophilic elements such as muscle may take 2–3 hours for decolorization, but the red blood cells retain the color.

6.   Transfer to methyl blue solution (F–140), 2–5 minutes.
7.   Rinse in water.
8.   Pass to 2% acetic acid, 15–60 seconds; rinse in water and examine; erythrocytes should be red; less strongly acidophilic elements, colorless or gray; and basophilic elements, blue.
9.   Dehydrate in 95% alcohol, then in absolute, and clear in xylene. Mount in xylene-resin.

Results: The blood vessels stand out clearly and are deep red. Somewhat thicker sections may be tried; they often produce striking results.

Boyer and Dunaway (*46*) devised a method which stains red blood cells deeply and makes the vessels of hamster embryos conspicuous. Their technic calls for special care in preventing blood loss before fixation. They section in paraffin at 10 or 15μ and stain by Weil's rapid method for myelin sheaths.

KNOX'S METHOD OF STAINING BLOOD VESSELS (*176*) is to produce a color reaction of the blood pigments with reagents. It gives good results whether the pigment is in cells or in plasma. He offers two technics, XIV–7 and XIV–8.

XIV–7.   FOR SMALL LIVING ORGANISMS.
1.   Immerse living specimens in a small dish of a saturated solution of benzidene dihydrochloride (F–29) for about 30 minutes.
2.   Add 3% hydrogen peroxide (R–102) drop by drop, until small bubbles appear around the specimen.
3.   When the blood vessels appear dark blue, fix in 70% alcohol acidified with 0.1% acetic acid.
4.   Dehydrate in 95% alcohol acidified with a trace of acetic acid, 2 or 3 changes of several hours each.
5.   Clear in benzene or xylene.
6.   Make whole mounts in xylene-resin or
6*a*.   Infiltrate in paraffin.

If a counterstain for whole mounts is desired, apply it between steps 3 and 4; borax-carmine is suggested.

If freehand sections are made, cut them after either step 3 or 4.

Results: Knox reports the successful application of this method to sabellid and serpulid polychetes, earthworms, small tadpoles, and fish larvae. We have used it with excellent results for tadpoles of various sizes and for small earthworms. It was not satisfactory in our hands for *Gambusia* and for *Lebistes reticulatus*, which were probably too large for penetration of the reagents. We have also used it for chick embryos (XI–7) where it produces very satisfactory demonstrations of the circulatory system that are useful for several hours.

XIV–8. FOR BLOOD VESSELS IN FIXED SPECIMENS.

1. Fix in 10% solution of formalin in sea water, or in formalin-hypertonic saline (F–86), 24 hours.
2. Cut large specimens into pieces and wash well in running tap water for several hours.
3. Incubate at 37°C, with constant gentle shaking, in sodium nitro-prusside-benzidine solution (F–30), 1 hour.
4. Rinse quickly in water. Place in 3% hydrogen peroxide, 2 ml/400 ml water at 37°C, with constant shaking for 1 hour.
5. Rinse quickly in water.
6. Dehydrate by the alcohol-xylene sequence.
7. Section at desired thickness; if desired, add a counterstain after spreading and deceration.

Results: The blood vessels are clearly demonstrated. They are more easily traced in thick sections.

Some of the smallest ducts of glands, and the secretory capillaries, may be demonstrated either by their contents or by histochemical technics which permit visualization of their walls. Histochemical methods recommended for this purpose are those of Baradi and Quinton-Cox (*17*) and of Wachstein-Meisel (*320*).

Capillary networks are also demonstrable by the same histochemical methods, which stain them selectively; see XIII–13. The methods should be applied to mesenteries.

CHAPTER XV

THE MICROSCOPE AND SIMPLE MAGNIFIERS

This chapter is necessarily brief and should be supplemented by other reading. Most microscope companies publish excellent small books on microscopes and microscopy kept up-to-date with descriptions of recent instruments and methods. The American Optical Company publishes one (8) and will furnish a modest number of copies without charge if a request is sent to the factory (A–2); for a larger number, a nominal charge is made. Bausch and Lomb have two handbooks in print; each is sold at a low price. One is on the theory of the microscope (28) and the other is on its use (75). The *Journal of the Royal Microscopical Society* (London) and most other journals concerned with microscopy print frequent reports on recent developments in miscroscope design and construction. Among the good books which deal with kinds of microscopes and their uses are those by Needham (233) and Barer (18). A study of microscope catalogs will give an excellent idea of the types which are available both for general and for special kinds of work.

OPTICAL PRINCIPLES OF MICROSCOPES

For an understanding of the optical principles involved in microscopy, four things must be borne in mind with regard to a ray of ordinary daylight:
1. It has appreciable breadth.
2. It travels in a straight line in a homogeneous medium.
3. It is bent (refracted) when it passes from one medium into another of different density.
4. It is composed of a number of different colored rays ranging from violet to red, and each of these has a different refractivity.

The amount of refraction undergone by light in a given case depends upon the differences in density of the two media which the light traverses. Thus glass is denser than air; hence, in passing from air through a glass plate, a ray of light is bent obliquely from its original course. On reaching the air again, however, it resumes its former direction, although it is displaced in position. It is on account of such displacement that an object in water, for example, appears to be at a different point than it really is.

On the other hand, after traversing a prism, a ray does not resume its former direction, but takes a new course upon leaving the prism (Fig. 11).

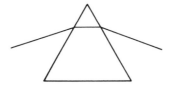

Fig. 11.—Path of a ray of light entering, traversing, and leaving a prism.

This new direction is always toward the base of the prism, and the amount of deviation depends upon the shape and density of the prism. If the base is down, then the ray is bent downward; if the apex is down, the ray still deviates toward the base; that is, it is bent upward.

LENSES.   Each of the two principal forms of lens is, in effect, two prisms: (*1*) with the bases placed together (Fig. 12*a*, a convex lens) and (*2*) with the apices together (Fig. 12*b*, a concave lens).

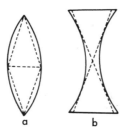

a   b

Fig. 12.—*a* is a convex (converging) lens; *b* is a concave (diverging) lens.

In the convex lens, since rays of light are refracted toward the bases of the respective prisms (Fig. 11), they will converge; in the concave lens, for the same reason, they will diverge. The terms converging lens and diverging lens, therefore, are used frequently as synonyms of the terms convex and concave lens. All lenses are modifications or combinations of these two types (Fig. 12).

If parallel rays of light pass through a convex lens (Fig. 13), they are so refracted as to meet in one point F which is termed, in consequence, the focal point or principal focus. If, on the other hand, the source of light be placed at the focal point, the rays of light will emerge parallel after traversing the lens. If parallel rays of light come from the opposite side of the lens, manifestly there will be a second focal point at *F'*. The two principal foci, *F* and *F'*, are termed conjugate foci and will be equidistant from the center of the lens if both sides of the lens have equal curvatures.

The ray *a-b* which passes through the center of the lens and the focal point (Fig. 13) traverses what is termed the principal axis of the lens. The optical center of the lens is a point *c* on the principal axis through which rays pass without angular deviation. The optical center may be within or outside the lens, depending upon the form of the lens. Any line, other than the principal axis, that passes through the optical center of the lens is termed a secondary axis. The line *ed* in Figure 13 is a secondary axis.

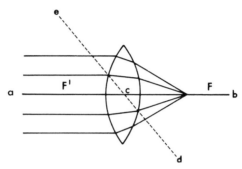

Fig. 13.—Paths of a ray of light through a converging lens; *F* and *F'* are conjugate foci; *c*, the center of the lens, and the line which traverses *c* is the principal axis of the lens; *e–d* is a secondary axis.

In a concave lens, parallel rays will diverge (Fig. 14), and the principal focus, *F*, of the lens is determined by the extension of the divergent rays until they meet at a point which lies on the same side of the lens as the source of light. Such a point has no actual existence and is known, consequently, as a virtual focus. The focus of a convex lens, on the other

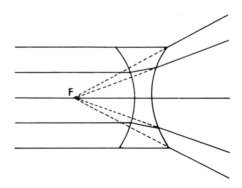

Fig. 14.—*F* is the virtual focus of this diverging lens.

hand, is real and may be determined readily by allowing the sun's rays, which are practically parallel, to pass through it and fall upon a screen. By moving the lens backward and forward, the spot of projected light varies in size and brightness. When smallest and brightest, the spot is at the focal point of the lens.

IMAGES.   In Figure 15, the object, represented by the smaller arrow, lies beyond the principal focus of a convex lens as in a photographic camera, for example, or the objective of a compound microscope.

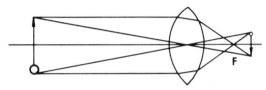

Fᴵɢ. 15.—Diagram of the lens of a camera or objective of a microscope; the arrow lies beyond the principal focus *F;* note that its image is reversed.

Light rays pass out in all directions from any luminous point. Hence one ray from any point on the arrow—the tip, for instance—will pass through the focal point *F* and one will pass through the optical center of the lens. Thus it is evident that the ray through *F* will emerge as one of the parallel rays upon leaving the lens, and the one through the optical center of the lens, since it traverses a secondary axis, will not be refracted; hence, the two rays must cross. Their point of intersection is the point at which the image of the arrow tip will be formed. The same fact may be determined, likewise, for any other point of the arrow, for example, the opposite end. Thus the distance from the lens at which the image is formed may readily be determined. In focusing a photographic camera, for example, the image comes sharply into view on the ground-glass plate at the back of the camera when the plate is brought into the plane in which these rays intersect beyond the lens. It will be observed from the figure that the image is reversed. The size of the image diminishes as the object lies farther beyond *F.*

If the object lies between the lens and the principal focus, as in Figure 16, parallel rays from the object will converge to meet at the conjugate focus *F'*, and an eye at this point will see the virtual image *ab* projected and enlarged without being reversed. The plane in which the image is formed is determined by finding the points of intersection of the secondary axes through points of the object with the imaginary elongation of the refracted rays, as shown in the figure. The image is magnified because the observer judges the size of an object by the visual angle which it subtends. The greater the convexity of the lens, the shorter is the focus; also, since the rays are bent more, the magnification is greater.

TYPES OF MICROSCOPES

THE SIMPLE MICROSCOPE.   The simple microscope (the ordinary so-called magnifier) operates upon this principle: the image of an object is projected and enlarged but not inverted (Fig. 16).

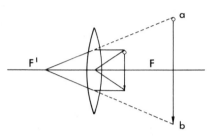

F<small>IG</small>. 16.—Diagram of a lens which acts as a simple microscope since the object (arrow) lies between the lens and the principal focus *F*, and is enlarged but not reversed.

The question arises as to whether there is an optimum distance between the simple microscope and an object. Why will not any point answer, so long as it is within the focal point? As a matter of fact, the object may be placed at any point within the focus, and it will be found that the nearer it is brought to the lens, the less it is magnified. There

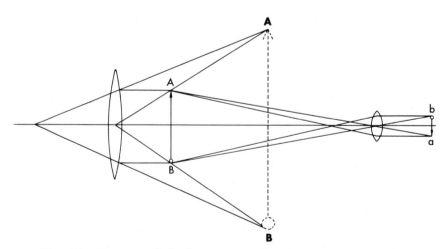

F<small>IG</small>. 17.—Diagram of the lens system of a compound microscope. The object *a–b* lies beyond the principal focus of the objective represented by the convex lens at the right; the ocular is represented by the lens at the left. Note that the image of *a–b* is reversed by the objective and that the eyepiece enlarges the image but does not reverse it.

is one most favorable point for observation, however, which is neither at the point of highest nor of lowest magnification, but an intermediate point at which the lens is most nearly free from chromatic and spherical aberrations. The eye forms an integral part of the optical arrangement when the microscope is being used. In our elementary exposition of the subject this fact is disregarded.

THE COMPOUND MICROSCOPE. The general principle of the compound microscope is represented in Figures 17 and 18A. The object

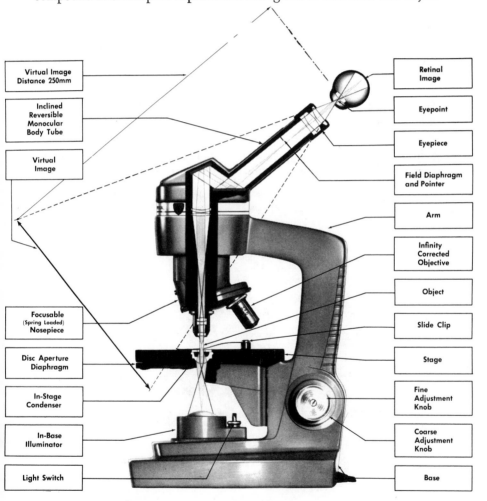

Fɪɢ. 18A.—Diagram of a compound microscope with part of the housing cut away to show the path of light from illuminator to eye. It may be profitably compared with Fig. 17, making due allowance for the extra prisms which the inclined ocular tube necessitates. (Courtesy of the American Optical Company.)

ab (Fig. 17) lies beyond the principal focus of the first lens or objective (really a system of lenses); hence the image *AB* is reversed. This image, in turn is viewed through a lens, the eyepiece or ocular, situated nearer the eye of the observer. The eyepiece acts as a simple magnifier, projecting and enlarging the real image *AB* but not reversing it again. As a matter of fact, the ordinary ocular of a compound microscope cannot be taken from the instrument and used as a simple magnifier because it is made of two plano-convex lenses which are so adjusted that the image from the objective of the compound microscope is not brought to focus until it has traversed the larger or field lens of the eyepiece (Fig. 18A). The image is examined, therefore, at a point between the two lenses of the eyepiece. Such an eyepiece is termed a negative eyepiece or ocular and is widely used today for microscopic work. The commonest form, the Huygenian, is an adaptation of an ocular designed originally by Huygens for the telescope. By contracting the area of the real image, the field lens of a negative ocular not only brightens the image but also increases the size of the field that can be examined. It is usually also designed, in conjunction with the eye lens, to help render the image achromatic. Positive eyepieces are also made. These produce an inverted image of the object below the system of ocular lenses. Such an

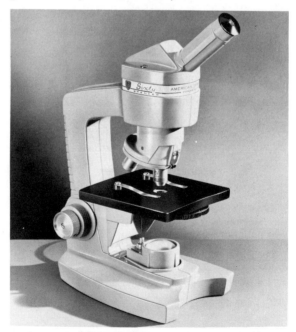

FIG. 18B.—This is a photograph of the microscope diagramed in 18A. It shows the body tube in a reversed position. This is an inexpensive and satisfactory student microscope. (Courtesy of the American Optical Company.)

ocular operates as a simple microscope. The Ramsden eyepiece is of the positive type.

A good objective includes two to five systems of lenses, as shown in Figure 19. A single system, in turn, may be a doublet (Fig. 20) or a triplet, each made of different kinds and shapes of glass. A good objec-

Fig. 19.—Four objectives with their lens systems exposed by the removal of a portion of the housing of each. Reading from left to right, these are 32 mm, 16 mm, 4 mm, and 1.8 mm focal length. Note that in each of the last three lenses there is at least one lens system which is a doublet. (Courtesy of the American Optical Company.)

tive is a very delicate piece of apparatus and must be handled with great care. Each component is very accurately ground, and the systems are spaced with extreme precision in order to get a clear image. The student, if not familiar with the parts of the compound microscope, should study Figure 18A with a microscope before him. See also Figures 18B and 21.

Fig. 20.—A doublet lens system made by the combination of the lenses *C* and *F.*

STEREOSCOPIC DISSECTING MICROSCOPES are compound microscopes with two oculars and with a pair of objectives for each magnification. They are often called binocular dissecting microscopes. They are constructed with prisms which provide erect images; thus they may be used for dissections as easily as simple microscopes. They are invaluable for many kinds of laboratory work. In general, they consist of two optically distinct tubes so combined that the objectives focus on the same point from different angles. A magnified, stereoscopic image is thereby provided so that objects that have depth stand out in pronounced relief. Adjustments of the ocular tubes may be made to provide the proper interpupillary distance for each observer. Adjustments for differences of focus between the right and left eye are easily made.

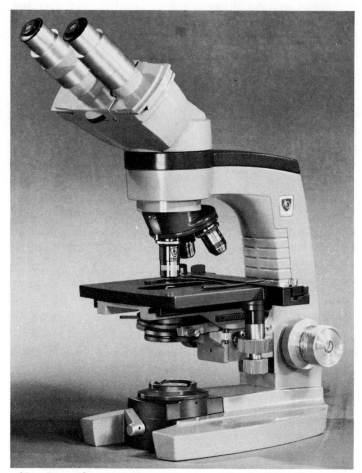

Fig. 21.—Binocular research microscope with a built-in illuminator. This model may have the binocular body turned through 180° to a more conventional position. With the oculars as illustrated, there is greater room for manipulation of the slide on the stage. Note the mechanical stage. (Courtesy of the American Optical Company.)

Many excellent stereoscopic dissecting microscopes are available. Figures 22A and 22B are instruments made by Bausch and Lomb. They represent similar microscopes arranged for two types of illumination. Lights may be provided for 22A by a table lamp or a light designed especially to give incident (reflected) light for dissecting microscopes. Transmitted light is provided for 22B by a substage mirror and a source of illumination. With many dissecting microscopes, a relatively simple adjustment will permit the use of either incident or transmitted light, or both simultaneously.

22A. is the same microscope as 22B, but lacks the substage assembly for the use of transmitted light. Only incident (reflected) light can be used to illuminate objects on its stage and it is of little use for studying translucent specimens. (Courtesy of Bausch and Lomb.)

Fig. 22B.—Binocular dissecting microscope that may be used with transmitted light, if the glass inset is placed in the stage and the substage mirror is used to obtain illumination. (Courtesy of Bausch and Lomb.)

NOMENCLATURE OR RATING OF OBJECTIVES AND OCULARS

Formerly there was a lack of uniformity among instrument makers in their marking of oculars and objectives to indicate their magnifications and other characteristics. Guyer (*142*, p. 203) recounts some of the designations used. The current methods of marking are informative and satisfactory.

Oculars are designated by the magnifications which they impart to the real image which is produced by the objectives; for example, 5× or 10×. Objectives are marked to indicate their numerical aperture, their focal length, and the magnification produced when used on a microscope with a tube length of 160 mm. If the objective is an apochromat, this also is indicated. Thus when the markings are 10×, 16 mm, N.A. 0.25, the objective provides an initial magnification of 10 diameters; it has a focal length of 16 mm, and a numerical aperture of 0.25. The N.A. is a measure of the efficiency of the objective, since it indicates the relative proportion of the light rays which traverse it to form an image. The formula originally proposed by Abbé is N.A. = $n \sin u$; n signifies the refractive index of the medium between cover glass and objective (air or immersion fluid), and u is one-half the angle of aperture.

DEFECTS IN THE IMAGE

SPHERICAL ABERRATION.   A simple convex lens, unless corrected, will not give a sharply defined image because it does not refract to the same degree all rays passing through it. Those which traverse its edges are brought to a focus nearer the lens (Fig. 23). This results not only in

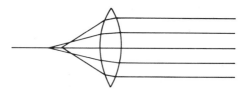

Fig. 23.—Lens producing a distorted image by spherical aberration.

an indistinct image but in a distortion of shape as well. Straight lines, for example, appear curved, and when the parts of the object in the center of the field are in focus, those nearer the margin are hazy and indistinct. This defect is greatest in strongly curved lenses; that is, since magnification increases with increased curvature, in high powers.

Spherical aberration is corrected by one or more of the following processes:
1. Cutting off the marginal rays.
2. Changing the shape of the surface of the lens.
3. Combining several lenses to make a system of lenses.

CHROMATIC ABERRATION. As with a prism, ordinary light in passing through a lens is broken up into its component colors. This process is technically termed dispersion. Since the colors are not all bent to the same extent, the result is that each color has a different focus; the ones that are bent most (violet rays) come to a focus nearest the lens, and those that are least affected (red rays) meet at a point farther away (Fig. 24). This failure of the color rays to meet in one focal point is termed chromatic aberration and, if uncorrected, causes the image of an object viewed through such a lens to be bordered by a colored halo.

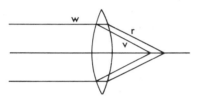

Fig. 24.—Lens producing chromatic aberration; *r*, red rays; *v*, violet rays.

The defect is corrected by properly combining glasses of different dispersive power but of comparable refractive power. Flint glass (silicate of potassium and lead), for example, has a dispersive power equal to about twice that of crown glass (silicate of potassium and lime), although their refractive powers are nearly the same. By combining a biconvex lens of crown glass with a concave lens of flint glass so constructed that its dispersive power will just equal that of the crown glass (Fig. 20), the error may, in large measure, be corrected. Such an arrangement does not interfere seriously with the refractive power of the lens so constructed. Unfortunately, no two kinds of glass have been found that have proportional dispersive powers for all colors, so that in the ordinary achromatic objective, only two of the different colors of the spectrum have been accurately corrected and brought to one focus. The colors left uncorrected form the defect known as a secondary spectrum. In the apochromatic objectives, three rays are brought to one focus, leaving only a slight tertiary spectrum. With apochromatic objectives it is best to use compensating oculars designed for them. The objective is under-corrected and the compensating ocular over-corrects. With this combination, there is very little chromatic abberation.

MICROSCOPE ACCESSORIES

CAMERA LUCIDAS are used for drawing. There are several types and each has a glass prism or thin glass plate so arranged that, when it is placed over the eyepiece of the microscope, the observer may see the image of the object under the microscope projected onto his drawing paper on the table.

Some form of the Abbé camera lucida is used by most workers. It consists of a cap which is fitted immediately above the eyepiece and which contains two right-angle prisms cemented together to form a cube. The lower prism is silvered along its cemented surface except for a small central opening through which the object under the microscope may be viewed; connected with the cap is an arm which bears a mirror, and this mirror may be so adjusted as to reflect the image of the drawing paper on the table onto the prisms from one side. The prisms are set so that the silvered surface of the lower one reflects this image upward to the eye of the observer which also, coincidentally, is viewing the magnified image of the object through the hole in the silvering. When proper adjustment of the light received from object and paper respectively is made, a pencil point may be distinctly seen when brought into the field of vision over the paper; consequently, the outline of the object may be accurately traced. The secret of success in working with a camera lucida is to have the illumination in the two fields properly balanced. Small screens of tinted glass are provided with the instrument for such regulation. It is helpful to work in a relatively dark room and to illuminate the paper with a small lamp, adjusting the amount of light by moving the lamp toward or away from the paper.

With the Abbé camera lucida, the microscope may be used in a vertical or in an inclined position. If the microscope stand is inclined, the drawing board upon which the paper rests must have the same inclination, or the outline when drawn will be distorted. Likewise, if the mirror of the camera is at any other angle than 45°, an adjustment of the drawing surface must be made; in short, the axial ray of the image and the drawing surface must always be at right angles to prevent distortion. This means that, if the mirror is depressed below 45°, the drawing surface must be tilted toward the microscope twice as much as the mirror is depressed. For example, if the mirror is depressed to 37° (8 below 45°), the drawing board must be raised 16°.

MECHANICAL STAGES are desirable accessories, useful in following objects in serial sections and in making enumerations of white blood cells and similar structures. Properly used, they make accurate counts possible. If they carry verniers, the positions of significant cells may be noted and recorded; it is easy then to return to the same place on a slide. Such notations cannot easily be transferred and used with other microscopes and mechanical stages. (Figs. 21 and 26 show microscopes with mechanical stages.)

FINDERS of various sorts are devices for relocating positions on slides with any microscope. Needham (233) describes a considerable number of these. Mention will be made here of types with which the writer is most familiar.

There are several kinds of instruments for marking the covers of slides with stylets that engrave the glass or that make circles of India ink. The stylets are parts of a device resembling an objective provided with the standard society screw. When the desired object is located with the proper objective, this lens is removed from the nosepiece and the marker substituted and used. Thomas (A–47) sells the Sheaff Object Marker, which has one stylet for engraving and another for marking a smoked slide to indicate the proper position on the master slide. See E–63.

Flatters and Garnett (A–22) sell a Mikrops Object Marker which carries fiber tips with small circular apertures. The tip, lightly inked, is pressed on the slide, leaving a circular impression around the object to be located.

SLIDE FIELD FINDERS are 3 × 1-inch slides marked with numbered grids on a part or on all of their surfaces. The type of marking and size of grid vary according to the maker. Edmund (A–19) sells one called the England Slide Field Finder. The entire surface is marked with a numbered grid having 1-mm openings. A laboratory-produced device has been used by the writer with success; it carries in a 22 × 70-mm space the numbers from 1 to 25,000. These were typed, photographed with suitable reduction in size, and the film mounted under a long cover.

All types of slide field finders are used in the same way with a mechanical stage. The object is located on the slide carrying the preparation; this slide is removed without disturbing the setting of the stage. The finder is placed on the stage and the numbers which appear in the center of the field recorded. When the object is to be found again, the finder is put in the mechanical stage at the setting indicated in the record, the finder is removed, and the slide bearing the object placed in the stage.

ILLUMINATORS. It is often difficult to use daylight for microscopic work, although with care and experience this may be satisfactory. It is, at best, variable. For work at night one must use another source of illumination, and the alternate use of daylight and artificial light may be difficult.

Fig. 25.—Microscope illuminator which has a rack for carrying filters. (Courtesy of the American Optical Company.)

There are various types of table microscope lamps which produce a uniform and dependable light source if light and mirror are carefully adjusted. Figure 25 is one example. A very satisfactory lighting device is the substage illuminator; it makes the use of a mirror unnecessary. Figure 18A shows a microscope with such an illuminator. Some substage lamps have a prong which fits into the hole into which the mirror prong usually fits; others fasten to the bottom of the condenser with a clip; still others lie directly on the table between the two arms of the microscope base and should be wedged into place so that they will not move. The simplest and most trouble-free arrangement of all is the lamp built into the base of the microscope; it is always in the proper place and needs little adjustment. Several manufacturers of dependable instruments now produce relatively inexpensive microscopes with a built-in lamp (see Fig. 18B). For research microscopes without built-in lights, the Ortho-Illuminator is invaluable (Fig. 26).

LIGHT FILTERS are necessary aids to good microscopy. Usually a blue disc is furnished with microscopes that have condensers. Unless the light source itself has such a filter, the use of this disc is almost essential, especially in studying stained blood slides. This type of filter gives daylight values to artificial illumination.

Neutral filters do not change the color of the light but cut down the intensity of illumination. Their use is more satisfactory than adjustments

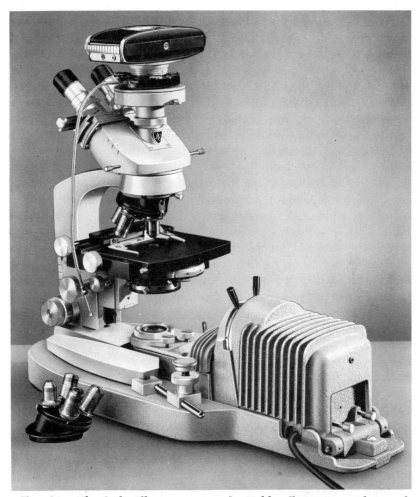

Fig. 26.—The Ortho-Illuminator provides Köhler illumination. This excellent instrument allows a number of changes in intensity and has easily adjusted red and green filters. It is shown here with microscope in position. (Courtesy of the American Optical Company.)

of the iris diaphragm. Since they are made to transmit varying amounts of light, ranging from $\frac{1}{2}$ to $\frac{1}{16}$ of the illumination delivered by the lamp, and may be used in various combinations, it is possible to obtain the degree of illumination desired. Filters of this sort are made by American Optical Company and Bausch and Lomb and are attached to a microscope lamp similar to that in Figure 25. It is also possible to obtain discs that fit into the substage condenser.

Green filters are desirable when studying Feulgen, aceto-orcein, and aceto-carmine preparations, since they make the chromosomes appear black and sharper in outline. Green filters are particularly comfortable to use for prolonged microscopic observations and unless the staining of a preparation is altered essentially by this color, they may be used habitually.

Polarizing filters used with ordinary microscopes will serve in place of special polarizing microscopes for many purposes. Most microscope makers sell such filters especially designed for their own instruments. Although they sometimes can be used on other microscopes, it is probably safer to buy the one designed for each make.

A central-stop diaphragm, which is often furnished with microscopes, will provide a reasonably good means of equipping a microscope for dark-field illumination. When this diaphragm is inserted in a slot in the condenser frame below its lenses, only marginal rays of light are admitted; this provides a dark background against which small objects appear brilliantly white. For research purposes, a dark-field condenser or other special equipment is usually used.

MICROMETERS are scales for measuring objects under the microscope. The stage micrometer carries a scale, usually 1 mm long, divided into one hundred 10-micron units. These smallest units are grouped into ten 100-micron units by lines numbered from 0 to 10. The scale is commonly mounted on a thick glass slide of standard size. An ocular micrometer is a circular glass disc with a scale of no fixed value ruled on it; it is generally inserted in the ocular between the eye lens and the field lens. By means of a stage micrometer, the values of the divisions of the ocular micrometer are determined and recorded for the known tube length and every combination of lenses to be used in measurement. Suppose that, with a 10× ocular and 16-mm objective, it takes four divisions of the ocular micrometer to correspond to one of the finer divisions of the stage micrometer; then, since the divisions of the latter are equal to 0.01 mm or 10 microns, each space in the ocular micrometer must be equal to 0.04 mm or 2.5 microns.

A filar or screw micrometer is a more convenient and considerably more expensive form of ocular micrometer; it is provided with delicate, movable spider lines that can be adjusted to the space to be measured by means of a fine screw with accurately cut threads. At the end of the screw is a graduated disc which records the distance between the spider lines. When this ocular micrometer has been calibrated with a stage micrometer, measurements can be made rapidly and with great precision.

MEASURING MICROSCOPIC OBJECTS

Measuring with a microscope is usually accomplished with an ocular micrometer, although there are other useful methods. If the objects are photographed, the prints may be compared with photographs of a stage micrometer made with the same combinations of lenses. If the photograph of all, or a part of the stage micrometer is measured and its magnification thus determined the measurement of the photograph of the specimen, divided by this magnification, will give its actual size.

In the same way a camera lucida may be used for measurements. The stage micrometer is outlined on a drawing sheet with the proper combinations of lenses and its magnifications determined. From these figures, the magnifications of the images drawn with the camera lucida may be determined.

It is also possible to use a microprojector (E–42) to throw first the image of the stage micrometer on the screen and after determining its magnification, project the objects to be measured. Under some circumstances this provides a very accurate measurement.

CARE OF THE MICROSCOPE

1. Always handle a microscope with due regard to the fact that it is a delicate and precise piece of equipment. Lift it by its arm with one hand and support its base with the other; hold it in a vertical position; set it down gently on the table.

2. Keep all of the lenses clean; never put away a microscope without cleaning ocular(s) and objectives, and the top condenser lens. After ordinary careful use, this cleaning should involve only wiping the lenses with fresh pieces of good quality lens paper, which are discarded after a single use, or brushing the lenses gently with a clean, soft brush. If the immersion lens has been used, wipe off the oil, moisten lens paper with xylene, wipe briefly, and wipe again with dry lens paper. If the instrument has been carelessly used, the objectives may have become clouded with water or other materials from an uncovered wet mount or smeared with mountant from a fresh slide or a broken one. The ocular(s) also may be smudged. All of these conditions produce a cloudy image; if the ocular is dirty, the blurred area will move as it is rotated in the tube. If after cleaning the ocular, the image is still not clear, each objective should be cleaned. Water will be removed by wiping; it may be necessary to moisten the lens paper with clean distilled water before drying the lens. Resinous mountants must be wiped away with one or more pieces of xylene-moistened paper.

3. If the image is still not clear, there may be dirt on the top surface of the upper lens of an objective. Remove this by blowing air over it from an ear syringe with a soft rubber tip; never use one made of hard rubber. It may also be necessary to wipe this surface.

4. Never remove an ocular from the tube and leave it uncovered, for small amounts of dust will drop in. Put another ocular in place, or one of the small plastic cups made especially for this purpose.

5. Keep the mechanical parts of the microscope clean, particularly the plane metal surfaces, by rubbing them with a good grade of oil on lens paper; remove surplus oil with fresh lens paper.

6. Dust the body of the microscope regularly with a soft cloth.

7. Store the microscope in its box or under a dustproof cover.

8. Damage to valuable microscopes from reagents may be avoided by using old ones without condensers for routine staining. However carefully done, differention under the microscope leaves various fluids on stage, condenser, and possibly objectives. It is possible to buy used instruments suitable for this purpose at relatively low cost.

CHAPTER XVI

DRAWING

by Elizabeth Smith Dean, with some additions

"I should make it absolutely necessary for everybody, for a longer or shorter period, to learn to draw. It gives you the means of training the young in attention and accuracy, which are the two things in which all mankind are more deficient than in any other mental quality whatever. . . ." Huxley.

Drawing is an important part of the work in morphology and anatomy. Treatment of the essential points of a subject can be condensed if the drawings accurately represent the dissections or microscopic preparations studied. The following simple directions are written mainly to aid the student in preparing his notebook. For more advanced technics of drawing, Zweifel's small but excellent paperback book (342) on biological illustration is heartily recommended.

It is important to recognize that laboratory drawing has no necessary relation to artistic ability. Students with no former experience in representing on paper what they see need not be discouraged. Clear-cut outline drawings can be made by anyone who *observes correctly* and uses sufficient care and patience in making his drawings.

MATERIALS FOR CLASSWORK may be selected from the following list:
pencils: 3H or 4H; HB; B.
pens: penholder and Gillott's or Esterbrook points for lettering.
ink: Higgins' waterproof India ink or Pelikan waterproof drawing ink.
ruler: transparent plastic, with one edge marked in millimeters, the other in inches.
erasers: soft eraser or art gum; kneaded rubber eraser.
penknife or pencil sharpener which will make a long point on a pencil.
sandpaper blocks for renewing the points on pencils.
coarse sandpaper glued to a block of wood for cleaning and sharpening the tips of erasers.
crayon pencils: red, blue, yellow, and at least one more color.
drawing paper of a good grade, or two-ply bristol board.

tracing paper.

draftsman's Scotch tape.

smudgers.

The pencils may be of any standard brand; the hardest is 4H; HB is a medium grade, and B is somewhat softer. The soft eraser and the kneaded eraser are for removing pencil lines; the latter can be used to erase large areas and can also be molded by the fingers into sharp points to erase small areas without damaging nearby lines. The colored pencils should be of good quality, so that they may be sharpened to a fine point. The draftsman's Scotch tape is useful for fastening drawing paper or drawing board to the table when it must not be moved, as during microprojection or camera lucida drawing.

This is not a large amount of equipment but should be adequate for most purposes.

GENERAL DIRECTIONS

Keep drawings as clean as possible; avoid fingerprints and frequent erasure. When laboratory work requires dissection, the drawings should be made in the laboratory as carefully and accurately as possible. They can later be traced, rubbed onto clean paper, and finished.

Since many biological objects are bilaterally or radially symmetrical, it is often timesaving to draw one half and then, by tracing and rubbing, make the other half. This is particularly helpful in making drawings of whole animals such as crayfishes.

Maintain uniformity in size and arrangement of drawings whenever possible. For example, in the development of the frog's egg, no increase in the size of the egg takes place from the single-cell stage to the end of the gastrulation; hence all drawings representing this series of development must be the same size. The neural tube, largest in circumference in the head, decreases gradually toward the posterior end of the body and must be drawn in correct scale in cross sections; otherwise the drawing will give an erroneous idea of its structure. Do not crowd the drawings upon the page. Exact margins and equal spaces between drawings contribute to a neat appearance. Place the title of the whole sheet of drawings at its top, centered. Place the title of each separate drawing, if there is more than one, directly below it together with information about magnification and other pertinent matters. For example the title of the sheet might be *RAT OVARY* and of the separate drawings *THE GERMINAL EPITHELIUM × 560* and *A PRIMORDIAL FOLLICLE FROM THE CORTEX × 870.*

XVI–1. LAYING OUT THE DRAWING AND MAKING THE OUT-LINE. If possible, measure the objects to be drawn. Use a ruler if the specimen is large, or an ocular micrometer if it is microscopic. Determine the size the drawing is to be; it should always be large enough so that all essential details of structure can be plainly shown.

Indicate the proposed length of the specimen by a single, light median line if it is bilaterally symmetrical or nearly so. Then indicate its main outline by dots at proper distances from the midline, using the ruler or the micrometer to determine dimensions and making necessary calculations if the size of the drawing is to be greater or less than that of the specimen. In using an ocular micrometer, drawing is much easier if one unit in the micrometer can be made to correspond to 1 mm or 1 cm on the drawing. However, to determine the true magnification at which the object is drawn, the value of the units in the ocular micrometer must be determined with a stage micrometer (p. 200).

When the outline of the object has been indicated by dots, join them with faint lines made by an HB pencil. Next add structures, placing dots and then connecting lines, as in making the outline. Now make all of the outlines neat, firm, and continuous, using an HB pencil. *Drawings should be shaded only if the student has had enough experience and/or instruction in drawing so that he can do it competently.*

Print labels at one or both sides of the drawing, depending upon its position on the paper. They should all begin or end at an equal distance from the edge(s) of the paper and should be connected to the structure named by a straight line, an extension of the lowest guideline called a leader, which is drawn with a ruler and ends on the structure in a minute dot about the size of a printed period. Make all leaders parallel to the top of the sheet of paper and to each other. Wherever possible, let them be equidistant from each other.

XVI–2. SHADING. Where differentiation of parts is desired it may be necessary to shade. Do this either by stippling or by lines. For making dots, use a special pen called the Leroy pen (E–39). These pens come in various sizes, each making a dot or a line of different width. They are inserted in the socket holder of a Leroy lettering pen and when pressed against the paper, the tip leaves a round, even impression. If properly made, the dots will be of uniform size. Degrees of shading are produced by varying the number but not the size of the dots.

XVI–3. INK DRAWINGS. Usually laboratory drawings are best executed in pencil. However, sometimes ink is desirable. If drawings are to be inked, carefully outline the whole picture in pencil and make all corrections before inking is started. Choose a type of pen most suitable for the work in hand. The choice must sometimes be made after duplicating a small portion of the pencil drawing and trying out various kinds and sizes of pens. Do not dip drawing pens but apply the ink with an applicator attached to the cork of the ink bottle.

XVI–4. LABELING. The results will not be satisfactory if the labeling is poorly done. Use an HB pencil; keep the point smooth and conical. Draw three parallel lines, 2 mm apart, as guidelines upon which to place the letters.

Place the letters moderately close to each other and keep the spaces between successive letters uniform. Leave larger spaces between words. If inexperienced in printing, take time to practice lettering before labeling drawings.

Many letters like *b*, *c*, and *g* contain an *o* combined with a straight line; hence it is necessary to learn to make an *o* properly. In making *b*, *d*, *p*, and *g*, be careful that the upstroke or downstroke is straight and joins the curve smoothly. The strokes of the *b*, *d*, *f*, *h*, *k*, and *l* extend to the uppermost guideline; the *o* portion of *b*, *d*, *g*, *p*, *q* lies between the middle and lower guides while the tails of *g*, *p*, *j*, *q*, and similar letters extend below the lower guidelines. The style shown in Figure 27 is easy to learn and is a good one to begin with.

A B C D E F G H I J K L M N O P Q R S T U V W X Y Z

a b c d e f g h i j k l m n o p q r s t u v w x y z

0 1 2 3 4 5 6 7 8 9

Fig. 27.—Simplified Gothic or "shop skeleton" letters and figures used in labeling drawings.

Indicate the relation of the size of the picture to the size of the specimen for all drawings. If the drawing is 10 times the size of the specimen state this by printing × 10, usually after the name of the animal or part. If it is only one-fifth as large, label it × $\frac{1}{5}$; if natural size, label it × 1.

CERTAIN TECHNICS FOR CERTAIN COURSES

XVI–5. ELEMENTARY COURSES IN BIOLOGY OR ZOOLOGY. Unshaded pencil drawings are best. They should be complete enough to be accurate but without repetitious detail. It is not, for instance, necessary to draw the appendages on both sides of a grasshopper. Similarly, cellular detail should be shown as accurately as possible, but in only a small part of a drawing of stratified epithelium.

XVI–6. ANATOMY. If many details are to be represented, or if the object is a complex one, make a preliminary drawing in pencil, erasing and revising as necessary until it is complete and accurate. Then this drawing, by now somewhat smudged, may be traced on tracing paper and rubbed onto a fresh sheet of good drawing paper. Rubbing is done by pressing gently upon the lines of the tracing, turned pencilled side down, with a smooth, rounded piece of metal such as the handle of a metal scalpel. Still better for the purpose are objects called domes of silence or gliders (E–26), which are fastened to chair legs so that they move easily over the floor. Place a blank piece of tracing paper upon the copy to prevent possible tearing. If the drawing cannot be reversed, turn the tracing paper over and trace the lines upon the back before rubbing.

XVI–7. EMBRYOLOGY. If the laboratory is provided with a few small microprojectors (E–42) which throw the image of a section on the table where it can be traced, much time can be saved and an accurate outline can be produced. The details are best filled in during observation with the microscope. A camera lucida may also be used for making outlines, although this takes more time (p. 196).

If neither microprojector nor camera lucida is at hand, an alternative method is available. A cover glass ruled into squares, or a net reticule, can be fastened into the ocular. Rule the drawing paper with very fine lines into the same number of squares as are on the cover glass or use graph paper of an appropriate kind. Draw with care the image seen in each ocular square in the corresponding square on the drawing paper. In such drawings, cells are not usually indicated. It is a decided advantage to have the drawing colored, especially if organs from the same germ layer are colored alike. Use the conventional three colors, for the germ layers: ectoderm, blue; endoderm, yellow; and mesoderm red; use these consistently throughout the sections, so that the development of the organs can be seen at a glance. Crayon pencils work up rapidly and give good results if the color is put on lightly, so that in the finished drawing the colors blend. To spread crayon evenly, use a blunt, rounded point and make long strokes with the side of the crayon. For example, in a cross section of a frog embryo, the neural tube with its optic cups is ectodermal in origin and the blue color immediately indicates its relationship to the ectoderm, which is similarly colored; the mesoblastic somites and mesenchyme are red; the lining of the archenteron is yellow. Choose a fourth color for the notocord and use it consistently. Vary the shade of each color; use a dark red for blood vessels by putting on a heavy layer of crayon and a light red for mesenchyme.

Distinguish neural epithelium and surface epithelium by two tones of blue. By this method a student has constantly before him the layers from which various organs develop, while the instructor can immediately see whether the student has a clear conception of the manner in which the organism is built up. Where cellular detail is desirable, a small segment may be left uncolored and in it the characteristic types of cells be shown.

XVI–8. HISTOLOGY. Histological drawings are usually best executed in pencil. Details must be shown. In general indicate these details, especially nuclear differences, by stippling. In intercellular matrices, such as connective tissue, represent the texture of the tissue by irregular lines. Lightly drawn lines give the effect of fibers and fibrils very well. Where various tissues of an entire organ are to be distinguished, cover the whole drawing with a light ground of blended graphite and work up the details with pen and ink. This combination is effective and has the added advantage of quick execution. It may be useful, in drawing slides stained with triple or quadruple stains, to use colored pencils on a small part of the drawing to show the characteristic color reactions of different structures. Use appropriate colors for granules of blood cells stained with a Romanowsky-type stain.

XVI–9. CYTOLOGY requires even more detailed drawing than does histology. Stippling and blended graphite for a background are both useful. A particular arrangement of the stipple dots gives the granular, alveolar, or reticular appearance of the cytoplasm. Avoid solid lines as much as possible; represent fibers by dots placed close together in a linear arrangement. Make chromosomes solid. Where the cell cytoplasm is homogeneous, a light ground coat of graphite may fill the outline of the entire cell, with cell parts stippled upon it.

CHAPTER XVII

COLLECTION, PRESERVATION, AND CULTURE OF INVERTEBRATE SPECIMENS FOR AN ELEMENTARY ZOOLOGY CLASS

It is not always easy to determine whether it is better to collect and prepare material for a freshman zoology class or to buy it. One must consider among other points, class size, location of the laboratory, instructor load, money available for class supplies, collecting facilities, and space needed for storage and for culturing. If collecting is not possible and the budget is limited, it may be desirable to buy a stock of organisms and to increase it by culturing.

As useful sources of information, the following books are recommended. *Culture Methods for Invertebrate Animals*, edited by Needham, Lutz, Welch, and Galtsoff, is a mine of information both on collection and culture methods. It was out of print for some time but has been reprinted by Dover Publications Company, in soft covers. For protozoa, Kirby's *Materials and Methods in the Study of Protozoa* is excellent. Hyman's series of publications on the invertebrates (McGraw Hill) contains much useful information concerning habitats; the phyla from Protozoa through Echinodermata and the smaller coelomate groups are covered.

There are numerous journals in which information concerning collection and culture methods may be found. A few of these are *American Journal of Hygiene, American Naturalist, Archiv für Protistenkunde, Biological Bulletin, Journal of Experimental Zoology, Journal of Protozoology, Physiological Zoology, Proceedings of the Zoological Society of London, Science, Transactions of the American Microscopical Society.*

GENERAL RULES FOR COLLECTING

All material should be labeled, as soon as taken, with data concerning the collecting site, time and date of collection, name of collector, temperature of habitat, and any other pertinent information. As soon as organisms are brought into the laboratory, they must either be placed in suitable containers under conditions which approximate their natural surroundings, or they should be fixed at once while they are in fresh condition.

The specimens may be carried in glass jars, plastic pails with covers, or in boxes or bags of heavy plastic. Whenever suitable, the latter type of container should be used since it is easily transported, whether empty or filled. Aquatic animals should be carried in the water from which they were taken; an additional supply of the same water should be secured and labeled to correspond with the specimens. Terrestrial animals such as earthworms should be provided with a quantity of the soil in which they were found.

Collecting equipment varies with the type of animals to be taken. Free-living aquatic specimens are collected with fine mesh nets, scoops with handles, pitchers of metal or enamel ware, or large pipets such as plastic basters (E–2). Plankton may be taken with nets of bolting cloth towed through the water behind a boat, or in some instances may be allowed to settle on slides. It is often necessary to resort to unconventional equipment. A good example is Dr. Patten's well-known method of collection of *Limulus* eggs from wet sand with a dust pan.

Material attached to stones, pilings, and other objects in the water should be removed in such a way as to avoid injuring the specimens. In some cases they may be scraped off rather roughly, but in others this treatment will produce enough damage to spoil the specimens. Putty knives are useful for detaching some delicate specimens from rocks. Heavy scalpels may be good instruments to use in prying organisms from wood. If the wooden support is not part of a structure such as a dock, but is a piece of waste wood or submerged tree trunk, some of the wood may be cut away with the specimen.

Often collections are made by a method which may be called indirect, whereby mud, soil, or aquatic vegetation likely to harbor the specimens sought is collected and brought to the laboratory. Mud and plants are placed in large shallow dishes of habitat water. The organisms generally leave the material on which, or in which, they were living and attach themselves to the walls of their containers, or they collect in visible masses which may be removed to culture dishes.

Collection of plankton on slides is probably more profitable in salt water than in fresh, but in any sizable body of water it may be rewarding. Clean slides are placed in slide boxes of wood or plastic with enough of the two larger surfaces cut away to provide adequate access of water to the slides. The boxes are tied with stout cord to hold the top and bottom together, and then suspended near the surface of the water from whatever point of attachment is available. They should be examined daily for specimens and when there are enough, one side of each slide is wiped clean and either studied in a container of filtered habitat water or fixed in a formalin-alcohol-acetic mixture (F–89) and prepared as a permanent slide (see chapter V). This method is especially useful for sponges, tunicates, some mollusks, and aquatic annelids.

If animals are small and terrestrial, they may be collected by removing small blocks of soil. The blocks, broken up somewhat, are placed in a Berlese funnel or similar piece of apparatus (E–4) and, with its help, the animals are separated from their environment. Adult insects of many sorts are best collected with insect nets. They may be kept in suitable cages or killed and preserved immediately.

Two types of organisms, parasites and commensals, are usually collected by removing them from the host and preserving them at once. Some may, however, be increased in numbers by transfer to new hosts. *Trypanosoma lewisi* is a good example of this. See also various methods in this chapter for cultivation of parasites *in vitro*. A list, which is far from complete, of parasites, symbionts, and their hosts follows.

COMMON PARASITES AND THEIR HOSTS

Protozoa

Endamoeba: E. histolytica, large intestine of man; *E. gingivalis,* mouth and especially gums of man; *E. invadens,* gut of snakes; *E. blattae,* house roaches.

Hydramoeba: H. hydroxena, gastrovascular cavity of hydra.

Trypanosoma: T. lewisi, blood of rats; *T. rotatoria,* blood of frogs; *T.* sp., many species of snakes.

Trichomonas: T. hominis, lower bowel of man; *T. gallinarum,* caecae and cloaca of turkey.

Giardia sp., mucosa of small intestine of most laboratory and domestic animals.

Trichonympha sp. and other symbionts, gut of termites.

Opalina sp., large intestine of amphibia.

Ichthyophthirius sp., skin of many kinds of fishes including goldfishes in aquaria.

Tetrahymena sp., hemocoele of various insects and certain small fish.

Nyctotherus sp., rectum of tadpole; cysts, gut of adult frogs.

Kerona sp., hydra, on ectoderm.

Monocystis sp., seminal vesicles of earthworms; guts of various invertebrates.

Hepatozoon sp., leucocytes of dogs, mice, and other mammals.

Eimeria sp., chickens and other domestic animals.

Plasmodium sp., red blood corpuscles, many birds and man.

Metazoa

NEMATODES, gut of most vertebrates; anterior nephridia of earthworms and lungs of common frogs. *Ascaris lumbricoides suum*, from pigs in abattoirs.

TREMATODES, gills and fins of marine and freshwater fishes; mouth and bladder of turtles; urinary bladder and lungs of frogs; bladder of other amphibians. Larval stages of trematodes are often present in the tissues of aquatic snails and may be released by finely mincing the visceral mass in water.

CESTODES, adequate supplies of fresh beef, pig, and sheep tapeworms may sometimes be obtained from slaughterhouses. Sacrificed cats and dogs may provide them. It is occasionally possible to make arrangements with veterinarians for securing parasites after administration of vermifuges. Cysticerci may be found in the abdomen of wild rabbits. Heavily parasitized specimens may show numerous cysticerci of *Taenia serrata* embedded in the peritoneum or liver. They should be removed to 37°C normal saline. Some mice harbor cysticerci of *T. crassicollis* in their livers.

CULTURE METHODS

Containers for cultures may be purchased as laboratory glassware; such glassware is however, expensive and for at least some purposes domestic glassware will do as well. Gallon jars with wide mouths in which mayonnaise, pickles, mustard, and similar foods are packed may usually be collected from the kitchens of institutions without charge and after washing, they are very suitable for culturing small, aquatic animals and for rearing and maintaining insects and even small mammals. For insects, the metal top should be replaced with wire netting and for mammals, with covers of hardware cloth. Or, one may buy glass jars of various sizes and at reasonable prices in variety stores. For smaller culture dishes, domestic glass containers such as those in which baby foods are sold are satisfactory. Stender dishes in the smaller sizes are well suited to protozoan cultures.

Some organisms have very exact food requirements, but there are a number of standard materials which will be eaten by many laboratory animals. Among these are Pablum, oatmeal, dry skim milk powder, and some of the Purina Chows. These or others favored by each laboratory should be kept on hand in sufficient quantity.

Protozoa

XVII–1.   DAWSON'S METHOD FOR *AMOEBA* (84).   For making cultures of large amoebae such as *A. dubia* and *A. proteus,* he collects water and plant material from various small streams and ponds. As containers he uses stacking finger bowls and syracuse watch glasses; for non-toxic water, referred to below simply as water, he finds most kinds suitable, using principally boiled spring, habitat, tap, or distilled water. The hay referred to is dry stems of timothy hay, cut in pieces 15–20 mm long and, like the wheat and oat grains, boiled 3–5 minutes directly before use.

The cultures are kept away from direct sunlight and thrive at room temperatures, although Dawson considers an optimum temperature to be 13–16°C. They should contain *Chilomonas paramecium,* which is almost always found in the water collected with the specimens. The pH of the cultures ranges between 6.4 and 7.2.

1. Place the collected material in clean finger bowls; include plant material with the water. Do not have more than 40 ml of material, altogether, in each bowl. Each day add about 10 ml of water until the total volume is about 70 ml. If amoebae are present, they will become abundant in 10–30 days. Begin examination for them at 10 days. Small crustaceans such as copepods and ostracods are inimical to the protozoans. Most other organisms that may be present are not harmful.

2. When amoebae become abundant, take up about 5 ml of amoebae and smaller organisms with a pipet and put them in a syracuse watch glass; select them with a dissecting microscope. Add 5 ml

of water in the next few days, and a piece of boiled timothy hay. Make as many of these cultures as convenient, because growth in them varies markedly from one to another.

3. Remove the specimens from each thriving culture made in step 2 to finger bowls, dislodging the amoebae with jets of culture water from a pipet; include all of the medium and specimens. Add water to make the volume up to about 30 ml, plus three pieces of hay and a wheat or oat grain. Every 5–10 days, add 10 ml of water and one or two pieces of hay also, if the culture seems to need it. Continue slow additions of water and hay until the culture volume is 65–70 ml. When they are well established, these cultures should contain numerous amoebae for at least a month.

4. To subculture when a maximum number of specimens has been reached in each dish, remove about one-half of the medium. Mix up the remainder thoroughly with jets of fluid from a pipet and remove about one-half of the organisms and medium to a clean finger bowl. Make a new culture there by step 3. To the remainder, add water and hay gradually until the volume is again 65–70 ml. These cultures will last several months to a year.

5. If large numbers of amoebae are desired, pick out 50–100 specimens from a thriving finger bowl culture and put them into another finger bowl. Add 10–30 ml of water and 3 pieces of hay, and treat as in step 3.

6. For classwork, make subcultures in syracuse watch glasses. Put in each glass 1 piece of hay, 3–4 ml of culture medium with the amebae, and the same amount of water. Make these 1–2 days before class use. The cultures will flourish and increase for at least 10 days and sometimes for as long as a month. They may be studied with a 16 mm objective and show fission and ingestion of food well. Whether the cultures are in syracuse watch glasses or finger bowls, the containers are stacked and the uppermost one covered with a piece of glass or an empty container.

XVII–2. *DIDINIUM*, a carnivorous ciliate, which preys largely on *Paramecium*, may generally be collected where the latter are abundant. Beers (25) recommends that sediment, submerged decaying leaves, and water from the edges of a pool or stream be included with the collected material; he points out that the specimens are usually encysted when collected and may be induced to excyst be placing them in a culture of *Paramecium* in timothy hay infusion. In such a culture they will rapidly devour the paramecia.

In order to maintain a stock of *Didinium*, they should be kept in the encysted form. Beers (25) recommends the following method:

1. Half fill vials with a stock culture of a few *Didinium* and many

and vigorous paramecia. When the paramecia have all been eaten, the *Didinium* will encyst.

2. Stopper the vial tightly, so that the fluid will not evaporate, and store.

3. When *Didinium* are needed, add fresh well-fed paramecia, in culture fluid, to a vial; they will shortly excyst.

Result: If vials are well stoppered, the cysts will remain viable for 5–6 years.

XVII–3. *EUGLENA.* Some species may be collected in cold, but not freezing, weather from hoof marks filled with green water in a horse pasture. They may also be found on the lip of dams in small, slow-flowing streams where the cement or stone is stained green. They often are closely associated with water plants from which they may be separated by gentle pressure on the plants in water. They frequently appear in wild, mixed culture. Various media are suitable for *Euglena* culture. One which is simple and convenient is made by adding commercial fertilizer (4–10–4), to the water. Rice (*263*), quoted by Kirby (*171*), uses it as follows: Add 1 g of fertilizer to 1 liter of water, heat to 80°C, and filter. Autoclave the filtrate, cool, and inoculate with *Euglena;* keep covered and in good light. Subculture at intervals, or add a little more fertilizer. Other media which are simple and suitable are 1% peptone in 1% citric acid and 0.1% solution of malted milk or dry skim milk in water.

XVII–4. GREGARINES OF CRICKETS can be produced in large numbers from infested crickets by the method of Parrish and Parrish (*244*). They found the usual incidence of infection to be 1–25 gregarines/cricket in about 25% of the population in their locality; they were able to increase it to 100 or more gregarines/host in about 99% of the population.

1. Collect and confine in a suitable cage a dozen or more crickets.

2. Place in the cage a watch glass of water with a cloth in the bottom and have water available in it at all times. Feed laying mash, Pablum, or Purina Laboratory Chow; added calcium, in the form of bone meal, prevents cannibalism.

3. Because the crickets often defecate on the cloth in the drinking water, it is soon contaminated with spores which are ingested with the water. Within a week, the colony is usually heavily infested.

4. When almost all fecal pellets show 1–10 cysts, sacrifice the hosts for study. See p. 11 for preparation of the material.

XVII–5. GREGARINES OF EARTHWORMS. Stegman (*301*) notes that most earthworms, particularly *Lumbricus terrestris*, are infested with *Monocystis* sp. These gregarines live in the seminal vesicles. Although not all stages will be found in one preparation of the vesicle mounted in 0.7% saline, several may be seen and if enough material is examined, the spores, trophozoites, zygotes, and the sporoblasts will be found. He refers students to Hegner's *Invertebrate Zoölogy*, 1933, for a description of these stages.

Packard (*241*) reports a source of gregarines which might serve if local earthworms are not infested. He uses *Thermobia domestica*, the bakehouse-oven fire brat, a silver fish, as a source of this material. More than half of his specimens contained parasites in the ventricular caecae and the posterior portions of the alimentary canal.

XVII–6 *PARAMECIUM.* This genus is nearly ubiquitous, and one seldom takes a collection of freshwater organisms without including some specimens. Several collections should be made in containers of about 1-liter capacity. Water and vegetation should both be taken. The samples, if left undisturbed in the laboratory for a day or two, are likely to show the paramecia collected near the surface in grossly visible masses. Cultures should be made from these collected specimens.

The culture methods which have been proposed for paramecia are numerous and varied, because they use bacteria principally for their food and because many mixtures support flourishing cultures of bacteria. Two very simple but adequate media will be given here.

A. *Hay infusions* have been used for a long time. Timothy hay is usually preferred. Wichterman (*334*) gives the following method of preparation. Cut heads and stems of clean dry timothy hay into 1-inch lengths. Place 1.5 g of the hay in a 250-ml Erlenmeyer flask in 240 ml of water, cover with an inverted beaker, and boil for about 15 minutes. Cool and allow to stand for about 24 hours before inoculation.

B. *Lettuce infusions* are also good for culturing paramecia. The material for many batches can be prepared at one time. Separate the leaves of a head of lettuce, place them on a tray or trays in the oven set at about 104°C, or at 225°F if a domestic oven is employed, and allow them to bake slowly. When they are dry, crisp, and brown, remove them and triturate either in a mortar or a Waring Blendor. Store the flakes in clean, dry bottles where they keep indefinitely. To make the infusion add 1.5 g/liter of hot water; boil 5 minutes, filter, and dispense in smaller flasks if the medium is to be used at once. If the infusions are to be stored, autoclave after plugging the mouths of the flasks with cotton.

The stock cultures are made in either medium by inoculating 1-liter jars of the medium with paramecia obtained by collection. The collected paramecia are transferred to syracuse watch glasses on the stage of a binocular dissecting microscope and removed with a pipet to the jar of culture medium. If desired, the paramecia may be first transferred to small stender dishes of medium, allowed to multiply there, and the inoculations made from these cultures to the larger ones.

For laboratory study of paramecia, see p. 9.

XVII–7. PARAMECIA IN FISSION STAGES. Wichterman (333) collects dividing paramecia by placing a thriving culture, well provided with bacteria, in a separatory funnel of about 2-liter capacity. The funnel is attached, in an upright position, to a ring stand. Since dividing paramecia tend to settle to the bottom of the culture dish, the withdrawal of a few milliliters of fluid, by occasionally opening the lower stopcock, will usually furnish an abundant supply of specimens in fission.

XVII–8. CONJUGATION in some species of *Paramecium* may be induced by certain environmental changes. If non-clonal, well-fed cultures are starved by transfer to a medium containing little food, they may begin conjugation in a few hours. This is not, however, an invariable result.

P. bursaria is an excellent species for demonstrating conjugation; several clones should be raised and a few members of the various clones brought together to determine whether they are of different mating types. It is somewhat more simple to purchase conjugation sets of *P. bursaria*. These consist of 2 mating types in separate cultures; when specimens from the 2 cultures are mixed conjugation occurs within a short time. After the purchase of the initial set, the separate cultures may be maintained and increased for future use.

XVII–9. *SPIROSTOMUM*, very large and interesting ciliates, are often found in stagnant pools. When conditions are suitable for their existence and the pool is permanent, one can almost always find specimens in abundance, and at all seasons of the year if the climate is relatively mild. Specht's culture method is simple and satisfactory (295).

1.   Boil together for a few minutes in a liter of spring water a few grams each of wheat grains and timothy hay. When this has cooled, add a tablespoon of cow manure, collected when fresh and kept in a closed jar.

2.   Inoculate this medium after 2 or 3 days with *Spirostomum*. The culture will rapidly attain a stable pH which is usually about 7.6, and the organisms will be present in large numbers. They tend to collect in grossly visible cream-colored masses.

3.   When the number of specimens appears to be decreasing, add another small amount of cow manure. Cultures thus renewed may last for a year.

XVII–10.   TETRAHYMENA of various free-living species may be collected from springs, roadside ditches, creeks, rivers, ponds, and lakes. Elliott and Hayes (99) have described the method which they have used in making collections in various parts of the world.
1.   Collect samples of about 100 ml, each of which consists of water, bottom mud, and other debris. Return these samples to the laboratory within a few hours after they are taken and place each one in a finger bowl.
2.   Sprinkle on the surface of the water a small quantity of Bactotryptone or proteose-peptone or dessicated fat-free milk. This will result in a considerable increase in the numbers of bacteria at first, and then of *Tetrahymena* if they were present in the sample.
3.   Make cultures by transferring specimens to a dried lettuce infusion containing bacteria.

XVII–11.   *VOLVOX GLOBATOR* may often be found in early spring in great abundance in small permanent pools containing duckweed and *Riccia*. When water from such pools, together with a few of the water plants, is placed in finger bowls so arranged that one side is strongly exposed to the light, the *Volvox* present will collect after a few hours at the most brightly lighted side of the dish. If the cultures are kept in conditions as nearly natural as possible, the organisms may live for some weeks in the laboratory. Any considerable rise in temperature above that of pond water is lethal. Small crustaceans feed on *Volvox* and should be excluded from the cultures. The sexual stages are most likely to be found in the ooze at the bottom of the culture.

Kirby (171) says that *Volvox* cultures have been maintained in soil extract. He recommends boiling equal volumes of garden earth and spring water for an hour, decanting after 2–3 days into sterile flasks, and diluting before use with 4–6 volumes of distilled water. The fluid should be placed over a layer of soil. He also cites the formula and method of culturing *Volvox* in an inorganic medium.

Metazoa

XVII–12.   *ARTEMIA SALINA*, the brine shrimp, is invaluable as study material and as a source of food for other aquatic invertebrates and for small vertebrates. The dried eggs may be purchased from biological supply houses and from dealers in tropical fish; they may be stored for long periods of time and are inexpensive. Directions for hatching are usually furnished with the eggs.

To produce *Artemia* larvae for food for hydra cultures, we have found this method satisfactory.

1. Make a solution of table salt in tap water; the concentration may vary from 4% to saturation; keep at a temperature a few degrees below 30°C. Place it in a shallow pan and sprinkle over its surface a pinch of *Artemia* eggs. They will hatch in 24–48 hours, and the larvae will collect on the bottom of the pan while shells and unhatched eggs will remain at the top.

2. Using a medicine dropper with a wide mouth, remove needed larvae to a cone of filter paper in a funnel. Rinse well under the tap and transfer to a small amount of water from the culture medium of the animal to be fed. To raise *Artemia*, transfer the newly hatched larvae to a fresh solution of salt water of the same concentration as their hatching medium. Bond (*234*, p. 205) considers a temperature of 30°C optimum with a range of 10–37°C. He recommends unicellular green algae (marine) as food; or a suspension of fresh yeast in water. Add small amounts of food daily or every other day.

The cultures profit from aeration. If greater salinity is desired, it should be provided by very gradual addition of sodium chloride or by permitting slow evaporation of the culture water. The larvae reach maturity in about 3 weeks.

XVII–13. COCKROACHES. Although it is relatively easy to trap available species of cockroaches in animal rooms of a laboratory, it is probably better to buy cultures of *Blaberus* which are now offered by several supply houses. They are considerably larger than *Periplaneta americana* and carry their egg masses until they hatch. The directions apply to *Blaberus* and *Periplaneta*.

1. Keep the insects in large battery jars with paper toweling on the bottom. Smear Vaseline or oil around the top, making a fairly wide band which they will not cross. Cover with hardware cloth, bent to fit the top of the jar tightly. We have found that another suitable container is a mayonnaise jar, gallon size; its lid should be pierced with numerous holes; such jars provide space for more specimens if they are laid on their sides.

2. Feed dog chow biscuits; any good brand of biscuits or of kibbled dog chow is acceptable. Pablum is also satisfactory.

3. Keep them always supplied with water by filling a wide-mouth bottle stoppered with cotton and inverting it in a flat dish.

4. When it is necessary to handle the cockroaches, place the culture jar in the coldest part of the refrigerator for 30 minutes or until

they are torpid. Without this precaution, it is difficult to prevent their escape when the jar is opened.

5.   Subculture before the container becomes overcrowded.

XVII–14.   *DAPHNIA* have been cultured by numerous experimenters with a variety of methods. Viehover (*317*) records a great many technics that he has tried, some adapted to ponds and others to laboratory containers. For the latter type, the following simple media may be used. The fluid used in all of them is any water that is safe for drinking.

1.   Dried shredded sheep or cow manure, 0.025%.
2.   Dried milk or malted milk, 0.01%.
3.   Cottonseed meal, 0.01–0.02%.
4.   Cultures of bacteria.

Ali (5) uses dechlorinated tap water in aquaria 75 × 40 × 40 cm and controls the temperature thermostatically. He holds it at 20°C. Temperatures much higher than this are harmful. In each aquarium he puts a few lettuce leaves and adds fresh ones every 20 days. He feeds 1 g of Fleishman's yeast, dissolved in a beaker of water, twice weekly and keeps the water level constant by adding amounts lost by evaporation. In all of these methods it appears that the important factors are a relatively low temperature and avoidance both of crowding of specimens and of an oversupply of food; both quickly ruin a culture.

XVII–15.   STEEN'S *DROSOPHILA* (*299*) PREPARATIONS show developmental stages with a complete metamorphosis. These preparations are not difficult to make, and each one may be used by successive students in a class with several laboratory sections.

1.   Prepare shell vials with cotton stoppers large enough to take 25 × 75 mm slides.
2.   Place about 0.5 ml of liquid banana agar on a slide, allow it to gel, and add a drop of yeast solution to its surface. Insert the slide in the vial together with a male and a female *Drosophila.*
3.   Lay the vial in such a position that the slide is horizontal. The eggs will be laid on the medium and development will take place there.
4.   For study, remove the slide from the vial and observe with a dissecting microscope; a hand lens will do if the microscope is not available. During the period of development, egg, larva, and pupa can all be observed.

XVII–16.   EARTHWORMS are best collected at night when it is raining or after a long continued drizzling rain. They are most plentiful in old gardens or rich lawns. The equipment needed is a flash light and a bucket. The worms come to the surface and may be picked up by hand. They should be left overnight in a covered bucket, with leaves or a small amount of freshly cut grass on the bottom. They may be selected for culture by placing them in water, a few at a time, and discarding any that seem injured or diseased.

They are cultured in rather large wooden boxes in each of which is placed a layer, about 30 cm deep, of a mixture of old leaves and leaf loam. This material should be kept moist but not wet; the box should be covered with glass or heavy polyethylene film. It is advisable to examine the culture every few days at first and to remove any dead or moribund worms. Not more than 50 worms should be kept in a 30 cm³ space. Since earthworms die at about 16°C, they must be kept in a cool place in summer. In the winter their boxes should be in unheated rooms. *Lumbricus* cannot be collected during the winter in most parts of the country; however *Allolobophora* may often be found near the bottom of manure or compost piles during cold weather.

For preservation, select specimens of good size and place them in a flat pan with sufficient water to cover them. Anesthetize them by adding a small quantity of methanol, and repeat this until the worms are quiescent. If the pan is put in the refrigerator the process will be hastened.

A. *Preservation in alcohol.* When the worms no longer respond to stimuli such as a slight prick, transfer them to 50% methanol for several hours; keep them as straight as possible; replace the 50% methanol with 70%, 12 hours; then place them in 95% alcohol for the same length of time. Store in 70% methanol.

B. *Injection with chromic acid* produces better specimens. After anesthetization is complete, submerge the worms in 1% chromic acid and then inject each specimen. Use an apparatus for continuous air-pressure injection (Fig. 10), with a clamp in the rubber tube to which the cannula is attached. Make the cannula of ¼-inch glass tubing, drawn to a sharp tip which will easily pierce the body wall of a worm, and have several cannulae in reserve in case of breakage. Fill the container *C* with chromic acid. Place *A* about 4 feet above *B*.

Pierce each worm with the cannula just posterior to the clitellum; direct its tip toward the posterior end of the worm and hold it parallel with the body wall to avoid piercing the alimentary canal. Inject the chromic acid slowly until the worm is turgid throughout its entire length. After injection is complete leave the worms in the chromic acid 4 hours. Wash thoroughly in running tap water 12–16 hours or until they are no longer yellow. Transfer to 50% methanol 2 days, 70% 2–3 days, and store in fresh 70% methanol. During the whole course of these procedures be sure that the worms are kept straight.

C. *Preservation by freezing* is satisfactory for short periods. The writer has not tried it for longer than a month, but there seems to be no reason why this period should not be extended. For freezing, anesthetize the worms in alcohol as above, straighten carefully, and freeze as rapidly as possible. Store in polyethylene bags in the freezer.

XVII–17. GRASSHOPPERS are frequently used for study of the characteristics of Orthoptera; usually the large lubber grasshoppers are chosen. The common commercial method of preservation is in alcohol, and specimens prepared in this way are not thoroughly satisfactory for dissection. It is better, if large grasshoppers are available, to collect the local species and to preserve them by freezing. The grasshoppers are easier to collect when they are in the last nymphal stage, before they can escape by flying. They may be caught in nets or pursued and picked up singly.

WALDBAUER'S FREEZING METHOD (323) is said by him to be applicable to caterpillars, grasshoppers, larvae of house flies, and buprestid beetles. It is probably equally satisfactory for cockroaches, crickets, and many other commonly used insects.
1.   Either kill the insects in a cyanide jar or render them torpid and inactive by subjecting them to low temperatures.
2.   Place each specimen singly in an envelope made of a small sheet of aluminum foil with every edge folded twice. Place the envelopes at once in the coldest part of the freezer. (Although the directions do not specify this, it is desirable to collect the envelopes, when freezing is complete, into polyethylene bags which can be labeled with the name and total number of the specimens.) Storage should be at -15°C or below.

XVII–18. HYDRA should be sought in spring-fed pools. They are commonly numerous for short periods after prolonged rains. In the autumn they are often found in pools on smooth dead leaves. Those collected just before cold weather begins may show gonads.
   Vegetation in likely pools and ponds, together with a considerable quantity of the water, should be collected and placed in large glass jars in the laboratory with a small amount of hornwort or *Chara* in each jar. In a few hours the hydra will be found attached to the sides of the vessel and to the plants. Cover the culture jars with glass and, if necessary, replace water lost by evaporation. Feed with small annelids, *Cyclops, Daphnia,* and other small crustaceans. Newly hatched brine shrimps, well washed to remove salt, are satisfactory food for small cultures, and particularly for class demonstration of feeding. For other methods

of feeding and culture of hydra, consult the articles of Loomis (*200, 201, 202*).

NEMATODES are ubiquitous. Cobb (*66*) recommends that for an introduction to this phylum a nonparasitic form be chosen. Soil nematodes are sometimes found in rotting fruit and vegetables lying on the ground. They may also usually be secured by burying small cubes of meat in the ground and investigating them in a day or two; if nemas are present, they generally collect where food is available. The vinegar eel, *Anguilla aceti*, occurs in vinegar made at home and in the bulk vinegar sometimes sold in stores. It may be subcultured in fresh vinegar and, since it is viviparous and transparent, shows all stages of development in adult females. Cultures may be obtained from supply houses if only factory-bottled vinegar is available.

XVII–19. SOIL NEMATODES are easily cultured. Chandler (*234*, p. 174) recommends the following technic:
1. Place a small quantity of manured soil in a piece of gauze or a fine sieve and wash into a small beaker of warm water.
2. Take a drop or two of material from the bottom of the beaker. Place it on the surface of nutrient agar (or salt agar, F–6) in a petri dish; cover and leave at room temperature 5–10 days.
Results: Large numbers of several species are usually present. They move slowly, impeded by the agar, and may be seen to ingest particulate matter, digest it, and egest wastes.

XVII–20. *RHABDITIS (PELIO) MAUPASI.* A good source of small parasitic nematodes is the earthworm. Stegman (*301*) advices the following procedure for the discovery and culture of these specimens.
1. Dissect a freshly killed earthworm pinned out under water. Make a mid-dorsal incision. It is important to avoid cutting the wall of the gut, since the contents cloud the dissecting field.
2. Pin back the body wall, cutting the septa if necessary, and examine the nephridia with a dissecting microscope in order to see whether they contain nematodes; they are visible through the thin wall. Infestation is usually not heavy.
3. If nematodes are seen, place the dissected specimen in a jar on wet blotting paper or paper toweling. Cover the jar and allow the worm to decompose at room temperature; if necessary, add more water to keep the preparation thoroughly saturated. The process should take from 5–7 days; it may be hastened by raising the temperature to 37°C. During this time the nematodes will reproduce, making a flourishing culture which shows all developmental stages.

3.   Study all stages in water. If fixed preparations are desired, see V–30.

XVII–21.   PLANARIA may be collected by lowering a piece of fresh beef 25–30 mm³ in size, at the end of a string, into a freshwater stream among the plants where planaria are known to occur or where their presence is suspected. At the end of half an hour, examine the meat and shake the planaria from its surface into a collecting jar. Replace the bait and repeat the process, putting most of the bait where collection is best. If planaria are abundant, a large supply may be collected in a few hours. Each jarful should be rinsed to remove remaining bits of meat and filled with fresh water from the collecting site. Keep cool on the return to the laboratory. Various authors recommend culturing as follows.

1.   Use glass, crockery, or enameled pans. The writer finds white ones especially useful because food debris shows in them easily. If necessary, use tap water which has been allowed to stand several days in the laboratory, but spring and well water are better.

2.   Feed 2 or 3 times weekly. First lower the water level in the culture pan, then add beef liver cut in thin strips; cover and leave undisturbed, 2–3 hours. Remove the liver, rinse the pans thoroughly with fresh water, and refill with fresh water. Pieces of clam and of earthworm may also be used for food; yolk of raw egg distributed along the bottom of the pan in a thin strand is useful.

The planaria may be left without food for a time, but it is still necessary to change their culture water twice or thrice weekly.

XVII–22.   ROTIFERS may be cultured in a solution of dried skim-milk powder by the technic of Lindner *et al.* (*196*). They use 1 g of non-fat dried milk powder/liter of water. The authors suspend this in tap water, but suggest that if the water is chlorinated it should be boiled. The cultures maintained at 20°C will thrive for several months. Subculturing may begin within a week.

REAGENTS AND SUPPLIES

In this appendix are listed the names of some of the reagents and of supplies that are used in various technics. Most of the dyes and some of their identifying characteristics appear here. Various chemicals and supplies for which the source might be difficult to find are included; many which are more readily obtainable are omitted. The address is given here of dealers who carry only the one item referred to in this appendix, and is usually not listed in Appendix IV. The name of a chemical, in italics, is the one approved by the International Union of Chemistry.

ABOPON: see Valnor mountant. R–196.

ACHROMYCIN: see tetracycline, R–190; Lederle or Cyanamid (A–33).

R–1. ACID ALIZARIN BLUE BB, C.I. No. (1063) 58610: used in the Quad stain (F–124).

ACID FUCHSIN: see fuchsin, acid. R–86.

R–2. ALCIAN BLUE, referred to by Lison (*197*) both as alcian blue 8G and 8GS. Conn *et al.* (*73*) call this alcian blue 8GX, C. I. No. 74240. Gurr (*141*) lists it as alcian blue with no letters following. It is in all instances apparently the same dye because all of these authors say that it was used by Steedman as a histochemical test for mucopolysaccharides (mucin).

R–3. ALIZARIN RED S, C.I. No. (1034) 58005: sodium alizarin sulfonate which stains bone both *in vivo* and *in vitro*.

R–4. ANILINE BLUE, ALCOHOL SOLUBLE, C.I. No. (689) 42775.

R–5. ANILINE BLUE, WATER SOLUBLE: cotton blue, C.I. No. (707) 42755.

R–6. ANILINE OIL: phenylamine: aniline: $C_6H_5NH_2$.

R–7. ARLEX GELATIN MOUNTANT preserves oil red O and hemalum well; made of commercial *d*-sorbitol syrup plus 10% of gelatin and 10 mg of Merthiolate/100 ml.

AUREOMYCIN: see chlortetracycline. R–43.

R–8. AZOCARMINE B, C.I. No. (829) 50090. Conn (73, p. 123) says that Heidenhein used either this or azocarmine G in his azan stain. B must be used in a stronger solution and with the application of more heat (56°C) to bring it into solution.

R–9. AZURE A: $C_{14}H_{14}N_3SCl$.

R–10. AZURE II: azure B, C.I. No. (720) 52010.

R–11. BALSAM, CANADA, a natural resin soluble in xylene; the refractive index is 1.5322. It is, in the writer's opinion, an unsatisfactory mountant. It yellows excessively with age and in time bleaches most stains. It should be supplanted by damar or synthetic resins.

BASIC FUCHSIN: see fuchsin, basic. R–87.

R–12. BAYBERRY WAX: many dealers.

R–13. BEECHWOOD CREOSOTE: a clearing reagent; most dealers.

R–14. BEESWAX: many dealers.

R–15. BENZIDINE: *p,p′*-bianiline: no longer available because it appears to be carcinogenic; use instead, benzidine dihydrochloride. See also R–64.

R–16. BENZIDINE DIHYDROCHLORIDE; $NH_2C_6H_4C_6H_4NH_2$-2 HCl: is often used in formulae which call for benzidine. It serves the same purpose and is less toxic.

R–17. BIOLOID MOUNTANT: a synthetic resin sold as crystals or in xylene or toluene solution; refractive index, in xylene, 1.5396; it tends to fade acid dyes; conserves hematoxylin, basic aniline dyes, and Schiff aldehyde complex; Will Corp. (A–52)

R–18. BORAX: sodium tetraborate: $Na_2B_4O_7 \cdot 10\ H_2O$.

R–19. BRILLIANT CRESYL BLUE, C.I. No. (877) 51010.

R–20. BUTANEDIOL: succinaldehyde: $CHO(CH_2)_2\ CHO$; Celanese Corp. of America. (A–11)

R–21. BUTYL ALCOHOLS: *n,-1-butanol*, $CH_3(CH_2)_2\ CH_2OH$; *tert-2-methyl-2-propanol* $(CH_3)_3\ COH$. Neither the normal nor tertiary butyl alcohol is directly miscible with water; ethanol is necessary for miscibility (see p. 60). The normal butyl alcohol has a less pleasant odor than the tertiary and is slightly less expensive. Eastman's practical grades are satisfactory. (A–15)

R–22. CALCODUR PINK 2BL, C.I. No. (353): benzo fast pink 2 BL: amadine fast rose 2 BL: chlorazol fast pink also appears to be a synonym; this is an azo-textile dye.

CANADA BALSAM: see balsam, Canada. R–11.

R–23. CARBON DIOXIDE, LIQUIFIED GAS: for freezing microtomes; obtainable in iron cylinders containing about 20 lb; sometimes available in 5-lb cylinders; emptied cylinders are exchangeable, so that payments are only for contents; many dealers.

R–24. CARBON DIOXIDE, SOLIDIFIED: dry ice; dealers in ice cream or from locker plants. It may be necessary to order in advance.

R–25. CARBON, FINE PARTICULATE: Peerless Black carbon preparation, particle size 27 mμ; Columbian Carbon Co., Research Laboratories. (A–13)

R–26. CARBOWAX: trade name for polyethylene glycols numbered 200, 300, 400, 600, 1000, 1500, 1540, 4000, 6000; Union Carbide Chemicals Co. (A–49)

R–27. CARMINE, POWDERED, C.I. No. (1239) 75470: used to make a number of stains and is fed, as a harmless dye, to various protozoa and some flat worms.

R–28. CARODIP: a plastic coating for sections mounted on 35-mm film; Carolina Biological Supply Co. (A–10)

R–29. CARYCINEL RED: $C_{19}H_{19}NO_2$; recommended by Lillie (*193*) as a stain for fat.

CEDAR OIL: see oil, cedar. R–145.

R–30. CELESTIN BLUE B, C.I. No. (900) 51010: a nuclear stain.

CELLOIDIN: see collodion. R–53.

R–31. CELLOSOLVE: *2-ethoxyethanol*: glycol monoethyl ether: $C_2H_5OCH_2CH_2OH$.

R–32. CELLULOSE CAPRATE: cellulose trideconate is a xylene-soluble mountant; refractive index of the solution is 1.4860 at 25°C and, of the dry resin, 1.4734. It sets in 30 minutes and preserves most stains well, although cobalt sulfide bleaches quickly. In our laboratory it was found very useful for mounting the sections of young embryos which are notably fragile with most mountants and shatter with careless handling. Heavy pressure applied 24 hours after mounting had no effect on the sections.

R–33. CEMENT, KRÖNIG'S: a mixture of colophony and white beeswax with a low melting point; Will Corp. (A–52)

R–34. CHARCOAL, ACTIVATED: for decolorizing Schiff reagent; 50-200 mesh; Fisher. (A–21)

R–35. CHLORANTINE FAST RED 5B: rouge chlorantine Lumiere 5B, C.I. No. 28160: $C_{36}H_{15}N_6O_{15}S_4Na_4$; Ciba Gessellschaft, Basel, Switzerland; and Gurr. (A–27)

R–36. CHLORANTINE FAST RED 7BL, C.I. No. 278: composition similar to R–35; Geigy Co., New York.

R–37. CHLORAZOL BLACK E, C.I. No. (581) 30235: Darrow (*82*) reports that National Aniline and Chemical Co. produces Erie black GXOO, and that du Pont produces pontamine black E; both seem to be almost identical with this.

R–38. CHLORETONE: *1,1,1-trichloro-2-methyl-2-propanol*: chlorbutol: chlorbutanol.

R–39. CHLOROFORM: for anesthesia, U. S. P. grade.

R–40. CHLOROFORM: for plastic embedding, technical grade.

R–41. CHLOROX: 5.25% of sodium hypochlorite in water; drug and household supply stores.

R–42. CHLORAZOL FAST PINK, C.I. No. (353): a vital dye for cartilage; see R–22.

R–43. CHLORTETRACYCLINE: an antibiotic which stains bone vitally; trade name, Aureomycin; Lederle. (A–33)

R–44. CHROME ALUM: chromium potassium sulfate: $CrK(SO_4)_2 \cdot 12 H_2O$.

R–45. CLARITE: a synthetic resin in toluene solution. This mountant is no longer available. Piccolyte resins are satisfactory substitutes.

R–46. CLEARCOL: a water-soluble quick-drying proprietary mountant; hardens in 1 to 5 hours; preserves fat stains well but crystal violet, staining amyloid, bleeds badly. Specimens may be mounted in it directly from alcohol. Refractive index, 1.4039; pH 1.5; H. Willard Clark. (A–12)

R–47. CLEARMOUNT: a proprietary mountant miscible with xylene, benzene, toluene, absolute alcohol, dioxane, and other solvents; neutral and said not to cause fading of stains; refractive index, 1.515. Edward Gurr, Ltd. (A–27)

R–48. CMC–10: Turtox mountant, aqueous; is especially useful for mounting small arthropods or portions of larger ones (fleas; ticks; mosquito larvae, pupae and adults). (F–61)

R–49. C.M.E. TISSUE SUPPORT RESIN: a plastic embedding medium useful in sectioning tissue containing undecalcified hard parts; Emaress Scientific Educational Arts and Crafts. (A–20)

R–50. COCCINEL RED: $C_{24}H_{30}N_2O_2$; recommended by Lillie (*193*) as a stain for fat.

R–51. COCHINEAL, C.I. No. (1239) 75470.

R–52. COLCHICINE: $C_{22}H_{25}NO_6$; an alkaloid poisonous in doses greater than 0.00066–0.0032 g; used in medicine and in histological technic; marketed under various proprietary names such as Colcemid-Ciba.

R–53. COLLODION: a cellulose tetranitrate; available under several names such as celloidin and Parlodion.
COLOPHONIUM: see rosin. R–175.

R–54. COLOR IN OIL: Prussian blue; paint supply dealers.

R–55. CONGO RED, C.I. No. (370) 22120.
CORROSIVE SUBLIMATE; see mercuric chloride, R–120.
COTTON BLUE: see aniline blue WS, R–5.

R–56. CRESYL VIOLET ACETATE: cresyl fast violet: cresyl violet: $C_{18}H_{15}N_3O_3$ is used by Klüver and Barrera as a neuron cell body stain; it is excellent for Nissl substance.

R–57. CRISTALITE: refractive index 1.515; a synthetic mountant with most of the properties of Clearmount; it dries more rapidly and is not miscible with alcohol; Gurr. (A–27)

R–58. DAMAR, sometimes spelled dammar: a natural resin superior to balsam; xylene-soluble up to 70%. Refractive index, 1.5317; tends to fade basic aniline dyes.

R–59. DARROW RED: $C_{18}H_{14}N_3O_2Cl$.

R–60. DECAL: a commercial decalcifying agent; Scientific Products. (A–44)
DEMINERALIZED WATER: see water, demineralized. R–199.

R–61. DENTISTS' STICKY WAX, provided in boxes of 12 sticks for about 85 cents. One box will seal a very large number of slides. Conger (*69*) recommends it for temporary preparations because it is solid at room temperature, flows on well when molten, adheres, and does not leak when under refrigeration. It cracks off cleanly when frozen with dry ice or liquid air. Kerr Manu-facturing Co., Detroit 18, Mich.

R-62. DETEC: Schain's Frozen Section Clarifier; Merck and Co., West Point. Pa.; most drug wholesalers and laboratory chemical distributors. (The composition of this product is not available.)

R-63. DEXTRIN: Will Corp. (A-52)

R-64. *o*-DIANISIDINE: 3,3'-dimethoxybenzidene: $CH_3O(NH_2)$ $C_6H_3C_6H_3(NH_2)OCH_3$; sometimes used in place of benzidine.

R-65. DIAPHANE: a semi-synthetic resinous proprietary mountant; specimens are mounted in it from 95% alcohol; refractive index, 1.5485; fair for basic aniline dyes; moderate fading of acid fuchsin and azure in eosin-azure; Will Corp. (A-52)

R-66. DIETHYL PHTHALATE: ethyl phthalate: $(COOC_2H_5)_2$; used for clearing whole specimens; Eastman Organic Chemicals. (A-15)

R-67. DIMEDONE: $(CH_3)_2$ $C \cdot CH_2 \cdot CO \cdot CH_2 \cdot CO \cdot CH_2$: British Drug Houses, Ltd. (A-7)

R-68. DIOXANE: *p*-dioxane: diethylene dioxide: $OCH_2CH_2OCH_2CH_2$; practical or technical grade, satisfactory; Carbide and Carbon Chemicals Corp. (A-9) and Eastman Kodak Co. (A-15); both supply a good grade.

R-69. DOW'S POLYETHYLENE GLYCOLS of numbers E200, E300, E400, E600, E1000, E500M, E1450, E4000 are water waxes used in infiltrating tissues. The higher numbers are most useful as water waxes (93); Dow Chemical Co. (A-16)

R-70. D.P.X.: a proprietary mountant; British Drug Houses, Ltd. (A-7) DRY ICE: see carbon dioxide, solidified. R-24.

R-71. ELVANOL: polyvinyl alcohol; Elvanol is a du Pont trade name. (A-17)

R-72. EOSIN Y, C.I. No. (768) 45380.

R-73. EPOXY RESIN: an extremely strong adhesive; usually furnished in two stock solutions which are combined, in specified quantities, just before use; hardware stores, hobby shops, variety stores, and numerous other places.

R-74. *ETHANEDIAL*: glyoxal: CHOCHO.

R-75. *ETHANOL*: ethyl (grain) alcohol: CH_3CH_2OH; usually purchased by educational institutions from distillers without payment of tax if the institution has been granted permission for such purchases by the Office of Internal Revenue. It is sold either at a concentration of about 96% or as absolute alcohol. The latter term is misleading since absolute alcohol is not entirely water free.

ETHER: see ethyl ether R-78.

R-76. ETHER: for use in plastic embedding; purified anhydrous grade is satisfactory.

R-77. ETHYL CHLORIDE: $CH_3 \cdot CH_2Cl$; for use in VI-7; purchase in a spray-type container is recommended.

R–78. ETHYL ETHER: *ethoxyethane:* diethyl ether: ether: sulfuric ether: $C_2H_5OC_2H_5$; C.P. grade should be used for anesthesia and as a nitrocellulose solvent.

R–79. ETHYL METHACRYLATE: Plexiglas: methacrylic acid: ethyl ester: $CH_2:C(CH_3)COOC_2H_5$; a plastic which may be used, with precautions, for embedding specimens.

R–80. ETHYL PHOSPHATE: triethyl phosphate: $(C_2H_5)_3PO_4$; a useful dehydrator; practical grade from a good source such as Eastman is satisfactory for histological work.

R–81. ETHYL PHTHALATE: C_6H_4-1,2-$(COOC_2H_5)_2$; Fisher. (A–21) ETHYLENE DIAMINE TETRACETIC ACID: EDTA; see Sequestrene and Versene, R–179 and R–197.

R–82. EUPARAL: a mixture of natural and synthetic resins in which material is mounted from alcohol; refractive index, 1.4776. It is ªvailable in natural yellow color for aniline dyes and green for hematoxylin; (A–22) and most dealers. This is a proprietary product; Flatters and Garnett Ltd.

R–83. FAST BLUE BB: fast blue BBN: diazo fast blue BB, C.I. No. 37175.

R–84. FAST GREEN FCF C.I. No. 42053: Conn et al. describe it as "closely related to light green SF yellowish . . . gives staining effects very much like light green and is considerably less subject to fading. . . . This dye is therefore to be recommended for such use as it has all the advantages of light green without the disadvantages." (73, p. 134)

R–85. FORMALIN: a saturated solution of the gas formaldehyde (HCHO) in water; often called strong formalin; about 40% by volume or or 37% by weight. Either the grade U.S.P. or A.C.S. is satisfactory for histological work. For dilutions, the saturated solution is considered to be 100%. Thus a 10% solution contains 10 ml of strong formalin and 90 ml of water. Formalin solutions are generally slightly acid. For most purposes this is either desirable or not harmful. When neutral formalin is necessary, Cowdry (77) recommends obtaining it by distillation. Lillie (193) prefers a soluble buffer. He adds 4 g monohydrated acid sodium phosphate, $NaH_2PO_4 \cdot H_2O$ and 6.5 g anhydrous disodium phosphate, $Na_2HPO_4/1000$ ml of 10% formalin.

R–86. FUCHSIN, ACID, C.I. No. (692) 42685 is used in van Gieson's stain and Mallory's connective tissue stain. Certification is especially important to insure permanent preparations.

R–87. FUCHSIN, BASIC, C.I. No. (677) 42510 should always be Commission Certified. The label on the container should state that it is for use in histology and cytology.

R–88. GELATIN: for most histological purposes, the gelatin sold for bacteriological technics is suitable. A good quality of gelatin sold for culinary purposes may also serve.

R–89. GELATIN, CALFSKIN: Eastman Organic Chemicals, Distillation Products Industries. (A–15)

R–90. GIEMSA STAIN: useful for both smears and sections; dry powder may be prepared in the laboratory (73, p. 255), but it is satisfactory to use the dye put out by various manufacturers. It is also possible to buy excellent stock solutions of this dye.

R–91. GLYOXAL: *ethanedial:* CHOCHO.

R–92. GOLD CHLORIDE, brown and yellow; most dealers. Gold chloride of commerce is ordinarily the yellow crystalline compound. The brown crystals sometimes sold are probably contaminated with metallic gold. For toning purposes either grade is probably satisfactory. The authors (339) of the method described in IX–14 recommend the brown crystals since they found that they stain muscle fibers less densely than the yellow crystals.

R–93. GUM ACACIA: gum arabic. This gum dissolves slowly in water, requiring about 24 hours and frequent stirring.

R–94. GUM SYRUP, ÁPATHY, MODIFICATION OF LILLIE AND ASHBURN. (F–22)

R–95. HARLECO EMBEDDING MEDIUM: H.E.M., is a water wax said by the manufacturer to have physical characteristics similar to those of Carbowax; m.p. 54°C; Hartman-Leddon Co. (A–28)

R–96. HARLECO SYNTHETIC RESIN: H.S.R.; one of the piccolyte resins; available in dry crystals or 60% solutions in xylene and toluene; refractive index, 1.5390; preserves most stains well; Hartman-Leddon Co. (A–28)

R–97. HEMATEIN, is derived by oxidation from hematoxylin and is commercially available in dry form.

R–98. HEMATOXYLIN, C.I. No. (1246) 75290 is a natural dye extracted from logwood; possibly more widely used than any other biological stain; it is used with a mordant which is either a constituent of the staining solution or applied before the staining solution is used.

R–99. HEPARIN: an anticoagulant; several dealers.

R–100. HEXAMINE: hexamethylenetetramine: methanamine: $(CH_2)_6N_4$. HIGGINS' INK: a colloidal suspension of carbon; a waterproof black drawing ink and useful as a non-toxic vital dye. See India ink R–106.

R–101. HISTOWAX: a mixture of paraffin and adjuvants in four melting point ranges; used for infiltration; Matheson, Coleman, and Bell. (A–36)

H.S.R. see Harleco Synthetic Resin. R–96.

R–102. HYDROGEN PEROXIDE as sold in drug and variety stores is a 3% aq sol. A 30% solution, sometimes called Superoxol, is sold by vendors of reagents. It is a strong oxidant and should be used with care.

R–103. HYDROWAX: a polyethylene glycol wax; T. Gerrard and Company, Ltd. (A–26)

R–104. HYPO: sodium thiosulfate: $NA_2S_2O_3 \cdot 5\ H_2O$.

R–105. HYRAX: a proprietary neutral synthetic resin, xylene soluble; most commonly used for diatoms but sometimes useful for unstained parasites; refractive index high: 1.822.

R–106. INDIA INK as a source of carbon for vital staining may be prepared by buying a cake of the solid form and rubbing it up in a small dish with normal saline until the mixture is sufficiently dark. A simpler method is to use Higgins' waterproof black drawing ink diluted with water, 1:1. Both kinds of ink may be obtained from dealers in art supplies. They are frequently sold in college book stores.

R–107. ISOPROPYL ALCOHOL: *isopropanol:* 2-propanol: $CH_3CHOHCH_3$; can usually be substituted for ethyl alcohol for dehydration preparatory to paraffin infiltration. It may be obtained 99% pure. Its use in staining procedures must depend on the solubilities of the stains used. For the washing and storing of slides the grade sold as rubbing alcohol is very inexpensive and satisfactory and may usually be purchased in pint bottles at chain grocery stores and drug stores.

R–108. JANUS GREEN B, C.I. No. 11050: used *intravitam* for staining mitochondria.

R–109. KINGSLEY'S BLOOD STAINS, STOCK SOLUTIONS: Hartman-Leddon Co. (A–28)

R–110. LATEX, for injection, is water soluble and colored red, yellow, or blue. Directions for use accompany each shipment; most supply houses.

R–111. LEMON JUICE, COMMERCIAL, for the method of Zinn and Morin (IX–14) is single strength reconstituted lemon juice, trade name Tempo, made by Henry Thayer Co., Cambridge 39, Mass. The preservatives used are sulfur dioxide and 0.1% sodium benzoate. It is possible that other brands would also be satisfactory.

R–112. LIGHT GREEN SF YELLOWISH, C.I. No. (670) 42095; a good plasma stain but fades badly if exposed to bright light; may be replaced by fast green FCF which gives similar results and is less subject to fading.

R–113. LUXOL, a trade name of the du Pont company (A–17), refers to several solvent blue dyes. Solvent, in this connection, means that the dyes are soluble in a variety of organic solvents. The Luxol dyes are unusual in being soluble in alcohol and in nitrogen-containing organic solvents such as pyridine.

R–114. LUXOL FAST BLUE ARN: du Pont C.I. Solvent blue 37; said by Salthouse (278) to have greater affinity for myelin than Luxol fast blue MBSN.

R–115. LUXOL FAST BLUE MBS: du Pont C.I. Solvent blue 38 was the dye first used by Klüver and Barrera to stain the myelin sheath. It is an alcohol-soluble amine salt of sulfonated copper phthalocyanine; no longer obtainable and was replaced by Luxol fast blue MBSN which has similar properties.

R–116. LUXOL FAST BLUE MBSN: Solvent blue 38, du Pont. See R–115.

R–117. LVN: low viscosity nitrocellulose.

R–118. LVN, R.S. ½ second: obtained from Hercules Powder Co. (A–29). It is dangerous to handle because of its inflammability and possible explosive capacity. It is shipped moistened with 30% /wt. of denatured absolute ethanol. Solutions such as those supplied by Randolph Products Co., Inc., Carlstad, N.J. are recommended to inexperienced workers.

R–119. MACNEAL'S TETRACHROME STAIN for blood may be bought as a dry stain and as a solution; Will Corp. (A–52)

R–120. MERCURIC CHLORIDE: $HgCl_2$ is very poisonous. Remove the reagent from one container to another with a glass or horn spoon, not a metal instrument.

R–121. *METHANOL:* methyl alcohol: carbinol: wood alcohol: CH_3OH; a suitable substitute for ethanol in tissue dehydration; also useful in dehydrating stained sections unless the dyes used are particularly soluble in it. If a good grade is used, it has a pleasant odor. It may be obtained almost free of water.

METHOCEL: see methyl cellulose. R–123.

R–122. METHYL BLUE, C.I. No. (706) 42780: a widely used dye for histological preparations.

R–123. METHYL CELLULOSE: sold by some dealers as Methocel; from most supply houses as a dry powder or in aqueous solution.

R–124. METHYL GREEN, C.I. No. (684) 42585.

R–125. METHYL METHACRYLATE: methacrylic acid, methyl ester: $CH_2:C(CH_3)$ $COOCH_3$; used for plastic embedding but the technic is more difficult than for Selectron resin; may be purchased as a powder, as a fluid containing an inhibitor, and in sheets which are used for construction of equipment. A trade name is Lucite.

R–126. METHYL SALICYLATE: synthetic oil of wintergreen; a useful clearing agent for whole preparations.

R–127. METHYL VIOLET 2B, C.I. No. (680) 42535.

R–128. METHYLENE AZURE A, C.I. No. (923) 52010.

R–129. METHYLENE BLUE, C.I. No. (922) 52015. Methylene blue chloride is the grade usually used for biological work. Conn *et al.* (73) state that it is used for a greater variety of purposes than any other biological stain with the possible exception of hematoxylin.

R–130. METHYLENE BLUE, POLYCHROME, Terry's formula; Steri-Kem Products. (A–46)

R–131. METHYLENE VIOLET, BERNTHSEN: $C_{14}H_{12}N_2OS$; this is an expensive dye used in MacNeal's tetrachrome stain.

R–132. MICHROME WATER WAX sets at 54°C to form translucent blocks which show no evidences of crystallization except at low temperatures; made by Gurr. (A–27)

R–133. MOLD RELEASE COMPOUND for plastic embedding; most supply houses. Kerosene is less expensive and works well if the inside of the mold is rubbed with it.

MOUNTANTS: see index.

R–134. NAPHTHOL AS PHOSPHATE: from Dajac Laboratories; see R–136.

R–135. NAPHTHOL BLUE BLACK: pontacyl blue-black SX, C.I. No. (246) 20470.

R–136. NEOTETRAZOLIUM CHLORIDE: blue tetrazolium; Dajac Laboratories, 5000 Langdon St., Philadelphia, Pa.

R–137. NEUTRAL RED, C.I. No. (825) 50040.

R–138. NEW FUCHSIN, C.I. No. (678) 42520.

R–139. NEW METHYLENE BLUE N, C.I. No. (927) 52030.

R–140. NIGROSIN, WATER SOLUBLE, C.I. No. (865) 50420.

R–141. NILE BLUE SULFATE, C.I. No. (913) 51180: used as a vital and supravital dye and as a fat stain.

R–142. NITROCELLULOSE: a general term for cellulose nitrates which are formed by the action of a mixture of nitric and sulfuric acids on cellulose. The cellulose can be nitrated to a varying extent with 2–6 nitrate groups/molecule; nitrocelluloses with low nitrogen content, up to tetranitrate, are not explosive; a nitrocellulose with a high nitrogen content is gun cotton. Low-viscosity nitrocellulose, LVN, is the type often used in microtechnic and the most common mixture used is LVN R.S. ½ second. The other type of commonly used nitrocellulose is referred to as celloidin, collodion, or Parlodion; the last is a trade name.

R–143. NONEX 63 B: a water wax described as polyethylene 1000 monostearate; Gemec Chemicals Co. (A–23)

R–144. OIL BLUE N or NA: recommended by Lillie (*193*) as a stain for fat.

R–145. OIL, CEDAR or cedar wood, technical grade, is a histological clearing agent; sometimes used as a mountant for Giemsa preparations. Lillie (*193*) says that for this purpose it is usually concentrated by heating until it has a refractive index of 1.5262 and solidifies at room temperature.

R–146. OIL ORIGANUM, Cretici: sometimes used in clearing whole specimens and sections.

R–147. OIL RED 4B. Conn *et al.* (*73*) call this a dye of uncertain composition. Lillie (*193*) recommends it as a stain for fat; he uses it as a supersaturated solution in isopropanol.

R–148. OIL RED O, C.I. No. 26125.

OIL OF WINTERGREEN: see methyl salicylate. R–126.

R–149. OILS, IMMERSION. There are several synthetic brands such as Crown, Cargille and Mersol of correct refractive index. When selecting an oil, the viscosity should be considered, since a type with high viscosity is best for an inclined stage.

R–150. ORANGE G, C.I. No. (27) 16230.

R–151. ORCEIN, C.I. No. (1242): may be extracted from a lichen or may be a synthetic product. The natural product is preferred by various workers for aceto-orcein stain-fixatives; for staining elastic tissue the synthetic product is probably better.

R–152. ORCINOL: *5-methyl-1,3-benzenediol:* $CH_3C_6H_3(OH)_2$.

R–153. OSMIC ACID: osmium tetroxide: OsO_4. The reagent is highly volatile and fumes are toxic; it should be handled with care. (F–160)

R–154. OXYTETRACYCLINE: an antibiotic which stains bone vitally; trade name, Terramycin; Pfizer. (A–39)

R–155. PARAFFIN FOR INFILTRATION, COMMERCIAL. Supply houses usually sell pure paraffin and paraffin with various adjuvants. The latter type is most often used and is satisfactory. Most firms market their wax mixtures under a trade name; one well known is Tissuemat. Turtox sells mixtures with the additions specified; these are slightly less expensive and are equally satisfactory. Most paraffin is available in various melting points. The type of preparation to be made and the temperature of the laboratory should both be considered in ordering. Recipes for making several mixtures will be found in the formula section.

R–156. PARALDEHYDE: $OCH(CH_3)OCH(CH_3)OCHCH_3$; Will Corp. (A–52)

R–157. PARLODION: trade name for nitrocellulose of the form often called celloidin or collodion.

R–158. PAROWAX: a domestic paraffin, sold by dealers in household supplies.

R–159. PERMOUNT: a proprietary synthetic naphthalene polymer dissolved in toluene; conserves aniline dyes and hematoxylin well; Fisher Scientific Co. (A–21)

R–160. PHENOLFORMALDEHYDE, black: a synthetic resin; Union Carbon and Carbide Co. (A–49)

R–161. PHLOXINE B, C.I. No. (778) 45410.

R–162. PHOSPHOMOLYBDIC ACID: often used, in weak solution, for stain differentiation.

R–163. PHOSPHOTUNGSTIC ACID is used much like phosphomolybdic acid.

R–164. PICCOLYTE RESIN: a beta-pinene polymer obtainable under this name as a dry resin from Turtox. Other piccolyte resin mountants are Harleco Synthetic Resin, H.S.R.; Permount; Kleermount, British Drug Houses, Ltd. (A–7)

R–165. PINACYANOL, C.I. No. 808: Eastman Kodak Co. (A–15)
PLEXIGLAS: see ethyl methacrylate. R–79.

R–166. PLEXIGLAS MOLDING POWDER: Rohm and Hass Co. (A–43)

R–167. POLYETHYLENE GLYCOL 1000 M.E. has an average molecular weight of about 1000; water soluble and used for infiltration of tissues; Gemec Chemicals Co. (A–23)

R–168. POLYETHYLENE GLYCOL DISTEARATE MW 1540: Kessler Chemical Co., Inc. (A–31)

POLYGLYCOLS, DOW: see Dow's polyethylene glycols. R–69.

R–169. POLYOTIC CYANAMID: A veterinary grade of tetracycline available from Cyanamid (A–33) at lower cost than that of other grades. It may be made up, buffered with NaHCO, a short time before use and kept refrigerated.

R–170. POLYVINYL ALCOHOL: PVA: Elvanol, du Pont (A–17): a synthetic polymer of vinyl alcohol, obtained as a light white powder of amorphous material; insoluble in ordinary fat solvents; water soluble; when dried, leaves a transparent, tough thin film that adheres closely to clean surfaces; resistant to dampness, water (except with long immersion), alcohol, xylene, and other solvents.

R–171. PONTACYL BLUE-BLACK SX: naphthol blue-black, C.I. No. (246) 20470.

R–172. PROTARGOL, as originally used by Bodian, is usually called silver proteinate. His material was obtained from Winthrop Chemical Co. It was unobtainable for a time but may now be purchased as Protargol-S from Winthrop Laboratories (A–53). A similar product used by Humason (*156*, p. 203) is available from Roboz Surgical Instrument Co. (A–42), which distributes Chroma (Grübler) products in this country. It is called silver protein for Bodian staining, Catalog No. 30960.

R–173. PVP–VA, E–735: vinylpyrrolidone: vinyl acetate copolymer E–735; an aqueous permanent mountant, setting in 30 minutes, which preserves the following stains well: oil red O for fat, hematoxylin (chromalum and Mayer's), PAS, aldehyde-fuchsin, alcian blue, celestin blue, azure A, methylene blue, toluidine blue, and the colored salts of various microchemical reactions. It leaches eosin at once. It is recommended as a substitute for glycerol-gelatin, when a suitable stain is used or for unstained specimens. Antara Chemical Co. (A–3)

R–174. RESORCIN-FUCHSIN: a good reagent for staining elastic tissue; Chroma. (A–42)

R–175. ROSIN: colophonium: colophony: the hard resin left after distilling off the volatile oil of turpentine.

R–176. RUBBER, CRUDE: available in thin sheets, smoked or unsmoked.

R–177. SAFRANIN O, C.I. No. (841) 50240.

R–178. SELECTRON, PLASTIC MONOMER is sold under a variety of names by different supply houses: from Ward's (A–51), it is Bio-Plastic; from Turtox (A–48), it is Turtox Embedding Plastic. There seems to be no difference in the products from different companies.

R–179. SEQUESTRENE: a chelating agent, useful in decalcification; it is a trade name for ethylene tetracetic acid, disodium salt, often called ETDA; Alrose Chemical Co. (A–1). See also Versene R–197.

R–180. SODIUM AMYTAL, Lilly, a proprietary anesthetic agent.

R–181. SODIUM HYPOCHLORITE is sold by some of the supply companies in 4-6% solution. It is cheaper and, for many purposes, as satisfactory to buy Chlorox, q.v.

R–182. SODIUM THIOSULFATE: $Na_2S_2O_3 \cdot 5\ H_2O$: hypo.

R–183. SPERMACETI WAX, Will Corp. (A–52)

R–184. STEARIC ACID, Will Corp. (A–52)

R–185. SUDAN BLACK B, C.I. No. 26150: used as a fat stain.

R–186. SUDAN BROWN, C.I. No. (81) 12020: used as a fat stain.

SUPEROXOL: see hydrogen peroxide, R–102.

R–187. TERGITOL 7: a wetting agent useful in a number of histological processes; Union Carbide Corp. (A–49)

R–188. TERPINEOL: $C_{10}H_{17}OH$; sometimes called synthetic oil of lilac; used in clearing.

TERRAMYCIN: see oxytetracycline. R–154.

R–189. TERTIARY BUTYL HYDROPEROXIDE, and other catalyzers for plastic embedding; Cadel Chemical Co. (A–8)

R–190: TETRACYCLINE: Achromycin: an antibiotic which is also a vital stain for bone. Polyotic is the trade name of the veterinary grade of tetracycline. (A–33)

R–191. THIONYL CHLORIDE: Will Corp. (A–52)

R–192. TOLUIDINE BLUE, C.I. No. (925) 52040: a useful stain for cartilage *in vitro*.

TRIETHYL PHOSPHATE: see ethyl phosphate. R–80.

R–193. TRIS: (hydroxymethyl) aminomethane; Fisher. (A–21)

R–194. TRYPAN BLUE, C.I. No. (477) 23850: a vital dye which stains many types of phagocytic cells and elastic membranes in some locations.

R–195. TWEEN 40: a polyoxyalkylene derivative of sorbitan monopalmitate; a surface active agent, and

TWEEN 80: a polyoxyalkylene derivative of sorbitan monooleate; Atlas Powder Co. (A–4)

R–196. VALNOR MOUNTANT, type ABP: a supersaturated solution of a borophosphate completely soluble in water. It conserves the staining of amyloid with crystal violet, and the staining of chromosomes with aceto-orcein and Giemsa; it fades hematoxylin; refractive index, 1.4241. Sold in 1-lb bottles by the manufacturer; Valnor Corp. (A–50)

R–197. VERSENE: a chelating agent, useful in decalcification; a trade name for ethylene tetracetic acid, disodium salt; often called ETDA; Bersworth Chemical Co. (A–6). See also Sequestrene. R–179.

R–198. VINYL ACETATE is usually sold as a 12% solution in acetone, colored red, yellow, or blue. It is not suitable for use in prepar-

ing animals for dissection because it becomes brittle when it
sets. It is excellent for making corrosion preparations; several
supply houses such as Ward's (A–51) and Turtox (A–48).
Ward's service bulletin No. 5 (1950) accompanies their ship-
ments (325).

R–199. WATER DEMINERALIZED, is an alternative to distilled water. It
is particularly useful where laboratories are not equipped with
stills. Tap water is passed through columns of ion-exchange
resins. The replaceable cartridges are of several kinds, one of
which produces water comparable to single distilled water and
another to triple distilled. Fisher Scientific Co. (A–21) markets
several types of demineralizers.

R–200. WATER WAXES: some of the well-known brands are Carbowax,
Dow's polethylene glycols, H.E.M. (Harleco Embedding Medium), Hydrowax, and Michrome Water Wax, q.v.

R–201. WRIGHT'S STAIN, DRY: most dealers.

R–202. XAM, GURR (A–27): maleic polymer with plasticizer; soluble in
xylene; sets in 2 days; requires weeks for drying; refractive index, 1.5401; preservation of hematoxylin stains is good; of cobalt
sulfide excellent; of methanamine silver, good; of Schiff's aldehyde stains, good; that of other aniline dyes, inferior; Prussian
blue completely bleached in 3 months.

R–203. XYLENE-RESIN, as used in directions in this book refers to synthetic resins, preferably piccolyte resins, or gum damar. It does
not mean balsam.

FORMULAE

In using these formulae, note certain points. For most solutions, a gram is roughly equated with a milliliter; a 1% solution of a dye is made with a gram of dye powder/100 ml of the solvent, and the dye need not be weighed on a precise chemical balance. But when the amount of a reagent is given in milligrams careful weighing on a good balance is essential. Water *always* means distilled water; if tap water is to be used it is specified. Unless otherwise noted, a reagent is to be used full strength; acetic acid means glacial acetic; however, ethanol is 95 or 96% unless absolute is specified. All bottles of solutions should be labeled with the correct name, date of making, and initials of the preparator.

ABOPON. See Valnor mountant, F–190.

F–1. ACETO-CARMINE, Belling (27)

acetic acid	45 ml
water	55 ml
powdered carmine, to excess	
ferric hydrate solution, trace	

Boil the carmine in the water and acetic acid; filter. This is the stock solution.

Working solution: Add to stock the ferric hydrate until a precipitate is imminent, then dilute with an equal quantity of stock solution.

F–2. ACETO-ORCEIN, LA COUR (181)

orcein	1 g
acetic acid, at 100°C	45 ml
water	55 ml

Dissolve the stain in the boiling acid, add the water, cool, and filter.

F–3. ACETIC-ORCEIN, TJIO AND WHANG (312)

Use F–2 formula, substituting 2 g orcein for 1 g.

F–4. ACETIC-ORCEIN-HYDROCHLORIC ACID MIXTURE (XII–5)

acetic-orcein (F–3)	9 parts
1N hydrochloric acid	1 part

F–5. ACID-ALCOHOL

ethanol, 70%	100 ml
hydrochloric acid	1 ml

F-6. AGAR, SALT, FOR NEMATODE CULTURE (XVII-19)

water	200 ml
sodium chloride	1 g
agar	3 g

Boil together until agar melts; pour into sterile petri dishes.

F-7. ALBUMEN, MAYER'S

To the white of one egg, add an equal quantity of glycerol and a small crystal of thymol. Mix in a Waring Blendor until full of foam, or beat well with an egg beater. Place the resulting mass in a cylindrical jar. When the foam has become much reduced pour the clear liquid below it into dispensing bottles and store in the refrigerator. There is no need to filter since the particulate matter is contained in the foam.

F-8. ALCIAN BLUE SOLUTION (197)

alcian blue 8G (Gurr), 1% aq sol	50 ml
acetic acid, 1%	50 ml
thymol	10–20 mg

Mix stain and acetic acid, filter, and add thymol.

F-9. ALCOHOL-ACETIC FIXATIVE

| alcohol, absolute or 95% | 3 parts |
| acetic acid | 1 part |

This is a general purpose fixative.

F-10. ALCOHOL DILUTION (142, p. 6). It is not economical to make dilute solutions from absolute alcohol. The 95% grade is satisfactory if used in the following way: subtract the percentage required from the percentage of alcohol to be dih-ted; the result is the proportion of water which must be added. For example, if 35% alcohol is required, subtract 35 from 95; thus 60 ml of water and 35 ml of 95% alcohol will produce a 35% solution. An easy way to use this method is to put 35 ml of 95% alcohol in a graduate and add water to the 95-ml mark.

F-11. ALDEHYDE FUCHSIN, GOMORI (127)

basic fuchsin, C. C.	0.5 g
ethanol, 70%	100.0 ml
paraldehyde, U. S. P.	1.0 ml
hydrochloric acid	1.0 ml

Mix dye in alcohol; add acid and paraldehyde. It should become deep violet in about 24 hours; it is then ready for use. Store in refrigerator; it does not keep well.

F-12. ALDEHYDE FUCHSIN, GABE'S MODIFICATION OF GOMORI'S (116)

Stock:

basic fuchsin	1 g
water, boiling	200 ml
hydrochloric acid	2 ml
paraldehyde	2 ml
ethanol, 70%	q.s.

Dissolve the dye in the boiling water, boil for about 1 minute, cool, and filter. Add the acid and the paraldehyde to the filtrate; leave in a stoppered flask at room temperature. At intervals test the solution by placing a drop on filter paper. The color gradually becomes lighter and the precipitate increases in quantity. When the deep red color of the basic fuchsin is gone, usually in about 4 days, filter and discard the filtrate. Dry the precipitate on the filter paper. Make a saturated solution of the precipitate in 70% alcohol. This stock solution will keep, at laboratory temperatures, for at least a year.

Staining solution:

stock	25 ml
ethanol, 70%	75 ml
acetic acid	1 ml

F–13. ALUM COCHINEAL

powdered cochineal	12 g
potassium alum	12 g
water	160 ml

Dissolve the alum in the water and boil the cochineal in the mixture for 20 minutes. Decant the clear supernatant, add water to the cochineal, and boil again. Decant and add to the first liquid, filter, and evaporate to 160 ml. Add a crystal of thymol to prevent the growth of molds.

F–14. ALUM HEMATOXYLIN, DELAFIELD'S

hematoxylin	4 g
ethanol, 95%	25 ml
ammonium alum, sat aq sol	400 ml
glycerol	10 ml
methanol	100 ml

Dissolve hematoxylin crystals in ethanol. Add the mixture to the ammonium alum solution and leave uncovered 3–4 days to ripen. (If quicker ripening is desired, add a small quantity of hydrogen peroxide.) When ripened, add the glycerol and methanol. The stain keeps indefinitely. It is usually better to dilute it with one or two parts of a saturated solution of ammonium alum.

F–15. ALUM HEMATOXYLIN, EHRLICH TYPE (*142*, p. 250)

Stock solution:

hematoxylin	2 g
ethanol, absolute	20 ml
ethanol, 45%	80 ml
acetic acid	10 ml
glycerol	100 ml
potassium alum	10 g

Dissolve the hematoxylin in the absolute ethanol and add the other ingredients. Ripen for about 6 weeks with occasional shaking.

Working solution (stable 6 months):

stock solution	10 ml
acetic acid, 45%	30 ml

F-16. ALUM HEMATOXYLIN, HARRIS' (*142*, p. 8)

hematoxylin	1.0 g
ethanol, 95%	10.0 ml
ammonium or potassium alum	20.0 g
water, heated	200.0 ml
mercuric oxide, red	0.5 g
acetic acid	8.0 ml

Dissolve the hematoxylin in alcohol with the aid of gentle heat. Dissolve the alum in water by heating. Mix the two solutions; bring to a boil and add mercuric oxide. As soon as the mixture becomes dark purple, cool by placing the container in cold water. When cool, add acetic acid. The solution may be reused. If it becomes too strong as it ages, dilute with water.

F-17. ALUM HEMATOXYLIN, MAYER'S (*269*, p. 155)

hematoxylin	1.0 g
water	1000.0 ml
sodium iodate	0.2 g
ammonium or potassium alum	50.0 g
citric acid	1.0 g
chloral hydrate	50.0 g

Dissolve hematoxylin in water, with gentle heat if necessary; add the sodium iodate and the alum. When the latter two ingredients are in solution, add the citric acid and the chloral hydrate.

F-18. ALUM HEMATOXYLIN, MAYER'S HEMALUM, KORN-
HAUSER'S MODIFICATION (*178*)

hematein	0.1 g
ethanol, 95%	5.0 ml
potassium alum, 5% aq sol	100.0 ml

Grind the hematein in a glass mortar with the alcohol. Add the potassium alum solution and mix well. Filter after 24 hours.

F-19. AMNIOTIC FLUID

Withdraw the fluid by sterile syringe from an intact amnion and dispense in sterile bottles. Store under refrigeration.

F-20. ANILINE FUCHSIN, ALTMANN'S (XII-13)

acid fuchsin	20 g
aniline oil	4 ml
water	100 ml

Mix aniline oil and water together, shake, and filter. Add the dye to the filtrate and mix thoroughly. After 24 hours, filter. Keeps for about 1 month.

F-21. ANILINE WATER (*142*, p. 241)

aniline oil	4 ml
water	90 ml

Shake together and filter through a wet filter. If a weak alcoholic solution is desired, add 20 ml of 95% alcohol.

F–22. APÁTHY'S GUM SYRUP, the modification of Lillie and Ashburn (*194*)

gum acacia (gum arabic)	50 g
cane sugar	50 g
water	100 ml
Merthiolate	15 mg, or
thymol	100 mg

Dissolve the gum and the sugar in the water at 55–60°C, with frequent shaking. Restore volume with water. Add either the Merthiolate or thymol as a preservative. Refractive index, 1.4170.

F–23. AQUEOUS HUMOR

Withdraw in a sterile syringe from the anterior chamber of the eye and store in a sterile container. Large animals are the best sources of this fluid.

F–24. AZURE A (XII–8)

azure A	0.25 g
water	100.0 ml
thionyl chloride	

Just before use, add 2 or 3 drops of the thionyl chloride to 10-12 ml of the dye solution. Store the solution of azure A in a stock bottle and the thionyl chloride in a glass-stoppered bottle sealed with paraffin. Use a rubber bulb pipet for delivering the thionyl chloride; the tip is drawn out to give the smallest drops possible by gravity. Rinse the pipet well after each use to prevent corrosion of the bulb by the thionyl.

F–25. AZURE-METHYLENE BLUE (VII–4)

A.	azure II or azure B, C.C.	1 g
	water	100 ml
B.	methylene blue chloride (R-129)	1 g
	borax	1 g
	water	100 ml

Mix equal volumes of A and B and filter just prior to use.

F–26. BAKER'S CALCIUM-CADMIUM-FORMALIN (*15*)

formalin, 10%	98 ml
calcium chloride	1 g
cadmium chloride	1 g

Both F–26 and F–27 may be used for fixation and storage of tissues containing phospholipids.

F–27. BAKER'S CALCIUM-FORMALIN (*15*)

formalin, 10%	99 ml
calcium chloride	1 g

F–28. BECKER AND ROUDABUSH'S FIXATIVE for cestodes (*24*)

ethanol, 95%	24 ml
formalin	15 ml

acetic acid   5 ml
glycerol   10 ml
water   46 ml

F–29. BENZIDINE DIHYDROCHLORIDE SOLUTION, KNOX (XIV–7)
Sprinkle the reagent on water, to excess, leaving it at least 1
hour. Use care in making this solution; it is toxic.

F–30. BENZIDINE SODIUM NITROPRUSSIDE, KNOX (XIV–8)
sodium nitroprusside   0.1 g
benzidine dihydrochloride, 0.5% sol in 2% acetic acid   25.0 ml
water   75.0 ml
Dissolve the sodium nitroprusside in 20 ml of the water; add the
benzidine solution, then the rest of the water; filter.

F–31. BEST'S CARMINE STAIN (XIII–5) (*142*, p. 164)
Stock solution:
carmine   2 g
potasssium carbonate   1 g
potassium chloride   5 g
water   60 ml
ammonium hydroxide   20 ml
Mix the first four ingredients, heat, and boil gently a few minutes, until the color darkens; cool; add the ammonium hydroxide. Ripen 24 hours.
Staining solution:
stock solution   10 ml
ammonium hydroxide   15 ml
methanol   30 ml
Mix thoroughly just before use. Do not filter.

F–32. BETHE'S FLUID (IX–15) (*142*, p. 253)
molybdate of ammonia   1 g
chromic acid, 2% aq sol   10 ml
hydrochloric acid   1 drop
water   10 ml

F–33. BLANK AND McCARTHY'S AFFIXATIVE AND SPREADING
SOLUTION (*39*)
potassium dichromate   0.2 g
gelatin   0.2 g
water   1000.0 ml
Boil the ingredients for 5 minutes and filter.

F–34. BLEACH, MAYER'S CHLORINE (*142*, p. 43)
potassium chlorate   0.1 g
hydrochloric acid   0.3 ml
alcohol, 70%   100.0 ml
Mix the potassium chlorate and hydrochloric acid in a flask
until the greenish chlorine fumes appear. Add the alcohol and
stopper the bottle. This solution should be made in a hood.

F–35. BLOOD SERUM
Obtain blood by venepuncture; store it in a sterile test tube un-

der refrigeration until the serum separates from the clot. Remove the serum and keep refrigerated.

F–36. BODIAN'S REDUCING SOLUTION (IX–12)

hydroquinone	1 g
sodium sulfite, anhydrous	5 g
water	100 ml

F–37. BODY FLUIDS in which tissues may be studied. See amniotic fluid, F–19; aqueous humor, F–23; blood serum, F–35.

F–38. BORAX-CARMINE, DILUTE ACIDULATED

hydrochloric acid, 1% sol in 70% alcohol	100 ml
Grenacher's borax carmine (F–39)	12 ml

Mix and stir well.

F–39. BORAX-CARMINE, GRENACHER'S (V–25) (*142*, p. 244)

borax, 4% aq sol	100 ml
carmine	2 g
ethanol, 70%	100 ml

Boil the borax solution and the carmine together, 30 minutes. Allow the mixture to stand 2–3 days, add the alcohol and filter.

F–40. BOUIN'S FIXATIVE: PFA

picric acid, sat aq sol	75 ml
formalin	25 ml
acetic acid	5 ml

General purpose; a few hours to several weeks.

BOUIN'S MODIFICATIONS: F–41 TO F–45.

F–41. B–15, ALLEN (*164*, p. 59)

PFA	100.0 ml
urea	2.0 g
chromic acid	1.5 ml

Add the chromic acid just before use. Fix small pieces about 1–2 hours.

F–42. B₃, ALLEN (*164*, p. 59)

picric acid, sat aq sol	75 ml
formalin	25 ml
acetic acid	10 ml
urea	10 g

Fix several hours to several weeks. After F–40, F–41, and F–42, wash briefly in water and transfer to 50%, then 70% alcohol in which they may be stored. Change the alcohol when it becomes deeply colored.

F–43. BOUIN-DIOXANE, PUCKETT (*257*) for amphibian eggs

Bouin's PFA	60 ml
dioxane	30 ml

Fix 1–3 days. Wash in dioxane and prepare by the dioxane-paraffin method.

F–44. BOUIN, HOLLANDE MODIFICATION, ROMEIS (*269*)

copper acetate	2.5 g
picric acid crystals	4.0 g

formalin   10.0 ml
water   100.0 ml
acetic acid   1.5 ml
Mix copper acetate with water and dissolve without heat by
stirring or shaking. Add picric acid and stir until dissolved; add
formalin and acetic acid. Fix several hours to 2 or 3 days.
Wash briefly in water; complete the washing in the graded
alcohols used for dehydration, adding a few drops of saturated
solution of lithium carbonate to each bath. It may be necessary
to make several changes of the 70% alcohol to remove most of
the yellow color. Store in alcohol without lithium carbonate.
This is a good general fixative.

F–45. BOUIN, MC CLUNG'S DIOXANE MODIFICATION (*164*, p. 60)
    picric acid, sat aq sol   50 ml
    acetic acid   10 ml
    dioxane   40 ml
    Fix one to several days; wash in dioxane.

F–46. BRECHER'S STAIN FOR RETICULOCYTES (*47*)
    new methylene blue N   0.5 g
    potassium oxalate   1.6 g
    water   100.0 ml

F–47. BUFFER, MC JUNKIN-HAYDEN FOR WRIGHT'S (VIII–15)
    monobasic potassium phosphate   6.63 g
    dibasic sodium phosphate, anhydrous   2.56 g
    water   1000.0 ml

F–48. CARBOL-FUCHSIN, CARR AND WALKER, (*61*)
    Stock A:
        basic fuchsin CF-41 (Matheson, Coleman, and Bell)   3 g
        ethanol, 70%   100 ml
    Stock B:
        stock A   10 ml
        phenol, 5% aq sol   90 ml
    Staining solution:
        stock B   45 ml
        acetic acid   6 ml
        formalin   6 ml

F–49. CARBOL-XYLOL
    Make a saturated solution of carbolic acid crystals in xylene.

F–50. CARNOY'S FIXATIVES (*142*, p. 228)
    I.   acetic acid   25 ml
        alcohol, absolute   75 ml
    II. acetic acid   10 ml
        alcohol, absolute   60 ml
        chloroform   30 ml

F–51. CARNOY-LEBRUN (*164*, p. 56)
    acetic acid   10 ml
    alcohol, absolute   10 ml
    chloroform   10 ml

Saturate with mercuric chloride. Fixation is rapid, 1–6 hours according to the size of the specimen. Wash in 95% alcohol, and store in 70% or 80% alcohol.

Carnoy's fixatives are poor for cytoplasm; excellent for nuclei, Nissl granules, and glycogen.

F–52. CATHEY'S PLASTIC INFILTRATION SOLUTIONS (VI–44)

I. methyl methacrylate, dried by shaking with anhydrous sodium
    sulfate(Na_2SO_4) and filtered   100.0 ml
    benzoyl peroxide (catalyst)   0.8 g

II. polyethylene glycol distearate MW 1540   6.0 g
    dibutylphthalate   4.0 ml
    solution I   27.0 ml

Mix in a glass-covered preparation dish and leave in a 50°C oven until the stearate has dissolved.

III. CASTING SOLUTION
    solution II   3 ml
    Plexiglas molding powder R–166 (Rohm and Hass)   1 g

Stir while Plexiglas is dissolving and remove bubbles with vacuum. If desired, this solution may be made up in larger quantities and stored in refrigerator and melted in 50°C oven just before use.

F–53. CELLULOSE CAPRATE MOUNTANT, LILLIE AND HENSON
(*195*)
    cellulose caprate   50 g
    xylene, histological grade   50 g

Dissolve the resin in the xylene. *The formula should be followed exactly;* different concentrations are not suitable.

F–54. CHAMPY'S FLUID (*142*, p. 231)
    potassium dichromate, 3% aq sol   7 ml
    chromic acid, 1% aq sol   7 ml
    osmic acid, 2% aq sol   4 ml

Make up fresh just before use. Fix 6–24 hours, and wash in water for the same length of time; useful as a fixative for mitochondria and lipids.

F–55. CHLORANTINE FAST RED SOLUTION (VII–6)
    chlorantine fast red 5B (or 7BL)   0.5 g
    water   100.0 ml

F–56. CHLORETONE SOLUTION, HARTNETT (II–8 and *148*)

Because Chloretone does not dissolve rapidly in water, Hartnett, (personal communication) recommends the following:
    Chloretone   200 mg
    ethanol, 95%   1 ml
    water   100 ml

Dissolve chloretone in ethanol; add the mixture to the water.

F–57. CHROMATING SOLUTION (IX–7, 8)
    zinc chromate   60 g
    formic acid   35 ml

water to make   1000 ml
pH should be 3.1

F–58. CHROMOTROPE 2R, staining solution (XIV–6)
chromotrope 2R (Grübler or National Aniline)   0.25 g
water   100.0 ml
acetic acid   1.0 ml

F–59. CITRATE SOLUTION, HYPOTONIC (XII–7)
sodium citrate crystals, analytical reagent   1.12 g
water, glass distilled   100.00 ml
This solution is equivalent to one-half of isotonic concentration.

F–60. CLEANING FLUID, ZIRKLE
water   20 ml
xylene   20 ml
n-butanol   20 ml
ethanol, 95%   40 ml
Dilute ammonium hydroxide may be substituted for water, and
carbon tetrachloride for xylene. This is excellent for cleaning
finished slides.

F–61. CMC–10 MOUNTANT, Turtox, (R–48) quick drying, aqueous; used
only for unstained, pigmented specimens, since most stains fade
in it and since it makes objects very transparent. Mount from
alcohol, lactic acid, glycerol, or water. Stains may be added to
the specimens by adding to the mountant one of the following:
a. 1% solution of methyl blue in lactophenol (F–126) until the
mixture is deep blue.
b. iron aceto-carmine (F–1) until mixture is medium red.

F–62. COLCHICINE SOLUTION (XII–5)
0.85% buffered sodium chloride solution (6.6 × 10⁻³M phosphate, pH7.0). Add to this either colchicine or Colcemid Ciba
(diacetylmethyl colchicine), 1 μg/ml.

F–63. COLE'S FIXATIVE (IX–15; *142*, p. 254)
water   50 ml
glycerol   50 ml
ammonium molybdate in excess
hydrochloric acid   15 drops

F–64. COLOPHONIUM-ALCOHOL (VII–4)
Stock solution:
colophonium (rosin)   10 g
ethanol, absolute   100 ml
Working solution:
stock solution   5 ml
ethanol, 95%   45 ml

F–65. CONGO-GLYCERINE, GAGE (*117*; *142*, p. 87)
glycerol   100 ml
Congo red, 0.5% aq sol   20 ml
Use on macerated preparations for study and mounting.

F–66. CONGO RED-STAINED YEAST for feeding small animals (*164*, p. 438)

yeast, compressed	3 g
Congo red	30 mg
water	10 ml

Boil mixture gently for 10 minutes. Dip a dissecting needle in the mixture and stir the culture to be fed with this needle.

F–67. CORROSIVE-ACETIC (XI–22)

mercuric chloride, sat aq sol	100 ml
acetic acid	5–10 ml

Fix small objects very briefly; larger ones for 4 to 24 hours. Wash well in running water. Remove mercuric crystals with iodine in dehydration (F–132) or by dehydration in Cellosolve.

F–68 CRESYL VIOLET SOLUTION (*174*)

cresyl violet (Matheson, Coleman, and Bell, or Bayer)	0.25 g
water	100.0 ml

Before use, add 5 drops of 10% acetic acid to 30 ml of the solution and filter.

F–69. DA FANO'S FIXATIVE*

cobalt nitrate	1 g
sodium chloride	1 g
formalin	10 ml
water	90 ml

* Da Fano, C. 1908. Ziegler's Beitrag 44: 495–525.

F–70. DAMAR

Make a solution by method F–145 for xylene-soluble resins.

F–71. DARROW RED (VII–5) for earlier samples of the dye.

Darrow red	50 mg
acetic acid 0.2 M (pH 2.7)	200 ml

Boil together gently, 10 minutes. Cool to room temperature and filter.

F–72. DARROW RED (VII–5)

Darrow red Cert. No. CD-1	50 mg
acetic acid-acetate buffer, pH 3.5	200 ml

Dissolve the stain in the buffer and filter. The earlier samples of this dye required a 10-minute boiling period, but this is not necessary with the new formulation. For staining celloidin sections, reduce the amount of stain to 25 mg.

F–73. DAVIDSON'S FIXATIVE, MODIFIED (XII–11)

alcohol, 95%	30 ml
formalin	20 ml
acetic acid	10 ml
water	30 ml

F–74. DEETJEN'S SOLUTION (VIII–8)

sodium chloride	0.75 g
manganese sulfate	0.50 g

sodium bicarbonate	0.01 g
water	100.00 ml

F–75. *o*-DIANISIDINE STAINING SOLUTION (XI–9)

A.* *o*-dianisidine (British Drug Houses, Ltd.) — 100 mg
ethanol — 70 ml

B. acetate buffer (0.1 M at pH 4.6):
acetic acid, 0.1 M — 102 ml
sodium acetate, 0.1 M — 98 ml

C. hydrogen peroxide, 30% solution
Working solution; make just before use
o-dianisidine solution (A) — 4.0 ml
acetate buffer (B) — 1.0 ml
water — 1.5 ml
hydrogen peroxide (C) — 0.2 ml
* lasts for about 1 week

F–76. DOWN'S POLYVINYL ALCOHOL MOUNTANT (*94*)
Stock solution:
polyvinyl alcohol — 15 g
water, 80°C — 100 ml
Dissolve the alcohol in the water in a steam bath.
Working solution:
stock — 56 ml
lactic acid — 22 ml
phenol — 22 g
This mountant clears small objects mounted directly from water.

F–77. ELFTMAN'S FIXATIVE FOR RAT PITUITARIES (VII–14)
chrome alum, $KCr(SO_4)_2 \cdot 12H_2O$ — 5 g
formalin — 5 ml
mercuric chloride, 5% aq sol — 100 ml
Mix immediately before use.
Fix 12–48 hours, at room temperature.

F–78. ENLOW'S PARLODION SOLUTION for sealing ground bone (X–3)
Parlodion — 28 g
butyl or amyl acetate — 250 ml
Dissolve the Parlodion in the butyl or amyl acetate. The proportions are critical and should not be changed. Store in containers which prevent evaporation. If only a small number of sections are to be treated, a smaller quantity of solution should be made.

F–79. EOSIN (VII–3)
eosin Y, C.I. No. (768) 45380 — 1 g
water — 200 ml
acetic acid — 1 ml

F–80. ETHYLENE DIAMINE TETRAACETIC ACID: EDTA (X–7).
This reagent is sold as Versene (R–197) and Sequestrene (R–179). Make of either a 5.5% solution in 10% formalin.

F-81. FAT STAINS IN CARBOWAX*
oil red O, or Sudan IV, or Sudan black B   1.2 g
Carbowax 400   100.0 ml
Heat to 60°C; when stain is dissolved, filter with suction; cool
to room temperature.
* Zugibe, F. T., Fink, M. L., and Brown, K. D. 1959. Stain
Tech. 34:33–37.

F-82. FAT STAINS, LILLIE AND ASHBURN (XIII–8)
Stock solution:
oil red 4B, oil red O, or Sudan brown   250–500 mg
isopropanol, 99%   100 ml
Make a saturated solution of the dye in isopropanol.
Working solution:
stock solution   6 ml
water   4 ml
This supersaturated solution is useful for several hours. Discard
after one staining session.

F-83. FEULGEN REAGENTS: DE TOMASI'S METHOD OF PREPA-
RATION (89)
Solution A (leuco fuchsin):
fuchsin, basic, C.C.   0.5 g
water at 100°C   100.0 ml
hydrochloric acid, 1N solution   10.0 ml
potassium metabisulfite ($K_2S_2O_5$)   0.5 g
Pour boiling water on the stain, shake thoroughly and cool to
50°C. Filter, add the 1N hydrochloric acid and the potassium
metabisulfite; shake, stopper well, and store in the dark 12-18
hours, when it should be decolorized. If it has a pinkish tint, add
500 mg of activated charcoal, shake well and filter. Store in the
dark, preferably refrigerated. It may be re-used until it becomes
pink.
Solution B:
hydrochloric acid, 1N   5 ml
potassium metabisulfite, 10% aq sol   5 ml
water   100 ml
See also Schiff reagents F–181 and F–182.

F-84. FLEMMING'S FLUID, strong formula
A. chromic acid, 1% aq sol   55 ml
acetic acid   5 ml
water   20 ml
B. osmic acid, 2% in 1% aq sol of chromic acid
Just before using mix four parts of A with one part of B. Fix
small pieces 24–48 hours. It may often be used to advantage
at temperatures as low as 0°C. Does not penetrate well. Wash
in running tap water 24–48 hours.

F-85. FORMALIN, BUFFERED, LILLIE (193, p. 32)
formalin   100 ml

water   900 ml
calcium or magnesium carbonate to excess
F–86. FORMALIN-HYPERTONIC SALINE (XIV–8)
    formalin   100 ml
    sodium chloride   20 g
    water   1000 ml
F–87. FORMALIN-PYRIDINE BATH
    formalin, commercial, not neutralized   20 ml
    pyridine, 2% aq sol   80 ml
F–88. FORMALIN-SALINE FIXATIVE FOR MAMMALS (IX–2)
    normal saline (0.9%)   900 ml
    formalin   100 ml
    FORMALIN SOLUTIONS: see R–85.
F–89. FORMOL-ACETIC-ALCOHOL, FAA
    formalin   10 ml
    acetic acid   10 ml
    alcohol, 70%   80 ml
F–90. FORMOL-ACETIC-ALCOHOL, BODIAN (IX–12)
    formalin   5 ml
    acetic acid   5 ml
    alcohol, 80%   90 ml
F–91. FORMOL-CALCIUM FIXATIVE (XIII–14)
    formalin, 10%   99 ml
    calcium chloride   1 g
F–92. FORMOL-NITRIC
    formalin, 10%   75 ml
    nitric acid   25 ml
F–93. FORMOL-SALINE WITH GUM ACACIA, FOR PERFUSION
    (*177*)
    sodium chloride   0.9 g
    gum acacia   2.4 g
    formalin   10.0 ml
    water, to make   100.0 ml
    Prepare in the same way as F–179. This formula is for use with
    guinea pigs. For cats and monkeys the amount of gum acacia is
    increased to 5.6 g. Adjust to pH 7–7.2 with NaOH for IX–7,–8
F–94. GAGE'S FORMALDEHYDE DISSOCIATOR (*117; 142*, p. 264)
    formalin   2 ml
    normal saline (0.9%)   1000 ml
F–95. GELATIN SOLUTIONS, FOR EMBEDDING
    gelatin, powdered   25 g
    water   50 ml
    Soak the gelatin in the water until the flakes are swollen. Melt
    over water at about 40°C; add sufficient warmed water to make
    100 ml of solution. If it is to be kept for some time, add 1%
    phenol and store in refrigerator. Use this 25% solution as a stock
    to make weaker solutions.

F–96. GENDRE'S FIXATIVE (XIII–5)

picric acid, sat sol in 95% alcohol	80 ml
formalin	15 ml
acetic acid	5 ml

This fixative preserves glycogen, particularly if used at a temperature near 0°C. Wash in 80% alcohol, several changes.

F–97. GIEMSA'S DILUTE STAINING SOLUTION (VIII–16)

stock stain, purchased (R–90)	1 ml
water, distilled	20 ml or
0.01M phosphate buffer, pH 6.0–6.5	20 ml

F–98. GILSON'S FLUID

nitric acid, 80% solution	4 ml
acetic acid	1 ml
alcohol, 60%	25 ml
water	220 ml
mercuric chloride	5 g

Fix for a few hours to several days. Material may be stored for several weeks without injury. This is an excellent general purpose fixative and seldom overfixes.

F–99. GIOVACCHINI'S MODIFICATION of the affixative of Rinehart and Abu'l-Haj (VI–31)

gelatin	15 g
water	55 ml
glycerol	50 ml
phenol	0.5 g

Dissolve gelatin in water by gentle heat and add glycerol and phenol.

F–100. GLASS-CLEANING SOLUTION

potassium dichromate, sat aq sol	100 ml
sulfuric acid, technical grade	100 ml

Mix with care, adding the acid to the dichromate solution in a Pyrex container.

GLYCEROL JELLY has long been a favorite mountant. It has, however, a number of disadvantages and can usually be replaced with a mountant which is easier to use and which makes a more permanent preparation, such as a polyvinyl alcohol mixture or PVP–VA. There are numerous formulae in the literature, all similar and of about equal merit.

F–101. GLYCEROL JELLY, HOYER'S, from the National Formulary, Ed. 8, 1946, p. 636, quoted by Mitchell and Cook (225)

gelatin	40 g
arsenic trioxide, sat aq sol	200 ml
glycerol	120 ml

Dissolve the gelatin in the arsenic trioxide solution with gentle heat, add glycerol, mix well, and cool. For most purposes, the quantities in this formula could be divided by 4.

F–102. GOLGI METHODS SOLUTIONS
COX-GOLGI (IX–6)
Solution A:

potassium dichromate, 5% aq sol	20 ml
mercuric chloride, 5% aq sol	20 ml
potassium chromate, 4% aq sol	20 ml
water	40 ml

Mix the first two solutions, then add the second two.
Use at least 25–30 times as much fixative as specimen, vol/vol.
Solution B:

ammonium hydroxide	5 ml
water	95 ml

F–103. GOLGI METHODS SOLUTIONS
FIXATIVE – PORTER AND DAVENPORT (IX–5)

silver nitrate, 0.5% aq sol	90.0 ml
formalin, commercial, not neutralized	10.0 ml
pyridine	0.1 ml

pH should be 5.5–6.0. If formalin is not acid, omit the pyridine.
If stain needs intensification, add 1 ml of 1% osmic acid solution.

F–104. GOMORI'S SUBSTRATE FOR ACID PHOSPHATASE (XIII–13)
Stock solutions:
  A. 0.5 M acetate buffer, pH 5.0, containing 1.2 g lead nitrate, $Pb(NO_3)_2$/liter.
  B. 0.1 M (about 3%) sodium glycerophosphate, Eastman product, catalog No. 644 (A–18)
      Both stock solutions are stable under refrigeration, with a few crystals of thymol or camphor added.
Working solution:

stock A	50 ml
stock B	5 ml

Add B to A, allow the precipitate to settle out, and filter.

F–105. GREGG AND PUCKETT'S FIXATIVE FOR FROG EGGS (*134*)

mercuric chloride, sat aq sol	90 ml
formalin	8 ml
acetic acid	2 ml

GRENACHER'S BORAX-CARMINE; see borax-carmine, Grenacher's, F–39.

F–106. GRIFFITH AND CARTER'S FIXATIVE FOR REFRACTORY
TISSUES (XI–18)

picric acid, sat sol in dioxane	85 ml
formalin	10 ml
formic acid	5 ml

Fix 1 day to 3 weeks; wash well in several changes of dioxane.

F–107. GRUNDMANN'S MOUNTANT FOR NEMATODES (V–30). See
also F–143.

lactophenol	5 ml

picric acid, sat aq sol	1 drop
methyl green, 1% aq sol	4 drops

Mix and let stand for 1 week; filter.

F–108. GUM MUCILAGE for attaching specimens to the freezing microtome (*142*, p. 71)

gum acacia, best grade	60 g
water	80 ml

Dissolve the gum in the water, stirring at intervals until all is
dissolved.

F–109. GUM SUGAR FORMULA (*142*, p. 71), an embedding medium for
frozen sections.

water	30 ml
sugar	q.s.
gum acacia	60 g
water	80 ml

Add sugar to 30 ml of water until a saturated solution is made;
filter it. Dissolve the gum acacia in 80 ml of water. When both
solutions are ready, mix them.

GUM SYRUP, APÁTHY, MODIFICATION OF LILLIE AND
ASHBURN (*194*). See Apáthy's gum syrup (F–22).

F–110. HAUPT'S GELATIN AFFIXATIVE (*149*)

gelatin	1 g
water	100 ml
phenol crystals	2 g
glycerol	15 ml

Dissolve gelatin in water at 30°C. Add glycerol and phenol;
stir well and filter. Store in stoppered vials under refrigeration.

F–111. HEIDENHAIN'S AZAN STAIN, SCHLEICHER'S MODIFICA-
TION (*164*, p. 248), slightly modified.

A. Azocarmine solution:

azocarmine B	0.1 g
water	100 ml
acetic acid	5 ml

Dissolve the stain in the water and the acid to make a clear solution. It may be re-used several times but may require further
addition of acetic acid.

B. Aniline blue-orange G solution (stock):

aniline blue, WS	0.2 g
orange G	0.4 g
water	100.0 ml
acetic acid	1.0 ml

Dissolve the orange G in the water and add the acetic acid;
add the aniline blue.

Working solution:

stock	10 ml
water	20 ml

Filter before use.

F–112. HEIDENHAIN'S SUSA

water	80.0 ml
mercuric chloride	4.5 g
sodium chloride	0.5 g
formalin	20.0 ml
acetic acid	4.0 ml
trichloroacetic acid	2.0 g

Dissolve the sodium chloride and mercuric chloride in the water. Add the other ingredients. Fix small pieces, no more than 10 mm thick, 3–24 hours. Rinse briefly in water, dehydrate in alcohol, or better, in Cellosolve, to remove mercuric chloride; a good general purpose fixative.

F–113. HELLY'S FLUID (*142*, p. 230)

potassium dichromate	2.5 g
mercuric chloride	5.0 g
water	100.0 ml
formalin	5.0 ml

Dissolve salts in water; add formalin just before use. Use on blocks of tissue no thicker than 5 mm. Fix 6–18 hours; wash in running water at least overnight.

F–114. HEMATOXYLIN, GOMORI (*125*)

hematoxylin, 1% aq sol	50 ml
chrome alum, 3% aq sol	50 ml
potassium dichromate, 5% aq sol	2 ml
sulfuric acid 0.5 N	2 ml

Mix in the order given. The solution may be used in 24 hours and lasts for 2 weeks if not kept too warm. Its surface should be covered by a metallic scum. Filter immediately before use.

F–115. HEMATOXYLIN, HEIDENHAIN'S

Mordant and differentiator:

| ferric ammonium sulfate, Fe $NH_4(SO_4)_2 \cdot 12 H_2O$ | 40 g |
| water | 1000 ml |

Select only the clear, violet crystals. Dissolve with occasional shaking and filter. Store in two bottles, one marked mordant, the second, differentiator. Never use the differentiator for mordanting. Some technicians dilute the differentiator 1:1 with water.

Stain:

hematoxylin crystals, C.C.	2 g
ethanol, 95%	20 ml
water	380 ml

Dissolve the stain in alcohol, shaking well at intervals. When the solution is deep, clear brown add the water. This solution, filtered after each use, may be re-used many times. It should be tested at intervals by pouring about 1 ml in a bottle and adding tap water. If a clear amethyst color develops the stain may be safely used.

F–116. HEMATOXYLIN, MALLORY'S PHOSPHOTUNGSTIC*

hematoxylin	0.1 g
phosphotungstic acid	2.0 g
water	100.0 ml

Dissolve the hematoxylin in a part of the water with gentle heat, and the phosphotungstic acid in the remainder. Mix the solutions when they are cool. Allow the stain to ripen for sev- weeks in a flask with a cotton stopper; or ripen it immediately by adding 10 ml of 0.25% aq sol of potassium permanganate. The fixative should contain mercuric chloride or the sections be mordanted with the solution of Peers, F–166.

* Mallory, F.B. 1901. Pathological techniques. p. 268.

F–117. HOYER'S MEDIUM is an example of glycerol jelly. For a suitable formula, see F–101.

F–118. INJECTION MASS (XIV–2)

chloral hydrate	40 g
carbon, fine particulate (R–25)	20-40 g
water	980 ml
Tween 80 (R–195)	20 ml
gelatin, 16% aq sol	q.s.

Mix well the chloral hydrate, carbon, and 950 ml of water in a blendor at room temperature. Mix Tween 80 in 30 ml of water and heat to about 40°C. Blend the whole for 20 minutes, add- ing at intervals 1–4 drops of caprilic alcohol to reduce bubble formation. Store this suspension in a chemically clean container. When ready to use, mix a portion of the carbon suspension with an equal amount of the gelatin solution which has first been warmed to 50–60°C.

F–119. INJECTION MASS: INDIA INK-GELATIN

calfskin gelatin (Eastman Organic Chemicals)	28 g
India ink, Higgins' waterproof	216 ml
water, demineralized, 90°C	200 ml

Dissolve the gelatin in the water with constant stirring; this takes about 20 minutes. Add the ink to the gelatin solution and inject at once. This formula is for a large specimen. For smaller ones the amounts should be much decreased.

F–120. INJECTION MASS FOR LYMPHATICS (XIV–5)

cedar oil	5 ml
color in oil (Prussian blue) (R–54)	5 ml
toluene	10 ml
diethyl ether	q.s.

Mix cedar oil and Prussian blue thoroughly and dilute with toluene. If coarse particles of color are present allow the fluid to stand several hours and decant; if necessary, filter through chamois skin. Just before injection add 1 ml of diethyl ether/10 ml of mixture of the first three ingredients.

F–121. KAHLE'S FIXATIVE (XII–8)

water	30 ml
ethanol, absolute	15 ml
formalin	6 ml
acetic acid	1 ml

Modification for *Drosophila* embryos:

water	37 ml
alcohol, 95%	32 ml
formalin	27 ml
acetic acid	4 ml

F–122. KINGSLEY'S STAIN (VIII–19); see also R–109.

Stock solution I:

methylene blue U.S.P., medicinal	0.065	g
methylene azure A	0.010	g
glycerol C.P.	5.0	ml
methanol C.P.	5.0	ml
water, distilled	25.0	ml
buffer, pH 6.9	15.0	ml

Stock solution II:

methylene violet (Bernthsen)	0.013	g
eosin, yellow, WS	0.045	g
glycerol C.P.	5.0	ml
methanol C.P.	10.0	ml
acetone C.P.	35.0	ml

The stain is quickly and simply prepared by mixing equal parts of the two stock solutions. It is usable for at least 8 months and is applicable to practically all hematological purposes.

F–123. KLÜVER AND BARRERA STAINS (IX–13)

Solution A:

Luxol fast blue MBS or MBSN, du Pont (R–115, 116)	1 g
ethanol, 95%	1000 ml
acetic acid, 10%	5 ml

Filter before use. Discard after use on frozen sections.

Solution B:

cresyl violet (Matheson, Coleman, and Bell or Bayer)	0.25 g
water	100.0 ml

Before using add 5 drops of 10% acetic acid to every 30 ml of solution; heat and filter; may be reused.

F–124. KORNHAUSER'S QUAD STAINS (VII–11) (83, p. 249)

Solution 1:

orcein, synthetic, C.C.	0.4	g
nitric acid, C.P.	0.4	ml
ethanol, 90%	100.0	ml

Solution 2:

aluminum sulfate crystals [$Al_2(SO_4)_3 \cdot 18\ H_2O$]	10.0	g
alizarin blue 2B	0.35	g

water 100.0 ml
acetic acid 0.5 ml
Boil together the first three ingredients in a covered flask for 10 minutes. Cool, filter, and add acid.
Solution 3:
phosphotungstic acid C.P. 4 g
phosphomolybdic acid C.P. 1 g
water 100 ml
An alternative to this mixture is to use either acid in 5% sol.
Solution 4:
orange G 2.0 g
fast green FCF 0.2 g
acetic acid 2.0 ml
water 100.0 ml

F–125. LACTIC-ACETIC-ORCEIN MOUNTANT–STAIN (329)
orcein, synthetic (Gurr) 2.0 g
acetic acid 50.0 ml
lactic acid, 85% 42.5 ml
water 7.5 ml
Mix the acids and water; add the stain. Specimens mounted in this make temporary preparations.

F–126. LACTOPHENOL for clearing temporary mounts, Becker and Roudabush (24)
phenol 10.0 g
glycerol 10.6 ml
lactic acid 8.2 ml
water 10.2 ml
This is especially good for nemas.

F–127. LAVDOWSKY'S FIXATIVE (142, p. 236)
formalin 10 ml
ethanol, 95% 50 ml
acetic acid 2 ml
water 40 ml
This is a general purpose fixative in which material may remain for several days without harm. The tissue should be washed in 70% alcohol.

F–128. LAVDOWSKY'S FIXATIVE, MOSSMAN'S MODIFICATION (142, p. 236)
formalin 10 ml
alcohol, 95% 30 ml
acetic acid 10 ml
water 50 ml
The added acetic acid is useful in decalcification of older mammalian embryos if changed at intervals.

F–129. LEAD DISODIUM VERSENATE (X–15)
versene acid 5.4 g

lead oxide   4.1 g
sodium hydroxide, 7.5% sol   18.0–19.0 ml
water   150.0 ml
Slurry the versene acid in the water; add the lead oxide. Heat the slurry to almost boiling with continual stirring. Add slowly 17 ml of the sodium hydroxide, maintaining the same temperature. Cool the solution to about 75°C and adjust to pH 7.0, using 1–2 ml of the sodium hydroxide for this. Add enough water to make the total volume of the solution 200 ml. This is a 5% solution.

LEUCO BASIC FUCHSIN (See F–83, F–181, F–182.)

F–130. LILLIE'S NEUTRAL BUFFERED FORMALDEHYDE SOLUTION, pH 7.0 (*193*, p. 32)
formaldehyde solution, 38–40%   100.0 ml
water   900.0 ml
acid sodium phosphate, monohydrate   4.0 g
disodium phosphate, anhydrous   6.5 g

F–131. LOCKE'S SOLUTION
sodium chloride   9.00 g
calcium chloride   0.25 g
potassium chloride   0.42 g
sodium bicarbonate (baking soda)   0.20 g
dextrin   0.25 g
water   1000.00 ml

F–132. LUGOL'S SOLUTION
iodine   6 g
potassium iodide   4 g
ethanol   10 ml
water   100 ml
Dissolve the iodine and potassium iodide in the alcohol by repeated shaking or stirring. Add the water.

F–133. LUGOL-TYPE SOLUTION (IX–1)
iodine   100 g
potassium iodide   200 g
water   1000 ml

LVN SOLUTIONS. See nitrocellulose solutions (R–142); (F–153, 154)

F–134. MAC NEAL'S TETRACHROME SOLUTION (V–7)
tetrachrome, dry (R–119)   0.15–0.3 g
methanol, neutral, acetone-free   100.0 ml
Warm the alcohol to 50°C; add the stain in small lots, shaking well after each addition. Keep at 37°C, stoppered, for 3 days, shaking occasionally; filter.

F–135. MAGNESIUM CITRATE SOLUTION, KRAMER AND SHIPLEY (X–6)
citric acid   80 g
magnesium oxide*   4 g

water, hot   100 ml
ammonium hydroxide (density 0.90)   100 ml
Dissolve the citric acid in the hot water; add the magnesium oxide and stir until a complete solution is made. Cool and add the ammonium hydroxide; dilute to 300 ml. After 24 hours, filter. Titrate with 5 N hydrochloric acid to pH 7.0–7.6 and add an equal volume of distilled water.
   * If the magnesium oxide contains much carbonate, it should be freshly ignited.

F–136. MALL'S DISSOCIATION SOLUTION (X–10)
water   77 ml
glycerol   20 ml
potassium hydroxide   1–5 g
   MAYER'S ALBUMEN. See albumen, Mayer's, F–7

F–137. MAYER'S CHLORINE REAGENT
potassium chlorate   several crystals
hydrochloric acid   0.5 ml
alcohol, 50%   5–10 ml
Combine acid and potassium chlorate and cover the tube. When chlorine fumes appear, add the alcohol. Prepare just before use.

F–138. MC CALLUM'S DISSOCIATION FLUID (V–10)
nitric acid   10 ml
glycerol   20 ml
water   20 ml

F–139. McMANUS' FIXATIVE* (IX–11)
cobalt sulfate or nitrate   1 g
water   80 ml
calcium chloride, 10% sol   10 ml
formalin   10 ml
   * McManus, J.F.A. 1946. The demonstration of certain fatty substances in paraffin sections. J. Path. Bact. 58: 93–5.
   MENZIES' PARAFFIN-BEESWAX-STEARIC ACID infiltrating mixture. See F–163.

F–140. METHYL BLUE SOLUTION (XIV–6)
methyl blue (National Aniline Co.)   0.5 g
water   100.0 ml
acetic acid   1.0 ml

F–141. MOFFAT'S REDUCING SOLUTION (XIII–12)
metol (p-methylaminophenol sulfate)   0.2 g
sodium sulfite   20.0 g
hydroquinone   0.5 g
borax   0.2 g
water   100.0 ml

F–142. MOFFAT'S SUBSTRATE (XIII–12), to demonstrate alkaline phosphatase.
sodium β-glycerophosphate, 3.2% aq sol   6 ml
calcium nitrate, 2% aq sol   9 ml

sodium barbitone (sodium-diethyl barbiturate),

10% aq sol	6 ml
silver nitrate, 0.5% aq sol	20 ml
water	19 ml

F–143. MOUNTANT, GRUNDMAN'S GLYCEROL (V-30); see also F–107.

glycerol, 50% aq sol	5.0	ml
methyl green, 1% aq sol	5	drops
picric acid, sat aq sol	1	drop

F–144. MOUNTANT, POLYVINYL ALCOHOL (PVA). See F–76.

F–145. MOUNTANTS, RESINOUS

Resinous mountants such as damar and many xylene-soluble synthetic resins may be prepared by dissolving the resin in such a quantity of suitable solvent as to make a solution thin enough to filter, and then concentrating it.

1. Place the desired amount of dry resin in a screw-cap jar which may be discarded after use.

2. Add an excess of the solvent; xylene or benzene is usually used. Place aluminum foil over the jar top and partially screw down the cap (or treat the jar lid with silicone grease). Shake at frequent intervals until all of the lumps of resin are dissolved. If the solution is thick add more solvent.

3. Filter into stock bottles or dispensing bottles as desired. Cover bottle tops with bond paper well secured and put in a warm place to evaporate part of the solvent. As the solution thickens, test it until it is of the proper viscosity for mounting; then close bottles to prevent further evaporation.

F–146. MOUNTANT, SPURR'S (297)

Formula I:

water	40	g
cadmium iodide, reagent grade, Baker	34	g
Elvanol 51–05, du Pont, low viscosity grade (R–71)	18	g
methanol	qs.	
fructose	8	g

Formula II: ph 4.85 at 24°C, for hematoxylin-stained sections:

water	40	g
cadmium iodide	4	g
Elvanol 51–05	16	g
methanol	qs.	
fructose	8	g

1. Slurry the Elvanol with absolute methanol, filter in a Buchner funnel and rinse several times with fresh methanol. Make a thin layer of the washed Elvanol in a glass container, dry overnight in a ventilated oven at 55°C. Grind in a mortar to a very fine powder.

2. Weigh a beaker and dissolve in it the cadmium iodide in the water, using heat; (a little more than 40 g may be used to allow

for evaporation). Avoid splashing the solution on the beaker walls. Cool the solution to about 20°C.

3. Add the polyvinyl alcohol while stirring with a speed-controlled motor-driven mixer. Stir 20-30 minutes, until few particles can been seen. Put the beaker in a water bath, gradually raising the temperature to 75°C; continue to stir until solution is complete.

4. Remove from water bath, add fructose when temperature does not exceed 70°C, and stir until dissolved.

5. Add sufficient water to restore mixture to weight of ingredients in the formula; stir well.

6. Cover and allow to stand overnight or until foam disappears. Mount specimens from water or from any grade of ethanol. The slides are permanent and dry quickly. Few stains bleed into the medium, but acridine red and acid violet do so. Hematoxylin sections should be mounted in formula No. II. The refractive index of the dried mountant is 1.6020.

F–147. MULLIGAN'S FLUID (IX–2)

carbolic acid crystals	40.0 g
copper sulfate crystals	5.0 g
hydrochloric acid	1.25 g
water	1000.0 ml

F–148. NEUTRAL RED when used as a vital stain is employed in weak solutions: for many purposes the solution should be only faintly pink.

F–149. NEWCOMER'S FIXATIVE (XII–2)

isopropanol	60 ml
propionic acid	30 ml
dioxane	10 ml
petroleum ether (petroleum benzine)	10 ml
acetone	10 ml

For Feulgen staining of tissues prior to embedding and sectioning. This solution is stable.

F–150. NILE BLUE SOLUTION (XIII–10)

Nile blue sulfate, sat aq sol	500 ml
sulfuric acid, 0.5%	50 ml

Boil in a reflux condenser for two hours. Filter, and repeat filtration before each use. Do not expose this solution to cold which causes it to precipitate.

F–151. NISSENBAUM'S FIXATIVE (237) (XII–9)

ethanol, absolute	3 ml
butanol, tertiary	2 ml
acetic acid	2 ml

Use at once after mixing.

NITROCELLULOSE SOLUTIONS. See R–142 and F–152, 153, 154.

F–152. DIRECTIONS FOR SAFE HANDLING OF LVN (Statement of

Hercules Powder Co.) This material is shipped in 30% by weight of denatured ethanol as a fluffy white mass. As soon as it is received, remove it from its container. Weigh it and immediately dissolve it in the proper amount of the desired solvent. Since it is very flammable, there should be no lighted burners or lighted cigarettes in the room or any electrical devices which may spark while the material is being weighed and the solutions made. Davenport (83) points out that since the cotton linters of which LVN is made contain a certain amount of gritty material, the solutions should be made some time before use and allowed to settle. The supernatant is decanted. All solutions must be stored in the dark to prevent deterioration.

SOLUTIONS OF LVN. See R–118.

F–153. LVN, 25% ALCOHOL-ETHER SOLUTION

LVN, RS ½ second, as received from Hercules
Powder Company   100.0 g*
ether, andydrous   140.0 ml
ethanol, absolute   110.0 ml

Put the LVN in a container which can be tightly closed, add the alcohol first, stir well, then add the ether. Close the container and shake at intervals until the LVN is completely dissolved. Store in the dark. Dilute with ether-alcohol 1:1/vol as needed.

* Of this only 70 g is LVN.

F–154. LVN, AMYL ACETATE SOLUTION (29)

LVN, as received from Hercules Powder Co.   400 g
amyl acetate   400 ml

This mixture dissolves without stirring. It may be kept in widemouth jars if a sheet of polyethylene is placed between jar top and lid. Dilute with amyl acetate to make 10, 20, 30, and 40% solutions. Store in the dark.

F–155. NICKEL SULFATE SOLUTION for anesthetizing protozoa, Bovee (43)

nickel sulfate ($NiSO_4 \cdot 6H_2O$)   0.4 g
water   1000.0 ml

Dissolve the crystals in the water. This is the stock solution; it keeps well.

F–156. NORMAL SALINE. See F–180.

F–157. ORTH'S FIXATIVE

potassium dichromate, 2.5% aq sol   90 ml
formalin   10 ml

Mix just before use. Fix 1–4 days; wash in running water for 12 hours. Store in 70% alcohol or 10% formalin. This is a good general fixative.

F–158. ORTH'S FIXATIVE, KOSE'S VARIANT

potassium dichromate, 3% aq sol   90 ml
formalin   10 ml

Mix just before use. Fix 1–3 days; wash 12–18 hours in running water. Used much as F–157; it preserves myelin well.

F–159. ORCINOL – NEW FUCHSIN (VII–9)

new fuchsin	2 g
orcinol, highest purity	4 g
water	200 ml
alcohol, 95%	100 ml
ferric chloride sol, U.S.P. IX	25 ml

Mix water, orcinol, and new fuchsin. Boil 5 minutes. Add ferric chloride and boil 5 minutes longer. Cool; filter, collecting the precipitate on the filter and, without drying, dissolve it in the alcohol. This is the staining solution. Pass specimen to 95% alcohol after deceration, stain 15 minutes at 37°C, differentiate 15 minutes in 70% alcohol. This does not stain tissue elements other than elastin.

F–160. OSMIC ACID SOLUTIONS, DIRECTIONS FOR HANDLING

The reagent is usually sold in 0.5-g amounts, sealed in a glass ampoule. It need not be weighed. Handle it with great care; its fumes are both irritating and dangerous. Prepare all glassware to be used in making the solution by very thorough washing, then rinsing several times in glass-distilled water.

1. Select a glass-stoppered bottle and put in it the proper amount of glass-distilled water to make a solution of the desired strength.

2. Wash the capsule containing the osmic acid as thoroughly as the glassware; if it carries a label, remove all trace of it. Nick the ampoule with a glass file, also well cleaned, and drop it in the bottle with the water. Shake well and, if this does not open the ampoule, introduce a cleaned glass rod and crush it. Stopper the bottle and shake at intervals until the reagent is dissolved. Leave the broken glass in the bottle. Store in the dark. The solution is useful until it darkens.

F–161. PAPAMILTIADES' FIXATIVE to follow lymphatic injection (XIV–5)

formalin	10 ml
aluminum sulfate	2 g
zinc sulfate	2 g
acetic acid	4 ml
water	90 ml

This fixative causes the injection mass to adhere to the walls of the lymphatics. Fix 5 days or longer. Wash briefly in water; dehydrate in dioxane or alcohol.

F–162. PARAFFIN, CARE AND PREPARATION

An oven should always be available, and set at a temperature a few degrees higher than the melting point of the hardest paraffin in current use. Provide it with twice as many enamel or stainless steel pitchers of 1 or 2 liters capacity as there are types of paraffin in use; label each container indicating the type of paraffin and its melting point, as: Tissuemat, 56°C. With wooden clothespins, clip filter paper cones to one half of the pitchers. When new paraffin is needed, set it to melt in a pitcher without a filter. When it is molten, filter it into the appropriate container. Pour the filtered wax into wide-mouth glass jars with straight sides and screw tops; label and store.

After each use of a jar of paraffin for infiltration, put it in the oven and allow it to remain molten until the particulate matter has settled. Then remove, cover, and store. This cleans the paraffin efficiently and may be repeated several times. When, however, a visible layer of dirt appears in the bottom of the jar, melt the whole mass, filter, clean the jar by wiping it while it is hot, and refill with filtered paraffin.

Collect all trimmings of paraffin blocks and when there is a sufficient amount, melt, filter, and reuse. This is not merely a matter of economy; paraffin improves with use.

It is important to follow these rules for keeping the wax meticulously clean because small particles of dirt in the block cause defects in sections and injure the knife edge. If there is an adequate stock of clean jars of paraffin for daily use and if used jars are cleaned at once it is little trouble to keep at hand a supply of clean paraffin. When much embedding in paraffin is being done, it is usually necessary to keep the oven going constantly.

PARAFFIN MIXTURES

If the commercial mixtures of paraffin and adjuvants are not satisfactory, it is possible to make excellent ones. Ordinary household paraffin to which two or three parts by weight of bayberry wax is added has a good consistency. Hance's rubber paraffin is probably the most satisfactory mixture. Its preparation is time consuming but saves expense.

F–163. PARAFFIN – BEESWAX – STEARIC ACID

Menzies (*221*) recommends a formula of paraffin-beeswax-stearic acid as an embedding mass suitable for cutting sections of 1–3μ.

paraffin (Shell Chemical Co., 125–130°F)	95 g
commercial beeswax	5 g
stearic acid, technical grade (mp 56°C)	10 g

Clarify the paraffin and beeswax in boiling water and decant. Melt the stearic acid, filter, and combine with the paraffin-beeswax mixture. The mass has a melting point of 51–52°C. Store and use in stainless steel, enamel, or glass; avoid any contact with copper.

F–164. PARAFFIN, HANCE'S RUBBER (*145*)

Stock:

chopped crude rubber (smoked or unsmoked)	20 g

paraffin 100 g

Heat paraffin smoking hot, add rubber and stir from time to time. Keep hot until the rubber melts, 3–4 hours.

Embedding mixture:

Parowax or similar product	100 g
stock	4–5 g
beeswax	1 g

Melt, mix, and filter through paper.

F–165. PARAFFIN-STEARIC ACID MIXTURE, one of WATERMAN'S FORMULAE (*164*, p. 43)

stearic acid, technical grade	80 g
spermaceti wax	15 g
bayberry wax	5 g
Parowax, or similar brand of paraffin	400 g

Melt the paraffin at 60–70°C; add the other ingredients and mix thoroughly; filter.

F–166. PEERS' BICHLORIDE MORDANT (*249*) is a saturated aqueous solution of mercury bichloride. Decerated and hydrated sections are treated in it in an incubator for three or more hours. After mordanting, mercuric chloride crystals are removed with iodine and thiosulfate.

F–167. PERENYI'S FIXATIVE

nitric acid, 10%	40 ml
alcohol, 95%	30 ml
chromic acid, 0.5%	30 ml

Mix just before use; fix 4–12 hours.

PFA. See Bouin's PFA, F–40.

F–168. PHLOXINE STAIN (VII–4)

phloxine B	1 g
water	100 ml
hydrochloric acid	1 ml

Dissolve stain in water, add acid, shake well, and allow precipitate to settle; or centrifuge. Decant supernatant and resuspend the precipitate in 100 ml of water; repeat three times; filter through Whatman No. 2 paper. Put the precipitate, on its paper, in the oven until it is just dry. Pulverize, dissolve in 95% ethanol, 0.5 g/100 ml, and filter. This is the stock.

Working solution:

stock	20.0 ml
ethanol, 95%	30.0 ml
acetic acid, 28%	0.5 ml

Filter.

F–169. PICRO-FUCHSIN, VAN GIESON, MODIFIED (VII–8)

acid fuchsin, C.C., 1% aq sol	10 ml
picric acid, sat aq sol	50 ml
zinc sulfate ($ZnSO_4$) 5% aq sol	50 ml

POLYVINYL ALCOHOL MOUNTANT. See F–76.

F–170. POLYVINYL ALCOHOL for quieting small organisms (*227*, p. 8)

    polyvinyl alcohol, type B, grade RH-349-N du Pont 12–14 g

    water   100 ml

    Stir the powdered alcohol into the water, in a glass beaker set in a steam bath, until the solution is as thick as heavy molasses. When all the bubbles have risen to the surface the solution should be glass-clear. Pour into a wide-mouth, stoppered bottle. It keeps indefinitely.

F–171. PONTACYL BLUE-BLACK SX. Also called naphthol blue-black*

    A. pontacyl blue-black SX   1 g

        water   100 ml

    B. potassium dichromate   2 g

        water   100 ml

    Mix three parts of A with one part of B, by volume.

    * Green and Wood. 1959. Stain Tech. 34:313–16.

F–172. PROTARGOL SOLUTION (IX–12)

    Protargol-S, C.C. (Winthrop Laboratories)   1 g

    water   100 ml

    copper   5 g

    Put the water in a shallow dish and sprinkle the Protargol on its surface. Allow it to dissolve without disturbance or stirring. When the solution is put in the staining dish with the slides, add the copper either in granular form or as clean, thin wire. The solution cannot be re-used. See Bodian (*41, 42*) for original directions.

F–173. PVP-VA MOUNTANT: Vinylpyrrolidone-vinyl acetate copolymer E–735 (PVP-VA, E–735); (R–173)

    Mix very well equal volumes of PVP-VA, E–735 (an ethanol solution) and water; the final concentration is 25% plastic in 50% aqueous ethanol. Store in clear glass jars or dropper bottles; coat their caps lightly with silicone oil to prevent sticking. Lamkie and Burstone (*182*), who give these directions, find that it is a superior aqueous mountant. They mount well drained slides directly from water, and report that the covers are immovable in 30 minutes. It leaches eosin immediately; azure A and toluidine blue slightly, although their metachromatic staining of cartilage, mast cells, goblet cells, and mucins is well preserved. The following stains are very well preserved: oil red O, for fat; hematoxylin; periodic acid-Schiff; aldehyde-fuchsin; alcian blue; celestin blue; and methylene blue. The colored salts of various microchemical reactions are also well preserved.

F–174. RELIEF STAINS FOR CILIATES AND FLAGELLATES (V–23)

    among those in common use are:

    1. cotton blue, 1% aq sol   1 part

        nigrosin, 1% aq sol   3 parts

        This stain is used in the method of Maneval (*208*).

    2. India ink, diluted

F–175. RINGER'S SOLUTION FOR AMPHIBIANS

sodium chloride	8.0 g
calcium chloride, anhydrous	0.2 g
potassium chloride	0.2 g
sodium bicarbonate	0.2 g
water	1000.0 ml
dextrose (may be omitted)	1.0 g

Sterilize if necessary with a Berkefeld filter.

F–176. RINGER'S SOLUTION FOR WARM BLOODED ANIMALS

sodium chloride	9.0 g
calcium chloride, anhydrous	0.24 g
potassium chloride	0.42 g
potassium bicarbonate	0.20 g
water	1000.0 ml

F–177. RISER'S STAIN (268)

Stock:

ferric ammonium sulfate, violet crystals	2 g
water (cold)	100 ml
sulfuric acid	2 ml
celestin blue B	1 g
methanol, absolute	10 ml
glycerol	10 ml

Dissolve the ferric sulfate in the water and add sulfuric acid. Bring to a boil, add stain, and boil for a few minutes. Cool and add the alcohol and glycerol.

Staining solution:

stock	1 part
water	3 parts

F–178. ROSSMAN'S FIXATIVE (XIII–5)

picric acid, sat sol in absolute alcohol	90 ml
formalin	10 ml

F–179. SALINE WITH GUM ACACIA FOR PERFUSION

sodium chloride	0.9 g
gum acacia, preferably tears	2.4 g
water, to make	100.0 ml

Put all of the ingredients together in a bottle and allow the mixture to stand until the acacia tears are dissolved. If you use powdered acacia, U.S.P., mix it with a small amount of water in mortar and rub it to a thick paste; add the rest of the water and stir well; when the acacia is dissolved, add the sodium chloride. Filter through gauze, several layers, or coarse filter paper, if the solution is clear. This formula is for use with guinea pigs. For cats and monkeys, the amount of gum acacia is increased to 5.6 g. Adjust to pH 7.0–7.2 with NaOH.

F–180. SALINE, NORMAL is sometimes called physiological or isotonic saline. It consists of sodium chloride and water; the amount of sodium chloride used varies from one group of animals to an-

other. It may be made up in large quantities if there is constant
need for it in the laboratory. For less frequent use, weigh out
the amount of salt needed to prepare 1 liter of solution, preparing as many portions as desired. They may be kept in packets
or envelopes of glassine paper, one packet to be added to a liter
of water as the solution is needed. The usual proportion of
salt/liter is:

1. for birds, 7.5 g
2. for frog, 6.5 g
3. for mammals, 9 g
4. for insects, 6–8 g

F–181. SCHIFF REAGENT, BARGER AND DELAMATER (*19*)

basic fuchsin	1 g
water	400 ml
thionyl chloride (SOCl$_2$) C.P.	1 ml
activated charcoal	1 g

Dissolve fuchsin in water; add thionyl chloride. Stopper flask
for 12 hours when solution should be decolorized. Shake with
charcoal and filter; pH 1.24. Store in well-stoppered bottle. Use
in a dark room at room temperature.

F–182. SCHIFF REAGENT, LILLIE, COLD (*192*)

basic fuchsin	1.0 g
sodium metabisulfite (Na$_2$S$_2$O$_5$)	1.9 g
hydrochloric acid, 0.15 N	100.0 ml
fresh, activated charcoal (R–34)	500.0 mg

Mix all ingredients except charcoal and shake by hand, at intervals for 2 hours, or use a mechanical shaker. The solution will
be clear and either yellow or light brown. Add the charcoal and
shake 1–2 minutes. Filter, measure, and make up to 100 ml
with water passed through the residue in the filter. Store at
0–5°C. It may be re-used. Discard when the solution becomes
pink.

F–183. SNIDER'S FIXATIVE–STAIN FOR NISSL BODIES (*289*);
(IX–9)

toluidine blue	1 g
water	15 ml
alcohol, 95%	20 ml
dioxane	65 ml

Mix alcohol and water and add the dye. Shake well before
adding dioxane.

F–184. SUBLIMATE-ACETIC FIXATIVE

mercuric chloride, sat aq sol	95 ml
acetic acid	5 ml

Fix small bits of tissue not more than 6 hours. Wash overnight
in running water.

F–185. SUDAN BLACK B (IX–11)

Sudan black B	0.75 g

ethylene glycol   100.0 ml
Stir the dye into the ethylene glycol heated to 100°C. Note that
the ethylene glycol is flammable and should be heated with
care on a hot plate. Filter while hot and again after it has
cooled to room temperature.

F–186. TELLYESNICKY'S FIXATIVE (*142*, p. 229)
  potassium dichromate   3 g
  acetic acid   5 ml
  water   100 ml
  Add acetic acid just before use. Fix 24–48 hours, wash in
  running water 6–12 hours; general purpose fixative.

F–187. TELLYESNICKY'S, SMITH MODIFICATION (XI–15)*
  potassium dichromate   0.5 g
  acetic acid   2.5 ml
  formalin, commercial   10.0 ml
  water   87.5 ml
  Mix just before use; satisfactory for frogs and tadpoles up to
  10 mm long.
  * Smith, B. G. 1915. The preparation of serial sections of frog
    embryos. Seventeenth Annual Report, Michigan Academy
    of Science, 77–80.

F–188. THIONIN, KLINGER AND LUDWIG (*173*)
  A. thionin, sat sol in 50% ethanol, filtered
  B. sodium acetate ($NaC_2H_3O_2 \cdot 3\ H_2O$)   9.714 g
      sodium barbiturate   14.714 g
      water, carbon dioxide-free   500.0 ml
  C. 0.1 N hydrochloric acid
  A, B, and C are stock solutions. To make the working solution
  use 40 ml of A, 28 of B, and 32 of C. The pH should be
  5.7 ± 0.2.

F–189. TOISSON'S DILUTING SOLUTION FOR ERYTHROCYTE
  ENUMERATION (VIII–10)
  sodium sulfate   8.0 g
  sodium chloride   1.0 g
  glycerol, neutral   30.0 ml
  methyl violet 2B   0.025 g
  water   160.0 ml
  Filter before use.

F–190. VALNOR MOUNTANT (Abopon, R–196); directions of Hrushovetz and Harder (*155*)
  1. Heat the material in a water bath to 60–70°C to make it
  less viscous; then measure the desired volume, including some
  of the crystals, and pour into a beaker.
  2. Add gradually phosphate buffer 0.2 M, pH 7.0, rotating the
  beaker gently until all of the crystals are dissolved. The amount
  needed is usually about one third of the measured volume of
  Valnor mountant.

3. To remove the microscopic debris which appears in some lots, heat the diluted solution to 80°C and filter, while hot, through Whatman No. 1 filter paper.

4. Store in dropper bottles of 30–50 ml capacity.

5. If, on cooling, crystals do not appear in the dispensing bottles, add some undissolved Valnor mountant, since the solution must be saturated. This solution fades hematoxylin; it conserves aceto-orcein and Giemsa's stains, and the coloration of amyloid with crystal violet.

VINYLPYRROLIDONE-VINYL ACETATE COPOLYMER; see PVP-VA MOUNTANT, R–173.

F–191. WACHSTEIN-MEISEL SUBSTRATE (*320*)

adenosinetriphosphate (ATP), 125 mg/100 ml, aq sol	20 ml
*Tris-maleate buffer, 0.2 M, pH 7.2 (*129*, p. 220)	22 ml
lead nitrate, 2% aq sol	3 ml
magnesium sulfate 0.1 M solution	5 ml

CONTROL SOLUTION: replace the ATP by an equal quantity of sodium glycerophosphate.

* Stock solution: maleic acid, 29 g; Tris, (hydroxymethyl) aminomethane, 30.3 g; water, 500 ml. Mix, add about 2 g of charcoal, and shake. Filter after 10 minutes. To 40 ml of stock add 20 ml of 1N (4%) NaOH and 40 ml of water. Add a few crystals of camphor.

F–192. WATTS' STAIN FOR EOSINOPHILS (VIII–21)

eosin, yellow	1 g
glycerol	50 ml
water	50 ml

F–193. WEIGERT'S IRON HEMATOXYLIN (VII–8)

Solution A:

hematoxylin	1 g
ethanol, 95%	100 ml

Solution B:

ferric chloride, 29% aq sol	4 ml
water	95 ml
hydrochloric acid	1 ml

To use, mix equal parts of A and B. It stains best when freshly mixed.

F–194. WORCESTER'S FIXATIVE (*246*)

mercuric chloride, sat sol in 10% formalin	90 ml
acetic acid	10 ml

This is an excellent general fixative which deserves wider use. It is particularly good for chick embryos and eggs of amphibians and fishes. Fix 2–24 hours, or more if the specimen is large, and wash about as long as the fixation period.

F–195. WRIGHT'S STAIN, methods provided by Matheson, Coleman, and Bell (A–36)

Method I, for immediate use:

Wright's stain, dry	0.3 g

glycerol, A.C.S.   3.0 ml
methanol, A.C.S.   100.0 ml
Place stain in a mortar of about 300-ml capacity and add
glycerol. With pestle, triturate to a uniform consistency, 3–5
minutes. Continue trituration while adding the alcohol in three
approximately equal portions. Place mixture in bottle and test
on a blood smear before filtering.

Method II, for use in about 24 hours:
Ingredients as above; place the stain in a stoppered bottle and
add methanol and glycerol. Shake occasionally. Test staining
quality before filtering. Store as a stock solution.

F–196. WRIGHT AND KINNICUTT'S DILUTING SOLUTION FOR
BLOOD PLATELET ENUMERATION (VIII–12)
Solution A:
brilliant cresyl blue   1 g
water   300 ml
Solution B:
potassium cyanide   1 g
water   1400 ml
Store Solution A in refrigerator. Mix two parts of Solution A
with three parts of solution B just before use; filter.

XYLENE-RESIN. See mountants, resinous, F–146.

F–197. ZENKER'S FIXATIVE (XI–17)
potassium dichromate   2.5 g
mercuric chloride   5.0 g
water   100.0 ml
acetic acid   5.0 ml
Dissolve the salts in the water with the aid of heat. This will
keep for some months.
Fix small cubes no more than 4 mm thick, or still thinner slices,
as short a time as is compatible with good penetration, 4–18
hours. Wash 12–24 hours in running tap water.

F–198. ZENKER-FORMOL (VIII–26)
Make Zenker's fluid without acetic acid and just before using
add 5 ml of formalin/100 ml.

F–199. ZINC CHROMATE SOLUTION for impregnation of nervous
tissue; Bertram and Ihrig (36)
It is important to use reagents of A.C.S. specification.
chromium trioxide (weigh in a hood)   27 g
zinc oxide   22 g
formic acid   35 ml
water, to make   1000 ml
Dissolve the chromium trioxide in 500 ml of water. Add the
zinc oxide, dilute with water to 900 ml, and stir vigorously
10 minutes. Add the formic acid slowly and stir until all solids
are dissolved, about 30 minutes. Add water to make 1000 ml.
The pH should be 3.1; measure with a pH meter which employs
a saturated calomel electrode and a glass electrode.

EQUIPMENT AND SUPPLIES

Many of the commercially available items noted below may be secured from most dealers in laboratory equipment. This is indicated by the phrase, most dealers. If they are sold by only one or only a few firms, the known source will be indicated. It must be emphasized that there are probably other sources for some of the items which are unknown to the writer and are consequently not listed. Their omission does not indicate that they are not desirable firms from which to buy the item in question.

Some pieces of equipment are either less expensively made in the laboratory work shop, or are at present not manufactured or at least not widely distributed. For these, directions by various authors are given or references to their original source of information.

If firms mentioned in this section supply several items mentioned here or in other parts of this book, their addresses are not given but should be sought in Appendix IV. For dealers who supply only one item, the address will be found with the description of that item.

E–1. BAGS, COLLECTING, WHIRLPAK are sold in two sizes by the National Agricultural Supply Co., Fort Atkinson, Wis. They have a tight closure and are useful both for collecting and for shipping; they are recommended by Fulton (115).

E–2. BASTERS are kitchen utensils of Pyrex or polyethylene, resembling a medicine dropper in proportions but of much larger size and with a large rubber bulb. They are extremely useful for collecting small organisms and taking samples of mud and sand; they hold about 100 ml.

E–3. BATHS, TISSUE FLOTATION are heated by light bulbs or are wired for thermostatic controls. They are, in the writer's opinion, less satisfactory for spreading than spreading tables. There are a number of types and prices; most dealers.

E–4. BERLESE FUNNEL, MODIFIED. A relatively inexpensive funnel sold by Turtox (A–48), catalog Nos. 130A175 or 130A1751. This same apparatus may be made in the shop, according to the directions published by Stegman (300).

E–5. BIBULOUS PAPER is a white absorbent paper, sold by supply houses in booklets of 50 or more sheets about 4 × 6 inches. A good quality of paper towel or filter paper may be used instead.

E–6. BLENDOR, WARING is a device for mixing solutions at various rates of speed. It may be replaced, for some purposes, by various types of kitchen blenders; most dealers.

E–7. BOARDS, DISSECTING are of metal or of wood and have arrangements of various kinds for holding the specimen firmly in place. They may be purchased from most dealers or constructed in the shop. A simple kind is a smoothly finished piece of wood, paraffined, with a series of cup hooks on the two longer sides, to which cords may be attached.

E–8. BOATS FOR CASTING PARAFFIN AND WATER WAX BLOCKS. Many workers prefer boats for embedding and make them of paper. Echols (95) recommends the use of heavy-duty aluminum foil. He gives directions for preparing boats quickly on wooden forms. Both paper and foil boats may be used for casting blocks of water wax.

E–9. BOXES, SLIDE, are made in a variety of sizes; those most commonly used are 25 place, 50 place, and 100 place. They are made of wood, of hard plastics, and of polyethylene. The wooden boxes warp and are not always accurately sized. They are sometimes too narrow or too wide. The plastic boxes are superior in that they are smaller, the lids fit better, and the sizing is accurate. The hard plastics may break when dropped.

E–10. CANNULA. A tube of metal, glass, or plastic; in microtechnic it is usually inserted in a blood vessel or small duct for injecting or removing a fluid. Glass cannulae are usually made in the laboratory.

E–11. CENTRIFUGE, HAND, MICRO. A device suitable for concentrating small organisms is an old-type glass salt cellar. These generally have a small central indentation in which the specimens collect as the dish is gently rotated. (Most modern salt dishes have a flat floor and are unsuitable.) They may be found in second-hand stores. (Dr. John Corliss, personal communication).

E–12. CLOTHESPINS, WOOD, spring type, for making squashes and holding cover glasses in place while mountant dries.

E–13. CONTAINERS FOR SHIPPING. A good storage and shipping container for small specimens can be made by cutting off the opened end of a fountain pen cartridge and cleaning it. The kind made by Shaeffer takes a 00 cork.

E–14. A CONTAINER FOR CLEANED COVER GLASSES may be conveniently made from a box in which seventy two 25 × 75-mm slides are packed, and two 3 × 5-inch library cards. Fold each card three times, then unfold and crease sharply along the ridges thus produced. Place both cards in the bottom of the box where they will furnish seven shallow troughs in which various sizes of covers may be stored. Keep covered when not in use. (E. M. Bullis, personal communication)

E–15. CONTAINERS—MISCELLANEOUS. In buying laboratory equipment it is desirable to consider not only pieces made of glass, but those of stainless steel and of various kinds of plastic. In some instances only glass will serve, but the metal and plastic have the advantage of greater durability. Often they cost no more than glass, sometimes less. The disposable plastic pieces such as petri dishes may be used several times and, with suitable equipment, may even be sterilized by vapor. For some purposes, the much less expensive containers designed for household use, both in glass and plastic will serve. Culture dishes which are very convenient are the gallon size mayonnaise, mustard, or pickle jars which may usually be obtained without cost from the kitchens of college dining rooms.

E–16. COOKY SHEETS, used with heating pads for spreading sections or keeping animals warm during perfusion; they should be of aluminum with three sides turned up about ¼ inch and the fourth side left open.

E–17. COUNTER, MECHANICAL, for blood cell enumeration is of the type usually referred to as a hand tally; most dealers.

E–18. COVER GLASSES are made in a variety of sizes and thicknesses. They are designated according to thickness as follows: No. 0 is 0.085–0.13 mm; No. 1 is 0.13–0.16 mm; No. 2 is 0.19–0.25 mm. No. 1 is a suitable thickness for most sections. Cover glasses are round (circles), square and rectangular. The circles range in diameter from 18–25 mm; the squares from 18–25 mm; and the rectangles from 22 × 30 mm to 24 × 50 mm. For larger slides, there are rectangles 35 × 50 mm and 45 × 50 mm. The price is by weight, and they are usually sold in ½ oz boxes. Good brands are sold by supply houses. Arthur H. Thomas (A–47) will cut special sizes to order and will also supply thicknesses other than those given here. A supply of clean cover glasses of various sizes should always be kept ready; see E–14.

E–19. COVER GLASSES (PLASTIC) are useful for some types of preparations and for freshman laboratory work. They are inexpensive enough to be considered disposable. A. H. Thomas (A–47) stocks 22-mm No. 2 squares. Turtox (A–48) also sells this size at a slightly higher price; the same firm offers circles, two sizes of rectangles, and sheets of the film from which desired sizes may be cut. All are of the same thickness. Since the plastic scratches easily such covers should not be used routinely for permanent preparations.

DEPRESSION SLIDE: see slide, depression, E–67.

E–20. DIAGRAMS for centering specimens and covers may be made on paper or cardboard. More durable are those prepared of plywood which may be marked easily with pencil. Glass cut with a scriber and with the grooves filled with pigment are also satisfactory. To prepare these, trace the outline of the slide and indicate the position and size of the label. In the space remaining draw two diagonal lines so that they intersect in the middle of the unoccupied space.

E–21. DIPPING TUBES are pieces of glass tubing with both ends fire-polished. To operate, hold the tip of the forefinger over the upper end and dip the lower end into the water until it comes just above the object desired; lift the finger and let the air out of the tube; the water will rush in at the lower end carrying the object with it. Replace the finger over the top of the tube and remove it; the water will remain in it as long as the finger is held firmly over the upper end. When the finger is removed, the water and the object pass out; useful for collecting.

DISHES, EMBEDDING: see molds for casting paraffin blocks, E–44.

E–22. DISHES, STAINING, McJunkin, for a single 3 × 1-inch slide; A. H. Thomas Co. (A–47)

E–23. DISHES, STAINING, FOR COVER GLASSES.
A. COLUMBIA JARS have molded grooves to hold five cover glasses. Their covers are loosely fitting glass lids or screw tops. For many purposes the latter are preferable. A. H. Thomas Co. (A–47)
B. CHEN STAINING ASSEMBLIES consist of glass jars and porcelain racks of several sizes to accommodate cover glasses of different sizes, shapes, and numbers. A. H. Thomas Co.
C. STAINLESS-STEEL COVER GLASS STAINING RACKS of several kinds carry different sizes of cover glasses. Some will carry as many as 30 covers; Lipshaw. (A–34)
   When staining assemblies are used, an economy may often be effected by purchasing the trays only and by securing boxes of a suitable kind to fit them from less expensive sources. Many household and variety stores will provide suitable containers for the trays.

E–24. DISHES, STAINING, FOR SLIDES.
A. COPLIN JARS are made of glass with molded ridges and slots; they will hold five slides 25 × 75 mm with a 25-mm end down. Their covers are loosely fitting glass lids or plastic screw tops. The latter are preferable.
B. STAINING BOXES are of glass and have ridges and slots. They will hold 10 slides, 25 × 75 mm, side down. They have loosely fitting glass lids.
C. STAINING ASSEMBLY is the term usually applied to a glass or metal box fitted with a removable tray made of the same materials; the tray holds the slides, with a side down. The box is deep enough to permit staining even 50 × 75 mm slides, but may be used for smaller ones. The capacity of the glass trays is 10 slides. The metal trays hold from 10–60 slides. Before using metal trays and/or boxes, it is important to ascertain by trial whether the stainless steel or nickel silver of which they are usually made will react with the stains to be used in them. They are said to be inert with respect to most histological reagents.
D. PLASTIC STAINING TROUGH is Gurr's designation of a staining as-sembly which he sells. (A–27) It accommodates 10 slides of the three usual sizes and has a tight cover and a lifting device which is a part of the

tray. Because these assemblies are of inert material, easy to use, occupy less space, and are less expensive than those made of glass or metal, they are worth considering.

The capacities of the glass and plastic boxes and assemblies can be almost doubled if the slides are inserted alternately straight across and obliquely so that each groove, except the first and last, holds the ends of two slides. Arranged in this way the coplin jar will hold 9 and the glass and plastic assemblies 19. The metal trays have slots which are too narrow to receive more than one slide.

E–25. DISHES, STENDER are made in the following outside diameters: 50, 60, 80, 100, and 130 mm and in heights of 30, 35, 40, and 50 mm. They have ground edges and plate glass covers and are suitable for culture work; most dealers.

DISSECTING TOOLS: see tools, dissecting, E–81.

E–26. DOMES OF SILENCE, sometimes called gliders, are made in a number of sizes; one about 3 cm in diameter is generally useful (XVI–6); hardware and variety stores.

E–27. EMBEDDING DEVICES have been designed and described by several workers. They are usually used for handling minute specimens. See references: Cory (76); Buck (52).

E–28. FABRIC for cleaning slides and covers before use must be lint-free and absorbent. Old linen handkerchiefs, linen table napkins, and dimity, a cotton dress material, are all suitable. The edges may be cut with pinking shears; hems should be removed before use. The cloths should be washed after each use.

E–29. FAUCET SUCTION PUMP, often called a filter pump, is an inexpensive device which produces enough negative pressure to filter many solutions, and to clean and dry pipets; most dealers.

E–30. FILM, 35-MM, without emulsion, for spreading paraffin sections; du Pont's Cronar; Carolina Biological Supply Co. (A–10)

FILTER PUMP: see faucet suction pump, E–29.

FLOTATION BATH: see bath, tissue flotation, E–3.

E–31. FORCEPS, COVER GLASS, various types; the tips should be fine and/or flattened. One type (Novy) has the lower blade flattened, the upper curved to meet it. This is a useful tool; most dealers.

E–32. FORCEPS FOR STAINING. Two useful types are Steward, for cover glasses, and Kirkbride, for slides; A. H. Thomas Co. (A–47)

E–33. FROGS FOR INDUCTION OF OVULATION. The Carolina Biological Supply House (A–10) sells these sets of frogs from late October through March.

GLASS MARKERS: see scribers, E–60.

E–34. HOLDER FOR LIVING TISSUE: a slide for holding living material in place for examination. Cut a 1 × 3-inch piece of Lucite from ⅜-inch stock, leaving the paper covering in place. Mark on the paper a ⅞-inch square in the center of this piece of Lucite, and make a line ⅞ inch long, ¼ inch from the left side of the square. In this line and in the two sides of the square parallel to it, bore six equidistant holes ¹⁄₁₆ inch in diameter. Bore four similar holes in the two other sides of the square—twenty holes in all, around the square. Whittle plugs of balsa wood, dab them with Duco cement, and insert in the holes so that they project on each side of the slide. Trim them level with the slide surfaces. Remove the paper from the plastic. A specimen may be spread on the slide and held in place by pins thrust into the plugs. Donaldson (*92*).

E–35. HOSE CLAMP for chromosome squashes, Julien (*165*); Hoffman's is a good type; Fisher No. 15-875. (A–21)

E–36. INCUBATORS for developing eggs are of all varieties and prices. The 100-egg size sold by Sears Roebuck and Co. is usually satisfactory and is much cheaper than those obtained from laboratory supply houses. It cannot, like the latter type, be used for other purposes than bird incubation. A careful study of catalogs is recommended; one must bear in mind that a means of ventilation is a necessity.

INFILTRATING OVEN: see oven, infiltrating, E–48.

E–37. LABINK is supplied in several colors and is used to write on glass or porcelain with a steel pen or brush. It is not affected by usual laboratory reagents or cleaning solutions but is affected by boiling water and steam sterilization; Alfred Bicknell Associates, Cambridge, Mass., and several dealers.

E–38. LANCET, BLOOD, disposable. Fisher's (A–21) #5-954A (250/pkt), #5-9545 (1000/pkt) is a good type; available also from several other dealers.

E–39. LEROY PENS are found in stores which sell drafting supplies and come in several sizes. They may be ordered by mail from a catalog from Keuffel and Esser Co. (A–32)

E–40. MACROTOME. Templeton (*309*) has described a device which permits the cutting of slices of fresh tissue 1 mm in thickness. It makes use of a mechanical stage to move the specimen and a single-edge razor blade attached to a bar.

MICRO COVER GLASSES: see cover glasses, E–18 and E–19.

E–41. MICRO MOUNT HOLDERS are slides of plastic thick enough to hold an embedded specimen in a central concavity, but with thin ends that fit the grooves of standard slide boxes; Ward's Natural Science Establishment. (A–51)

E–42. MICROPROJECTORS: microscopes which throw the image of a section or whole mount on a screen or a paper; they must be used in a subdued light. Bausch and Lomb makes one suitable for low-power work. They are very useful to survey fields and to use in drawing outlines of complicated objects such as sections of embryos.

E–43. MICROTOME MOTORS. A rotary microtome may be equipped with a small motor which turns the wheel and leaves both hands free for dealing with the ribbon. An inexpensive and satisfactory type is that sold for attachment to sewing machines. It is provided with a foot pedal by which the speed may be controlled. It is essential to choose a model which will turn the wheel in the direction away from the operator. Supply houses offer various models which are satisfactory but more expensive.

E–44. MOLDS FOR CASTING PARAFFIN BLOCKS.
1. polyethylene ice cube trays, cut apart into separate compartments.
2. porcelain embedding dishes of various sizes; A. H. Thomas. (A–47)
3. petri dishes of the smallest size, both top and bottom.
4. syracuse watch glasses.
5. small glass dishes of any origin, with a flat bottom and sides slightly flared toward the top.
6. embedding dishes as offered by various dealers.
7. paper boats.
The ice cube molds will release the paraffin by slight pressure on bottom or sides; dishes 2–5 should be wiped with a light coating of glycerol before use.

E–45. MOLDS FOR PLASTIC EMBEDDING are most satisfactory if they are made of glass or highly polished metal. Good molds of various sizes and shapes may be made by fitting together slides or other pieces of glass. Pyrex glass and ordinary glass containers made for domestic purposes may be chosen with due regard to the size of the specimen to be cast. Petri dish halves are often suitable. Rings of glass or metal are good for making small circular castings. See Ward's and A. H. Thomas' catalogs for these.

E–46. NEUTRA-STAT: the device of Richards and Jenkins (266) for eliminating static electricity during paraffin sectioning. A head at the tip of a flexible tube contains an alpha-emitting strip; this ionizes the air and discharges static electricity from the ribbon when placed close to it during sectioning. It is obtainable from some laboratory supply houses including Gardner Laboratory, Inc., Bethesda 14, Md.

E–47. OBJECT CARRIERS are devices on which blocks of tissue are mounted for sectioning. There are several types.
A. OBJECT DISCS are of metal, with stems, and are bought from the manufacturer of the microtome used. They are more difficult to use than other types, are expensive, and have no satisfactory area for labeling.
B. BLOCKS, PHENOLIC RESIN, sometimes called fiber blocks, may be purchased under the name of blocks, embedding, from A. H. Thomas (A–47). These come in several sizes and have parallel slots on the sur-

face to which the specimen is attached. They are very satisfactory and superior to wooden blocks for nitrocellulose-embedded specimens.

C. BLOCKS, WOODEN, may be made inexpensively in the shop from dowel sticks or from pieces of hard, fine grain wood. They should be 2–3 cm long with their ends 2–3 cm on a side. The cuts should be made so that the ends are cross sections of the wood in order that the paraffin may penetrate readily. It is practical to place the specimens on these blocks for storage and to label them by writing on the side in pencil.

OBJECT DISCS: see object carriers, E–47.

E–48. OVEN, INFILTRATING, CURTIN'S (*81*) is an excellent contrivance. His directions for making it follow:
1. Buy a small, portable, steel-top oven. These are usually 10 × 12 inches at the base and about 11 inches high. It need not be insulated.
2. Place a carefully fitted sheet of hard board or asbestos in the open bottom. If desired, bolt this sheet to the flange.
3. If the shelf is to be used, cover it with hardware cloth to better support jars.
4. Bore a hole in the top of the oven of a size which will just permit the passage of an electric cord covered with rubber insulation. Insert the cord, connect it to a light receptacle inside the oven and to a plug at the other end. Provide a 75-watt bulb.
5. With jars of paraffin in the oven, adjust the height of the bulb so that at least the lower third of the paraffin will remain unmelted.

This oven costs less than five dollars to make. It is virtually dustproof and permits temperature regulation so that the specimens always rest on an unmelted base and are thus infiltrated at exactly the melting point of the paraffin.

PLASTIC TRAY: see tray, plastic, E–82.

E–49. PIPETS, COLLECTING, BANTA are 200 mm long and have a glass bulb 35 mm in diameter; for catching small specimens too quick to be taken in a gauze net; A. H. Thomas Co. (A–47)

E–50. RAZOR BLADES for use in razor-blade holders are usually of the double-edge type. While most ordinary thin blades will serve, the stainless steel kinds are the most satisfactory. Wilkinson's Sword Blade brand is particularly good. Some of the single-edge blades which are of uniform thickness except at the cutting edge are excellent.

E–51. RAZOR-BLADE HOLDER, for holding safety razor blades; AO Spencer. (A–2); used with E–50 to section paraffin blocks.

E–52. RESTRAINING DEVICES FOR INJECTION OF SMALL ANIMALS. It is sometimes difficult to inject small animals subcutaneously without the help of an assistant. A very simple device described by Keyl and Smith (*168*) makes the procedure relatively simple. This is a sheet of clear plastic 5 × 6 inches, in one corner of which an opening is cut obliquely to the edges of the sheet; its outer border is about 2⅛ inches from the corner.

The device is used by laying the plate with its longest dimension parallel to the vertebral column of the animal and pulling the dorsal skin through the opening. The injection is made into the tent of skin thus formed. Restraining cages of plastic are available from supply houses but are more expensive.

E–53. RIBBON BOXES. A satisfactory type is the shallow cardboard container in which ladies' hose are sold. Many dealers will save these for customers, on request. A label is attached to the lid and the inside dusted before use. A sheet of construction paper of slightly rough surface is cut to fit each box. Dark sheets make it easier to see the ribbons.

E–54. RIBBON WINDERS for paraffin sections are useful in cutting serial sections. One is made by AO Spences (A–2). Hance (*144*) gives directions for making simple and satisfactory substitutes for the more expensive commercial one.

E–55. RINGS FOR CASTING PLASTIC MOUNTS may be of glass (see E–56) or of metal. The latter are furnished by Ward's. (A–51)

E–56. RINGS AND RECTANGLES FOR MAKING CELLS for whole mounts are available, ready made, from several sources: glass rings of several diameters and heights from Ward's, Thomas, and Fisher; cellulose acetate rings and rectangles from Turtox. These last have a fairly wide range of sizes and four thicknesses. Since the thickness is from 0.01 to 0.04 inches, it is necessary, in making a thick cell, to build up the rings or rectangles by cementing together as many as necessary for the depth desired.

E–57. RINGS FOR SPREADING THIN MEMBRANES. Two rings are needed for each spread, one of which fits inside the other loosely enough to allow the edges of the membrane between them. A. H. Thomas (A–47) sells a suitable type called Retaining Rings; convenient sizes are 9/16 inch and 3/4 inch, inner diameter.

ROLLER: see ribbon winder, E–54.

SALT CELLAR: see centrifuge, hand, micro, E–11.

E–58. SARAN WRAP is a thin transparent plastic film sold in grocery stores for domestic purposes. There are numerous other similar plastic sheets in these stores which are probably equally good.

E–59. SCALPEL, RIBBON CUTTING, has a cutting edge 10 mm long at its tip.

E–60. SCRIBERS (glass markers) are provided with tips of carborundum, diamond, or tungsten carbide. The last type is inexpensive and is easy to use, because it has a fine, sharp point; many dealers.

E–61. SECTION CARRIERS are devices by which loose frozen or celloidin sections are transferred from one reagent to the next for staining and, if necessary, for dehydration.
A. A GLASS SIEVE which fits into a petri dish or finger bowl is described

by Peters (*250*). It is made by Braun-Knecht-Heimann Co., San Francisco 19, Calif.

B. JACOBSON'S CARRIER (*160*) was devised for frozen sections but would be equally useful for nitrocellulose sections. It is made by piercing the bottom of a 250-ml propylene beaker and the sides to a height of about 1 mm. After drilling the holes, the edges are carefully smoothed to prevent damage to the sections.

E–62. SECTION LIFTER: a generally useful device which has a flat metal blade; a wooden handle rather than a metal one is desirable. There should be several sizes available. They are particularly useful to lift specimens gently from one reagent to another; many dealers.

E–63. SHEAFF MICRO OBJECT MARKER, A. H. Thomas Co. (A–47), catalog No. 6730-B.

SLICING GUIDES are devices for making thin slices of tissue which will be readily penetrated by reagents. They are usually made in the laboratory shop. Below are directions for making two different types. See also macrotome, E–40.

E–64. SLICING GUIDE FOR SMALL ORGANS, Bernstein and Harman (*34*).
Materials: a fine-tooth, double-edged comb, preferably with the teeth 1 mm apart; a bar of Lucite about 10 mm thick and 12 mm wide; 2 nuts and bolts; double-edged razor blades with one edge protected.
Construction: divide the comb longitudinally into 2 equal halves and bolt them to the sides of the Lucite bar, passing the bolts through holes drilled at both ends of the comb and through the bar. Choose the drilling sites in such a way that the upper surface of the bar, which serves as a cutting platform, lies just above the bases of the comb teeth; make sure that the teeth are perfectly aligned.
Use: place a small organ such as a rat's brain on the Lucite bar. Pass the razor blade through the teeth of the comb which act as a guide for cutting uniform slices of macroscopic thickness. See also macrotome, E–40.

E–65. SLICING GUIDE FOR PARTS OF MODERATE SIZE. Stagg and Tappen (*298*) have devised a guide for accurate sectioning of decalcified bones which could be adapted for use with other materials also. It is made of three 1 × 5-cm bars of aluminum 35 cm long, held together by brass screws. Parallel cuts are made across the sides of the trough, 1.5 mm wide and 1 cm apart, with a machinist's circular saw. A double row of 3 brass bolts with freely rotating concave brass discs on their ends are inserted through the sides, equidistant from each other; they provide a clamping mechanism to hold the bone firmly in place. They are supplemented by molding clay packed around the bone.

A similar trough of hard wood could be constructed in a shop which lacks facilities for cutting metal. In either aluminum or wood, the relative proportions can be varied to fit objects of various sizes.

SLIDE BOXES: see boxes, slide, E–9.

E–66. SLIDES, MICROSCOPE, for sections and whole mounts are usually made of glass and may be purchased in these sizes: 25 × 75 mm; 37 × 75 mm; and 50 × 75 mm. The first size is in most common use; the others are for embryological preparations of some kinds, for large paraffin and celloidin sections, and for whole mounts of large organisms. The grade which Arthur H. Thomas calls clinical, is satisfactory for most work. There are several excellent brands offered by supply houses. Some slides are sold as prewashed and ready to use. They are sometimes really clean and they are often suitable for whole mounts, but they may be quite unsuitable for blood smears or for spreading paraffin sections. Test for chemical cleanness by placing a drop of water in the center of the slide. If it flattens and spreads, the surface is clean, but if it remains as a rounded drop the slide should be washed in a detergent, or in acid alcohol, or placed overnight in a glass-cleaning fluid (F–100) followed by thorough rinsing in water. All washed slides should be dried with lint-free cloths (E–28) and stored in dustproof boxes.

E–67. SLIDES, DEPRESSION, for the prolonged study of living specimens are available in a variety of sizes and styles. There are two types which are most generally useful: thin ones with a polished concavity and a thicker, molded kind which has a smooth depression with straight sides, Figure 1. The upper surface of this slide is ground. Plastic depression slides may also be had.

E–68. SLIDES, SILICA AND PLASTIC. It is sometimes necessary, in microchemical tests for potassium, sodium, and other materials which may be constituents of glass slides, to use those made of silica or Vinylite; A. H. Thomas Co. (A–47). Other types of plastic slides, such as those offered by Turtox (A–48), are economical to use in freshman zoology classes.

E–69. SLIDE WARMING TABLES are used for spreading and drying sections and drying slides after mounting. Both A. H. Thomas Co. (A–47) and Lipshaw (A–34) offer several models. They are excellent but expensive. Ball (16) describes the construction of one with a bimetallic thermoregulator which is very good. The writer has made spreading tables suitable for student use by placing a heating pad with a 3-speed switch between two aluminum cooky sheets, each with one open end. The switch should usually be set at medium for spreading paraffin sections.

SPREADING TABLE: see slide warming table, E–69.

STAINING DISHES: see dishes, staining E–22 and E–23.

STENDER DISH: see dishes, stender, E–25.

E–70. SYRINGES, LUER TYPE, B. D. Yale, are supplied with glass tip or with needle-locking tip of corrosion-resistant metal. Either tip accepts the standard slip-on needle. Sizes of 1-, 2-, 5-, and 10-ml capacity are most generally useful. A 1-ml capacity syringe, generally called tuberculin, is graduated in 0.01 ml.

E–71. SYRINGE, METAL, FOR INJECTING MASSES (as latex, and vinyl acetate); capacities 10, 25, and 50 ml, with glass barrel enclosed in metal except for a window; rubber covered plunger. Ward's (A–51) catalog Nos. 563 A, C, and E. Turtox (A–48), catalog No. 310A7011.

E–72. SYRINGE, TUBERCULIN, is a luer syringe graduated in 0.01 ml.

E–73. SYRINGE NEEDLES are supplied in gauges (diameters) ranging from 27–18, the higher numbers indicating smaller gauges. They are of stainless steel and fit luer syringes with a plain glass tip, and with the Luer-Lok top. They also attach, with adapters, to a veterinary-type syringe.

E–74. THORNS for pinning specimens on cork are superior to metal pins, since they are not affected by reagents. There is no commercial source for these; they should be collected when a suitable tree or shrub is discovered. Hawthorn trees provide very good sharp ones as do barberries and some of the locust trees.

E–75. TIDE is a household detergent obtainable in grocery stores. It is the only one known to the writer which is not toxic to organisms and cells.

TISSUE CARRIERS FOR HISTOLOGICAL PROCESSING are devices for transferring tissues from one solution to another; usually used for fixation and preparation for infiltration. They are of many kinds; some may be made in the laboratory or shop while others are purchased; see E–76.

E–76. TISSUE CARRIERS, COMMERCIAL are of several types. It is desirable to consult catalogs and compare prices. They include:
a. metal boxes or tubes which are perforated.
b. plastic boxes, usually with arrangements for labeling and with or without interior divisions into compartments. Some are cheap enough to be disposable; some are provided with weights which overcome the buoyancy of the plastic, so that the carrier floats suspended in the various fluids.
c. metal and porcelain carriers, which float or are partially submerged, include Gooch crucibles with corks and perforated metal tubes with corks. Lipshaw (A–34), A. H. Thomas (A–47), and Fisher (A–21) offer a variety of tissue carriers.

E–77. TISSUE CARRIERS produced in the laboratory and which may be made without specific directions are:
a. cones made of folded pieces of lens paper.
b. gelatin capsules of various sizes which should be perforated for the entrance of fluids.
c. tubes of glass or plastic, each end of which is covered with cheesecloth.

Carriers for which directions for making are helpful are the following:

E–78. HOLDERS FOR SMALL ORGANISMS (*319*)
1. Cut cellulose acetate test tubes in ¾-inch lengths.
2. Soften one end of a piece in acetone or apply plastic or celluloid cement to it.

3. Attach lens paper to the treated end by pressure.

E–79. THE CARRIER OF HORNER AND ARNOTT (*153*) is made from full-size ice-cube trays. Four or five $\frac{1}{16}$-inch openings are made in the bottom of each compartment of the tray by drilling or perforating with a hot needle. Specimens are placed in each compartment of the tray and the tray itself put in a Pyrex baking dish and covered with a sheet of glass. The writer modifies this device by:

1. always beginning the holes from the inside of the tray since the surface pierced last usually shows irregular projections. These hold the tray from the bottom of the dish.
2. making more holes than suggested for specimens which require rapid draining.
3. selecting a glass pan for the reagent container which is provided with a lid.

E–80. MELNYK'S TISSUE CARRIER (*218*) is made from part of a poly-ethylene ice-cube tray with small compartments. The number of sections in the piece cut from the tray may be chosen so that the device will fit into an available dish into which the reagents are poured; in his model, a 12-compartment tray $2\frac{1}{2} \times 1\frac{7}{8} \times \frac{1}{2}$ inch fits a rectangular ridged staining box.

Most of the bottom of each compartment is removed with a No. 4 cork borer. The openings are covered with Lumite-Woven Saran base filter fabric, style 1009000, 52×52 mesh from Chicopee Mills, Inc., 47 North Street, New York 13, N. Y. It is applied by heating the bottom of the tray to the melting point on a hot plate and applying the fabric quickly and with uniform pressure on both fabric and tray. The polyethylene body is reported to be unsatisfactory to use in xylene and phenol at room temperatures and in glacial acetic acid, acetone, ethyl acetate, and aqua regia at 60°C.

E–81. TOOLS, DISSECTING. A suitable assortment for most dissecting, preparatory to removal of tissue for histological work includes straight and curved scissors, fine forceps with curved and with straight points, heavy forceps, one or more section lifters, and scalpels. Many workers prefer the scalpels with replaceable blades which are sold in several sizes and styles.

TRANSFER TRAYS: see section carriers, E–61.

E–82. TRAY, PLASTIC for II–9. This may be made by cementing together, with epoxy resin, pieces of ethyl or methyl methacrylate; these are cut to such dimensions that the resulting box will accommodate frogs of the size usually used in a laboratory. It is also possible to buy suitable trays of plastic or glass at variety and hardware stores and from supply houses.

E–83. TRIMMING JIGS are sometimes used to make the edges of paraffin blocks parallel. Lorenzo (*203*) describes one which can be made in the shop. Matthews describes another (*212*).

E–84. VIALS, SHELL, have a uniform diameter and no indentation at the top. They are made in a variety of sizes ranging from 25×8 mm to 80×25 mm; most dealers.

E–85. WARM STAGES which will keep specimens at desired temperatures while they are studied are available from some dealers. Satisfactory ones may be devised. A recent paper by Reeve and Makower (*262*) gives directions for constructing one using a 3½-inch square plate of electrically conductive glass.

E–86. WEIGHTS FOR COVER GLASSES are used to hold the cover in place on some types of whole mounts and thick sections until the mountant has set. It is usually possible to improvise these. One may use shell vials with a diameter less than that of the cover glass and partially filled with mercury, lead shot, or water; piles of copper pennies; weights from old balances. Spring clips in which tension is adjustable, and wooden spring clothespins may be used instead of weights.

ADDRESSES OF DEALERS IN EQUIPMENT, REAGENTS, AND SUPPLIES

A–1. ALROSE CHEMICAL CO., Providence, R. I.

A–2. AMERICAN OPTICAL CO. (AO Spencer), Instruments Division, Buffalo 15, N. Y.

A–3. ANTARA CHEMICALS, General Aniline and Film Corp., New York, N. Y.

A–4. ATLAS POWDER CO., Wilmington, Del.

A–5. BAUSCH AND LOMB OPTICAL CO., INC., Rochester, N. Y. 14602

A–6. BERSWORTH CHEMICAL CO., Framingham, Mass.

A–7. BRITISH DRUG HOUSES LTD. Distributor in the United States, Ealing Corp., Cambridge 40, Mass.

A–8. CADEL CHEMICAL CO., 205 Chicago St., Buffalo 5, N. Y.

A–9. CARBIDE AND CARBON CHEMICALS CORP., Division of Union Carbide and Carbon Co., 30 E. 42nd St., New York 17, N. Y.

A–10. CAROLINA BIOLOGICAL SUPPLY CO., Burlington, N. C. 27216

A–11. CELANESE CORP. OF AMERICA, New York, N. Y.

A–12. CLARK, H. WILLARD, 33 South High St., Melrose 76, Mass. 02176

A–13. COLUMBIAN CARBON CO., Research Laboratories, 214 44th St., Brooklyn 32, N. Y.

A–14. CYANAMID: see Lederle Laboratories, A–33.

A–15. DISTILLATION PRODUCTS INDUSTRIES, Eastman Organic Chemicals Department, Rochester 3, N. Y.

A–16. DOW CHEMICAL CO., Executive Offices, Midland, Mich.

A–17. I. E. DU PONT DE NEMOURS, Electrochemical Department, 7 S. Dearborn St., Chicago 3, Ill. and Wilmington, Del.

A–18. EASTMAN ORGANIC CHEMICALS DEPT., Division of Eastman Kodak Co.; see A–15.

A–19. EDMUND SCIENTIFIC CO., Barrington, N. J. 08007

A–20. EMARESS SCIENTIFIC EDUCATIONAL ARTS AND CRAFTS, P. O. Box 445, Loma Linda, Calif. 92354

A–21. FISHER SCIENTIFIC CO. has sales-stock distribution centers in Boston; Chicago; Fort Worth; Houston; New York; Odessa,

Texas; Philadelphia; Pittsburgh; St. Louis; Union, N. J.; Washington, D. C.; Edmonton, Montreal, and Toronto, Canada.

A–22. FLATTERS AND GARNETT, LTD., 309 Oxford Road, Manchester 13, England.

A–23. GEMEC CHEMICALS CO., 120 Moorgate Road, London, E. C. 2, England.

A–24. GENERAL ANILINE AND FILM CORP., Dyestuff and Chemical Division, 2445 E. 26th St., Los Angeles, Calif.

A–25. GENERAL BIOLOGICAL SUPPLY CO., 8200 S. Hoyne Ave., Chicago 20, Ill. (Turtox)

A–26. T. GERRARD AND CO., LTD., London W. I., England.

A–27. EDWARD GURR, LTD., 42 Upper Richmond Rd. West, London, S. W. 14, England.

A–28. HARTMAN-LEDDON CO., 5821 Market St., Philadelphia 39, Pa.

A–29. HERCULES POWDER CO., Wilmington, Del.; Parlin, N. J.

A–30. K AND K LABORATORIES, INC., 177 93rd Ave., Jamaica 33, N. Y.

A–31. KESSLER CHEMICAL CO., INC., State Road and Cottman Ave., Philadelphia 35, Pa.

A–32. KEUFFEL AND ESSER; offices in numerous cities in the U. S. A., including Anchorage, Alaska; Toronto and Montreal, Canada.

A–33. LEDERLE LABORATORIES, a division of American Cyanamid Co., Pearl River, P. O. Box 149, New York, N. Y. 10965

A–34. LIPSHAW MANUFACTURING CO., 7446 Central Ave., Detroit 10, Mich.

A–35. LUCIDO DIVISION, NOVADEL-AGENER CORP., 1740 Military Rd., Buffalo, N. Y.

A–36. MATHESON, COLEMAN, AND BELL, East Rutherford, N.J.; or Norwood, Ohio.

A–37. MEINECKE AND CO., INC., 225 Varick St., New York 4, N. Y.

A–38. PFALTZ AND BAUER, INC., Empire State Building, New York 1, N.Y.

A–39. PFIZER LABORATORIES, Division of Charles Pfizer and Co., Inc., 235 E. 42nd St., New York, N. Y. 100017. Address inquiries to Professional Services Dept.

A–40. PHIPPS AND BIRD, INC., 6th at Bird St., Richmond, Va. 23205

A–41. POWELL LABORATORIES, Gladstone, Ore. 97027

A–42. ROBOZ SURGICAL INSTRUMENT CO., INC., 810 – 18th St., N. W., Washington, D. C.

A–43. ROHM AND HASS CO., Washington Square, Philadelphia 5, Pa.

A–44. SCIENTIFIC PRODUCTS, Evanston, Ill.

A–45. STAR BAND CO., Broad and Commerce Sts., Portsmouth, Va.

A–46. STERI-KEM PRODUCTS, Whittier, Calif.

A–47. ARTHUR H. THOMAS CO., Vine St. at Third, P. O. Box 779, Philadelphia 5, Pa.

A–48. TURTOX, 8200 S. Hoyne Ave., Chicago 20, Ill.

A–49. UNION CARBIDE CORP., CHEMICALS DIVISION, 270 Park Ave., New York, N. Y. 10017; 230 Michigan Ave., Chicago, Ill.

A–50. VALNOR CORP., 16 Clinton St., Brooklyn 1, New York, N. Y.

A–51. WARD'S NATURAL SCIENCE ESTABLISHMENT, INC., P. O.
    Box 1712, Rochester, N. Y. 14603

A–52. WILL CORP., Rochester 3, N. Y.; Atlanta 1, Ga.; New York 52, N. Y.;
    Baltimore 24, Md.; Buffalo 5, N. Y.; S. Charleston 3, W. Va.

A–53. WINTHROP LABORATORIES, 1450 Broadway, New York 18, N. Y.

A–54. WYANDOTTE CHEMICAL CORP., Wyandotte, Mich.

GLOSSARY

Many terms used in the text are defined as they are introduced or are explained in one of the appendices. Such definitions are referred to in the index. Other terms will be already known to the reader or may be easily found in standard works of reference. The glossary contains only words or abbreviations which may be difficult to locate, which are important enough to require special notice, or which have a rather limited meaning in the field of microtechnic.

ADJUVANTS: helpful substances; in this book used particularly in connection with various materials which are added to commercial or domestic brands of paraffin to make mixtures which section and ribbon well.

AFFIXATIVES are compounds used in making sections adhere to a slide. It is possible to spread paraffin sections which adhere perfectly without affixatives if meticulous care is used; the use of an affixative makes good results more certain.

A.C.S., on the label of a reagent, indicates that it is of a grade approved by the American Chemical Society.

BLOCK: The use of this term should be restricted to an embedded specimen (specimen in its embedding medium). It is often confusingly applied to the object carrier on which a block is mounted.

BLOCK STAINING: synonymous with bulk staining and in toto staining. It refers to the staining of a specimen before infiltration. The most commonly used dyes for this purpose have been hematoxylin and alum cochineal. Recently Schiff's reagent (pp. 153 and 167) has been successfully used in this way.

BLOCKING: the formation of a block by embedding or casting.

BUFFY COAT is the layer of leucocytes which collects above the red blood corpuscles in a sample of oxalated blood. In a normal specimen it is a thin layer.

CASTING a block is synonymous with embedding; the term is usually reserved for specimens infiltrated in wax or plastic.

CATALYSTS for plastic embedding increase the rate of polymerization. Benzoyl peroxide is commonly used.

C.C. indicates certification by the Biological Stain Commission. Stains carry the certification label if they have been examined by members of the Commission or its agents and found to conform to standards established by the Commission.

291

COUNTERSTAINS usually demonstrate cytoplasmic and intercellular substances and are to be contrasted with nuclear stains; most counterstains are applied after nuclear stains.

DECERATION: the removal of embedding wax from spread sections with xylene or a reagent of similar characteristics. The process is called, somewhat laboriously, deparaffinization; it is also called dewaxing.

DEWAXING: *see* deceration.

DIFFERENTIATION: the removal of excess dye by a dye solvent from overstained objects; a part of regressive staining. It should result in precise coloration of a cell or tissue element; *see* p. 152 for Heidenhain's iron hematoxylin method. Differentiation is also employed to remove excess stain in progressive staining.

DISSOCIATION: the separation of tissue elements from each other so that they may be seen as whole objects; the process is usually carried on by fluids which soften or dissolve the substances holding the tissue elements together. It may be completed by teasing; *see* p. 39. For examples, *see* pp. 38, 39, and 130.

DOUBLE EMBEDDING: the use of one infiltrating agent followed by embedding in another; for instance, infiltrating with water wax and embedding in paraffin.

EMBEDDING: the enclosure of a specimen in a substance which will harden into a firm mass, in preparation for sectioning. Specimens are usually, but not always, infiltrated with the same substance. *See* p. 86.

FORMALDEHYDE, $H \cdot CHO$, is a gas often produced by partial combustion of methanol. The name preferred by the International Union of Chemistry, but seldom used in microtechnic, is methanal.

FORMALIN is a saturated solution of formaldehyde in water; the solution is usually considered as 100% when employed in formulae or in making dilutions. (*See* R–85.)

FORMOL, a trade name, is an older term for formalin. It is not in common use now but is generally retained as part of a compound name assigned when formol was in general use: example, picro-formol-acetic.

HARLECO: a brand name used by Hartman-Leddon Company.

HEINZ BODIES are normally found in small numbers in red blood corpuscles. The number is increased in certain types of hemolytic anemia.

HISTOPHAGOUS: tissue-eating; characteristic of certain organisms, either scavengers or parasites.

INDIA INK: synonym, Chinese ink; a term which describes a number of mixtures, all of which have a base of carbon. When used in microtechnic as a vital dye, it almost always means a commercial preparation of colloidal carbon, such as Higgins' India ink or Pelikan drawing ink. The ink is injected intravascularly, intraperitoneally, or subcutaneously.

INFILTRATION is the process of permeating a cube, slice, or fragment of tissue with a supporting medium such as paraffin or nitrocellulose in a liquid state. Following infiltration, the medium is hardened by cooling in the paraffin process, or by evaporation of the solvent in the nitrocellulose technic.

LEUCO DYES (LEUCO BASES) are colorless compounds made when a dye is reduced. After oxidation, there is a restoration of color, but the chromophore is probably a slightly different compound than in the original dye. Schiff's reagent is a leucobasic fuchsin and methylene blue may be employed in the leuco (reduced) form.

LIGATION: tying a blood vessel with a thread or other ligature to slow blood flow or to stop it either temporarily or permanently.

LIGHT MICROSCOPE refers to conventional microscopes, distinguishing this type from electron microscopes.

MACERATION is a method of dissociation by which cement substances between tissue elements are dissolved.

MEDIUM is a term which should be correctly used and often is not; the plural, media, is frequently employed when the singular, medium, should be used; *see* p. 216.

MICHROME is a brand name used by Edward Gurr, Ltd.

MIKROPS is a brand name used by Flatters and Garnett, Ltd.

MITOTIC POISONS are substances which interfere with the normal process of mitosis and are used to advantage in increasing the number of metaphase plates. Their action is to stop the process at metaphase, when the chromosomes have separated; they prevent cytokinesis.

MOUNTANTS are fluids used in mounting; *see* Mounting, A. For an exhaustive study of mountants of all sorts, see the report of Lillie, R. D., Zirkle, C., Dempsey, E. W., and Greco, J. P., 1953. Stain Tech. 28: 57–80.

MOUNTING is a term used in two ways:

A. It means covering a specimen on a slide with mountant and a cover glass; in a few cases the mountant may be omitted (*see* p. 44).

B. It means affixing frozen or nitrocellulose sections on a slide before staining them.

NET RETICLE (RETICULE) is a set of engraved lines on a glass disc, arranged to enclose square spaces of equal size. The disc is inserted in the eyepiece of a microscope at such a level that it and an object on the stage will be in focus at the same time.

OBJECT CARRIER: the device upon which a block is mounted; it may be a metal disc with a stem, a fiber block (so-called), a piece of wood, or any other body which carries a block on its surface and is inserted in the object clamp of a microtome.

OVERSIGHT METHODS are staining technics which give a general picture of an organ or tissue because they demonstrate many of its components. Good examples of oversight methods are Kornhauser's Quad stain and Mallory's connective tissue stain. Hematoxylin and eosin is another example, but it is more difficult to interpret.

PERFUSION is the injection of a liquid or liquids through the circulatory system at normal arterial pressure of an animal; it usually begins with normal saline until the blood has been washed out and is followed by a dye or fixative. Pulsating perfusion, recommended by some authors, simulates arterial pulsation by interrupting the flow at regular intervals.

PLASMAL REACTION is a staining of substances other than DNA, which sometimes occurs when leucobasic fuchsin is applied to specimens. It may be prevented in some material by an extraction of the plasmal-reactive substances with methanol-chloroform previous to the staining process.

REFRACTORY TISSUES are those difficult to infiltrate with paraffin. The refractory character is usually imparted to them by a high content of yolk or blood.

RIBBON: In the cutting of wax blocks which are properly trimmed each section adheres to the preceding one, forming a continuous ribbon of sections. The word is used in this connection both as a noun and a verb.

SACRIFICE: to kill an animal at the termination of an experiment, or to provide material for microscopical study.

SECTIONING: the cutting of thin slices of frozen or embedded tissue at a known thickness, measured in microns, on a machine called a microtome. Some plant tissues may be cut without embedding, but most animal tissues must be supported.

SERIAL SECTIONS are sections kept in serial order as they are cut; they are mounted or spread on the slide in the same order. Although material in any embedding medium may provide serial sections, they are most easily made after paraffin embedding.

SUBSTRATE is a substance which is acted upon by an enzyme. The relation between substrate and enzyme is generally specific, each enzyme acting upon a single substrate. The more recent conventions of terminology make the relationship between them clear. The enzyme name ends in -ase, and its first part indicates the substrate. For example, adenosine triphosphate, the substrate, is broken down by adenosine triphosphatase, the enzyme; lipids are acted upon by lipases.

SUPRAVITAL STAINING: *see* vital staining.

SURFACE ACTIVE AGENTS are substances which usually concentrate at boundaries, for example, the boundary between a solid and a liquid. In microtechnic, such agents are useful in spreading paraffin sections and in facilitating penetration of fluids into tissues. Tergitol, for example, added in small quantity to a stain, will usually shorten the staining time appreciably. *See* also Tween 40 and Tween 80, R–195.

TEASING: the mechanical separation of fibrous tissue components such as muscle cells (fibers) and fibers of tendons. The instruments used are needles with which the intercellular and interfiber substance is gently torn so that each unit is separated from its neighbor. Teasing may be preceded by maceration.

U.S.P. on the label of a reagent indicates that it is the grade approved for inclusion in the *U.S. Pharmacopeia.*

VITAL STAINING is the coloration of (1) cells, (2) intercellular materials, and (3) intracellular substances following the injection or ingestion of nontoxic dyes. The staining is either long-lasting or permanent, but harmless. Examples: (1) Cells are stained by taking up such colloidal materials as India ink, the pigments used in tattooing, or trypan blue; (2) intercellular materials such as the matrix of bone is colored by ingestion of alizarin red S (p. 131) or injection of chlorazol pink (p. 131); (3) fat, an intracellular substance, is stained after ingestion of a solution of Sudan III.

Supravital staining should be carefully distinguished from vital staining. The dyes used are toxic. They are applied to cells shortly before removal from the body, or to cells removed from the body but still living. In both cases the cells survive for short periods. Thus staining of the mitochondria of pancreatic cells by perfusion of the pancreas with Janus green and staining of the mitochondria of leucocytes on a glass slide are both examples of supravital staining.

WATER WAXES: polyethylene glycols, soluble in water. They are available in a variety of grades of hardness (*see* p. 76) and are useful for such purposes as the conservation of materials destroyed by reagents used in paraffin and nitrocellulose technics.

XYLENE, *o*-xylene, $C_6H_4(CH_3)_2$, is referred to as xylol in older literature. It is a commonly used clearing agent and solvent. Compounds such as carbolxylol, formulated when xylol was the common term, usually retain that spelling.

XYLENE-RESIN is a mountant made of resin which is usually dissolved in xylene; it is also soluble in toluene, benzene, and other similar reagents.

BIBLIOGRAPHY

1. Ackerman, G. Adolph. 1958. A combined alkaline phosphatase-PAS staining method. Stain Tech., 33: 269–71.
2. Adams, J. A. and Travis, B. V. 1935. Two new species of gregarine protozoa from the firebrat, *Thermobia domestica* (Pack.) (Thysanura). J. Parasit. 21: 56–59.
3. Agrell, Ivar P. S. 1958. Whole mounts of small embryos attached directly to glass slides. Stain Tech. 33: 265–67.
4. Albrecht, Mildred H. 1954. Mounting frozen sections with gelatin. Stain Tech. 29: 89–90.
5. Ali, M. A. 1959. A suggested method for Daphnia culture. Turtox News 37: 203.
6. Allen, Ezra. 1919. A technique which preserves the normal cytological conditions in both germinal and interstitial tissue in the testis of the albino rat (Mus norvegicus albinus). Anat. Rec. 16: 25–37.
7. Altmann, R. 1894. Die Elementarorganismen und ihre Beziehungen zu den Zellen. Leipzig: Veit Co.
8. American Optical Company, 1958. Oscar W. Richards. The effective use and proper care of the microscope.
9. Angulo, A. W., Hessert, E. C., Jr., and Kownacki, V. P. 1958. A carbon-gelatin injection mass for minute vascular and respiratory passages. Stain Tech. 33: 63–66.
10. Anthony, Adam. 1959. Tissue sectioning with the freezing microtome. Stain Tech. 34: 288.
11. Armitage, Kenneth B. 1960. The use of Daphnia to demonstrate biological phenomena. Turtox News 38: 118–21.
12. Ashley, Laurence M. 1946. A rapid method of handling paraffin sections. Turtox News 24: 41–44.
13. Baird, I. L. and Henson, O'Dell W. 1961. Sectioning and staining whole heads of small animals. Stain Tech. 36: 173–76.
14. Baker, J. R. 1945. Cytological technique. London: Methuen and Co., Ltd.
15. Baker, J. R. 1944. The structure and chemical composition of the Golgi element. Quart. J. micr. Sci. 85: 1–72.
16. Ball, Harold J. 1958. An inexpensive slide warming table. Turtox News 36: 248–49.
17. Baradi, A. F. and Quinton-Cox, R. 1963. Staining secretory capillaries of exocrine glands with techniques for specific phosphatases. Stain Tech. 38: 121–25.
18. Barer, R. 1956. Lecture notes on the use of the microscope. Oxford: Blackwell Scientific Publications.
19. Barger, J. D. and DeLamater, E. D. 1948. The use of thionyl chloride in the preparation of Schiff's reagent. Science 108: 121–22.

20. Barr, Murray L. 1959. Sex chromatin and phenotype in man. Science 130: 679–85.

21. Barr, M. L. and Bertram, E. G. 1949. A morphological distinction between the neurones of the male and female, and the behaviour of the nucleolar satellite during accelerated nucleoprotein synthesis. Nature, Lond. 163: 676–77.

22. Barron, D. H. 1934. Amyl acetate: A useful solvent for embedding masses. Anat. Rec. 59: 1–3.

23. Bauer, H. 1933. Mikroskopisch-chemischer Nachweis von Glykogen und einigen anderen Polysacchariden. Z. mikr. anat. Forsch. 33: 143–60.

24. Becker, E. R. and Roudabush, R. L. 1935. Brief directions in histological technique. Ames, Iowa: Collegiate Press, Inc.

25. Beers, C. D. The culture of Didinium nasutum, in Needham *et al.*, 234 p. 100–3.

26. Bell, J. Thomas, Jr. 1959. Polyoxyethylene sorbitan monopalmitate (Tween 40) as a vehicle for oil red O fat stain. Stain Tech. 34: 219–21.

27. Belling, John. 1926. The iron-acetocarmine method of fixing and staining chromosomes. Biol. Bull. 50: 160–62.

28. Benford, James R. 1951. The theory of the microscope. Rochester: Bausch and Lomb.

29. Bennett, H. Stanley. 1940. Nitrocellulose in amyl acetate as an embedding medium. Anat. Rec. 76: 233–39.

30. Bensley, C. M. 1939. Comparison of methods for demonstrating glycogen microscopically. Stain Tech. 14: 47–52.

31. Bensley, R. R. 1911. Studies on the pancreas of the guinea pig. Amer. J. Anat. 12: 297–388.

32. Bergan, P. 1955. Aceto-orcein and Feulgen stains for anatomy and cytology of trematodes. Stain Tech. 30: 305–10.

33. Berger, Patricia J. 1962. Blood letting from the eye of an amphibian. Turtox News 40: 55.

34. Bernstein, P. W. and Harman, P. J. 1955. A simple slicing guide for small organs. Stain Tech. 30: 193–94.

35. Bertram, E. G. and Ihrig, H. K. 1957. Improvement of the Golgi method by pH control. Stain Tech. 32: 87–94.

36. Bertram, E. G. and Ihrig, H. K. 1958. Zinc chromate solutions for impregnation of nervous tissue. Stain Tech. 33: 187.

37. Bertram, E. G. and Ihrig, H. K. 1959. Staining formalin-fixed nerve tissue with mercuric nitrate. Stain Tech. 34: 99–108.

38. Best, F. 1906. Ueber Karminfärbung des Glycogens und der Kerne. Z. wiss. Mikr. 23: 319–22.

39. Blank, H. and McCarthy, P. L. 1950. A general method for preparing histological sections with a water-soluble wax. J. Lab. clin Med. 36: 776.

40. Blank, H., McCarthy, P. L. and DeLamater, E. D. 1951. A non-vacuum

freeze-dehydrating technic for histology, autoradiography and microbial cytology. Stain Tech. 26: 193–97.

41. Bodian, D. 1936. A new method for staining nerve fibers and nerve endings in mounted paraffin sections. Anat. Rec. 65: 89–97.

42. Bodian, D. 1937. The staining of paraffin sections of nervous tissue with activated Protargol. The role of fixatives. Anat. Rec. 69: 153–62.

43. Bovee, Eugene C. 1958. Nickel sulfate as an anesthetic for protozoans. Turtox News 36: 78–79; and 1963, personal communication.

44. Bowen, C. C. 1956. Freezing by liquid carbon dioxide in making slides permanent. Stain Tech. 31: 87–90.

45. Boyd, I. A. 1962. Uniform staining of nerve endings in skeletal muscle with gold chloride. Stain Tech. 37: 225–30.

46. Boyer, C. C. and Dunaway, M. L. 1953. Staining in lieu of micro-injection for the study of embryonic blood vessels. Stain Tech. 28: 147–48.

47. Brecher, George. 1949. New methylene blue as a reticulocyte stain. Amer. J. clin. Path. 19: 895–96.

48. Breder, C. M., Jr. and Nigrelli, R. F. 1933. Lamellibranch leucocytes as living material for class room demonstration. Science 78: 128.

49. Brewer, H. E. and Shellhamer, R. H. 1956. Stained ground sections of teeth and bone. Stain Tech. 31: 111–14.

50. Bridges, Calvin B. 1937. The vapor method of changing reagents and of dehydration. Stain Tech. 12: 51–52.

51. Bruesch, Rulin. 1942. Staining myelin sheaths of optic nerve fibers with osmium tetroxide vapor. Stain Tech. 17: 149–52.

52. Buck, John B. 1938. A device for orienting and embedding minute objects. Stain Tech. 13: 65–68.

53. Bulmer, D. 1959. Dimedone as an aldehyde blocking reagent to facilitate the histochemical demonstration of glycogen. Stain Tech. 34: 95–98.

54. Burdi, Alphonse R. 1965. Toluidine blue-alizarin red S staining of cartilage and bone in whole-mount skeletons *in vitro.* Stain Tech. 40: 45–48.

55. Caramia, F. G. and Angeletti, P. U. 1962. Differentiation of serous and mucous components of salivary glands by alcian blue and a counter-stain. Stain Tech. 37: 125–27.

56. Carame-Vivas, M. J. 1962. A method for holding small aquatic invertebrates. Turtox News 40: 60–61.

57. Carbowax Brochure. 1960. Carbowax polyethylene glycols. New York: Union Carbide Chemicals Co.

58. Carolina Biological Supply Co. 1949. Killing paramecia in bulk. Carolina Tips 12: 32.

59. Carolina Biological Supply Co. 1959. Carolina introduces the slide strip. Carolina Tips 22: 37–38.

60. Carothers, E. Eleanor. 1928. The collodion method and serial sections. Science 67: 400–401.

61. Carr, D. H. and Walker, J. E. 1961. Carbol fuchsin as a stain for human chromosomes. Stain Tech. 36: 233–36.
62. Cather, James Newton. 1958. Fixing and staining the chromosomes in eggs of invertebrates. Stain Tech. 33: 146–47.
63. Cathey, William J. 1963. A plastic embedding medium for thin sectioning in light microscopy. Stain Tech. 38: 213–16.
64. Celarier, Robert P. 1956. Tertiary butyl alcohol dehydration of chromosome smears. Stain Tech. 31: 155–57.
65. Chauncy, H. H., Smarsh, A., and Kronman, J. H. 1964. False cellular localization of aminopeptidase caused by resinous mounting media. Stain Tech. 39: 131–34.
66. Cobb, N A. 1931. The use of live nemas (Metoncholaimus pristiurus) in zoological courses in schools and colleges. The Collecting Net 6: 276–77.
67. Cole, E. C. 1936. A new methylene blue technic for permanent preparations. Stain Tech. 11: 45–47.
68. Cole, W. V. 1951. Some observations on the comparative histology of the motor end plate. Trans. Amer. micr. Soc. 70: 239–44.
69. Conger, Alan D. 1960. Dentists' Sticky Wax: a cover-sealing compound for temporary slides. Stain Tech. 35: 225.
70. Conger, A. D. and Fairchild, L. M. 1953. A quick-freeze method for making smear slides permanent. Stain Tech. 28: 281–83.
71. Conn, H. J. 1939. Cautions in the use of dioxane. Stain Tech. 14: 152.
72. Conn, H. J. et al. 1960. Staining procedures. Ed. 2. Baltimore, Md.: Williams and Wilkins Co.
73. Conn, H. J. et al. 1961. Biological stains. Ed. 7. Baltimore, Md.: Williams and Wilkins Co.
74. Corliss, John O. 1953. Silver impregnation of ciliated protozoa by the Chatton-Lwoff technic. Stain Tech. 28: 97–100.
75. Corrington, Julian D. 1961. Getting acquainted with the microscope. Printed for Bausch and Lomb, Rochester 2, N.Y.
76. Cory, Brother Lawrence. F.C.S. 1955. An electrically heated device for paraffin-embedding of specimens to be sectioned. Turtox News 33: 126–28.
77. Cowdry, E. V. 1948. Laboratory technique in biology and medicine. Ed. 2. Baltimore, Md.: Williams and Wilkins Co.
78. Cox, W. H. 1891. Imprägnation des centralen Nervensystem mit Quecksilbersalzen. Arch. mikr. Anat. 37: 16–21.
79. Crippa, A. 1951. Sulla utilizzazione del tetracetata di piombo come ossidante in istochimica. Boll. Soc. ital. Biol. sper. 27: 599–601.
80. Crossmon, Germain. 1940. The selective staining of red blood cells. Stain Tech. 15: 155–58.
81. Curtin, Charles B. 1956. An inexpensive embedding oven for the laboratory. Turtox News 34: 248.
82. Darrow, Mary A. 1940. A simple staining method for histology and cytology. Stain Tech. 15: 67–68.

83. Davenport, Harold A. 1960. Histological and histochemical technics. Philadelphia and London: W. B. Saunders Co.

84. Dawson, J. A. 1928. The culture of large free-living Amebae. Amer. Nat. 62: 453–66.

85. Dean, D. and Hatfield, P. A. 1963. Holding small aquatic invertebrates for observation. Turtox News 41: 43.

86. De La Pava, S. and Pickren, J. W. 1963. An iodine stain for gross neuropathological examination of brain stem and spinal cord. Stain Tech. 38: 295–96.

87. Demke, Donald D. 1952. Staining and mounting helminths. Stain Tech. 27: 135–39.

88. Desmet, V. J. 1962. The hazard of acid differentiation in Gomori's method for acid phosphatase. Stain Tech. 37: 373–76.

89. de Tomasi, J. A. 1936. Improving the technic of the Feulgen stain. Stain Tech. 11: 137–44.

90. Diller, Irene Corey. 1945. Smear methods for mammalian tissues, including tumors. J. tech. Methods Bull. int. Ass. med. Museums 25: 73–76.

91. DiStefano, Henry S. 1952. Feulgen hydrolysis with perchloric acid. Stain Tech. 27: 171–74.

92. Donaldson, John C. 1957. A slide for holding fresh tissue. Turtox News 35: 280.

93. Dow Brochure, 1959. Polyethylene glycols. Midland, Mich.: Dow Chemical Co.

94. Downs, W. G. 1943. Polyvinyl alcohol, a medium for mounting and clearing biological specimens. Science 97: 539–40.

95. Echols, Robert M. 1955. Aluminum foil boats for paraffin casting. Stain Tech. 30: 65–67.

96. Ehrlich, P. 1886. Ueber die Methylenblaureaktion der lebenden Nervensubstanz. Biol. Centralbl. 6: 214–24.

97. Elftman, Herbert. 1952. A direct silver method for the Golgi apparatus. Stain Tech. 27: 47–52.

98. Elftman, Herbert. 1959. Combined aldehyde-fuchsin periodic acid-Schiff staining of the pituitary. Stain Tech. 34: 77–80.

99. Elliott, A. M. and Hayes, R. E. 1955. Tetrahymena from Mexico, Panama, and Colombia with special reference to sexuality. J. Protozool. 2: 75–80.

100. Ellis, Richard A. 1957. Histochemical demonstration of endogenous dehydrogenase systems by supravital perfusion. Stain Tech. 32: 191–94.

101. Enlow, Donald H. 1954. A plastic-seal method for mounting sections of ground bone. Stain Tech. 29: 21–22.

102. Enlow, Donald H. 1961. Decalcification and staining of ground thin-sections of bone. Stain Tech. 36: 250–51.

103. Fesco, Edward J. 1954. Blotting paper cells for whole mounts. Stain Tech. 29: 319–20.

104. Feulgen, R. and Rossenbeck, H. 1924. Mikroskopisch-chemischer

Nachweis einer Nucleinsäure von Typus der Thymonuclein-säure und die darauf beruhende elektive Färbung von Zellkernen in mikroskopischen Präparaten. Hoppe-Seyl. Z. (für physiologische Chemie) 135: 203–48.

105. Ford, C. E. and Hamerton, J. L. 1956. A colchicine, hypotonic citrate, squash sequence for mammalian chromosomes. Stain Tech. 31: 247–51.

106. Ford, E. H. R. and Woollam, D. H. M. 1963. A colchicine, hypotonic citrate, air drying sequence for foetal mammalian chromosomes. Stain Tech. 38: 271–74.

107. Foulkes, R. H. and Beher, W. T. 1955. Vital staining with two dis-azo textile dyes. Stain Tech. 30: 37–39.

108. Fox, C. A., Ubeda-Purkiss, M., Ihrig, H. K., and Biagioli, D. 1951. Zinc chromate modification of the Golgi technic. Stain Tech. 26: 109–14.

109. Frings, Hubert. 1948. Dried skim milk powder for rearing protozoa. Turtox News 26: 33–37.

110. Frost, H. M. 1958. Preparation of thin undecalcified bone sections by rapid manual method. Stain Tech. 33: 273–77.

111. Frost, H. M. 1959. Staining of fresh, undecalcified, thin bone sections. Stain Tech. 34: 135–46.

112. Frost, H. M., Villaneuva, A. R., and Roth, H. 1960. Tetracycline staining of newly forming bone and mineralizing cartilage *in vivo*. Stain Tech. 35: 135–38.

113. Fry, F. E. J., Cucin, D., Kennedy, J. C., and Papson, A. 1960. The use of lead versenate to place a time mark on fish scales. Trans. Amer. Fish. Soc., 89: 149–53.

114. Fullmer, H. M. and Lillie, R. D. 1956. A selective stain for elastic tissue (orcinol-new fuchsin). Stain Tech. 31: 27–29.

115. Fulton, Macdonald. 1962. A convenient plastic bag for collecting small animals. Turtox News 40: 39.

116. Gabe, M. 1953. Sur quelques applications de la coloration par la fuchsine-paraldéhyde. Bull. Micr. appl., Ser. 2, 3: 153–62.

117. Gage, Simon Henry. 1936. The microscope. Ed. 16. Ithaca, N. Y.: Comstock Publishing Co., Inc.

118. Galtsoff, Paul S. 1956. Simple method of making frozen sections. Stain Tech. 31: 231.

119. Gatenby, J. B. and Beams, H. W. 1950. The microtomist's vademecum. (Bolles Lee). Ed. 11. Philadelphia: The Blakiston Co.

120. Gelei, J. von. 1935. Eine neue Abänderung der Klein'schen trockenen Silbermethode und das Silberliniensystem von Glaucoma scintillans. Arch. Protistenk. 84: 446–55.

121. Giovacchini, Rupert P. 1958. Affixing Carbowax sections to slides for routine staining. Stain Tech. 33: 247–48.

122. Glegg, R. E., Clermont, Y., and Leblond, C. P. 1952. The use of lead tetraacetate, benzidine, o-dianisidine and a "film test" in investigating the periodic acid-Schiff technic. Stain Tech. 27: 277–305.

123. Glick, D. 1949. Techniques of histo- and cytochemistry. New York: Interscience Publishers, Inc.
124. Goland, P. P., Jason, R. S., and Berry, K. P. 1954. Combined Carbowax-paraffin technic for microsectioning fixed tissues. Stain Tech. 29: 5–8.
125. Gomori, G. 1941. Observations with differential stains on human islets of Langerhans. Amer. J. Path. 17: 395–406.
126. Gomori, G. 1946. The study of enzymes in tissue sections. Amer. J. clin. Path., 16: 347–52.
127. Gomori, G. 1950. Aldehyde fuchsin: a new stain for elastic tissue. Amer. J. clin. Path. 20: 665–66.
128. Gomori, G. 1950. An improved histochemical technic for acid phosphatase. Stain Tech. 25: 81–85.
129. Gomori, G. 1952. Microscopic histochemistry. Principles and practice. Chicago: University of Chicago Press.
130. González, Romeo. 1959. The removal of mercury after fixation in sublimate-containing mixtures. Stain Tech. 34: 111–12.
131. Gray, Peter. 1954. The microtomist's formulary and guide. New York and Toronto: The Blakiston Company, Inc.
132. Gray, Peter. 1958. Handbook of basic microtechnique. Ed. 2. New York, Toronto, and London: McGraw-Hill Book Co., Inc.
133. Greenstein, J. S. 1957. A rapid phloxine-methylene blue oversight method for formalin-fixed material. Stain Tech. 32: 75–77.
134. Gregg, V. R. and Puckett, W. O. 1943. A corrosive sublimate fixing solution for yolk-laden amphibian eggs. Stain Tech. 18: 179–80.
135. Griffiths, I. and Carter, M. E. 1958. Sectioning refractory animal tissues. Stain Tech. 33: 209–14.
136. Grundmann, Albert W. 1955. Improved methods for preparing and mounting nematodes for study. Turtox News 33: 152–53.
137. Guillery, R. W., Shirra, B., and Webster, K. E. 1961. Differential impregnation of degenerating nerve fibers in paraffin-embedded material. Stain Tech. 36: 9–13.
138. Gunthorp, Horace. 1920. To kill cats for laboratory use. Science 11: 87.
139. Gurr, Edward. 1956. A practical manual of medical and biological staining techniques. Ed. 2. London: Leonard Hill (Books) Ltd. New York: Interscience Publishers, Inc.
140. Gurr, Edward. 1959. Methods of analytical histology and histochemistry. Baltimore, Md.: Williams and Wilkins Co.
141. Gurr, Edward. 1960. Encyclopedia of microscopic stains. Baltimore, Md.: Williams and Wilkins Co. Edinburgh, Scotland: Neill and Co., Ltd.
142. Guyer, Michael F. 1953. Animal micrology. Ed. 5. Chicago: University of Chicago Press.
143. Hale, Arthur J. 1952. The effect of temperature and of relative humidity on sectioning of tissues embedded in polyethylene glycol wax. Stain Tech. 27: 189–92.

144. Hance, Robert T. 1916. A simple paraffin ribbon winder. Anat. Rec. 10: 523–26.

145. Hance, Robert T. 1933. A new paraffin embedding mixture. Science 77: 353.

146. Harman, W. J. and Corliss, J. O. 1956. Isolation of earthworm setae by use of histophagous protozoa. Trans. Amer. micr. Soc. 75: 322–33.

147. Harris, Richard S. 1956. A serum-film technic for bone-marrow smears. Stain Tech. 31: 39–44.

148. Hartnett, John C. 1954. A convenient method for anesthetizing the frog. Turtox News Vol. 32: No. 3; and 1962, personal communication.

149. Haupt, A. W. 1930. A gelatin fixative for paraffin sections. Stain Tech. 5: 97–98.

150. Haushalter, E. R. and Bertram, E. G. 1955. A pulsating perfusion-fixation method for laboratory animals. Anat. Rec. 121: 435.

151. Heller, R. E., Thomas, R. W., and Davenport, H. A. 1947. Staining nerve fibers with methylene blue. An evaluation of variables used in an immersion technic. Stain Tech. 22: 111–18.

152. Hillemann, H. H. and Lee, C. H. 1953. Organic chelating agents for decalcification of bones and teeth. Stain Tech. 28: 285–87.

153. Horner, H. T., Jr. and Arnott, H. J. 1961. The use of a multiple-compartment tray for processing many specimens at one time. Stain Tech. 36: 204–5.

154. Hotchkiss, R. D. 1948. A microchemical reaction resulting in the staining of polysaccharide structures in fixed tissue preparations. Arch. Biochem. 16: 131–41.

155. Hrushovetz, S. B. and Harder, C. E. 1962. Permanent mounting of unstained and aceto-orcein stained cells in the water-soluble medium, Abopon. Stain Tech. 37: 307–11.

156. Humason, Gretchen L. 1962. Animal tissue techniques. San Francisco and London: W. H. Freeman and Company.

157. Humason, G. L. and Lushbaugh, C. C. 1960. Selective demonstration of elastin, reticulum, and collagen by silver, orcein, and aniline blue. Stain Tech. 35: 209–14.

158. Itikawa, O. and Ogura, Y. 1954. The Feulgen reaction after hydrolysis at room temperature. Stain Tech. 29: 13–15.

159. Jackson, B. and Dessau, F. I. 1955. Streptococcal desoxyribonuclease for the removal of Feulgen-stainable material. Stain Tech. 30: 9–11.

160. Jacobson, Stanley. 1963. Handling sections in bulk with special reference to the Nauta technic. Stain Tech. 38: 262–63.

161. Jee, W. S. S. and Arnold, J. S. 1960. India ink-gelatin vascular injection of skeletal tissues. Stain Tech. 35: 59–65.

162. Jimenez, F. A. and Schneider, E. 1962. The Schain frozen section clarifier. Stain Tech. 37: 121–23.

163. Johnels, Alf G. 1955. Suppression of costaining of nonnervous tissue in Protargol technics. Stain Tech. 30: 169–72.

164. Jones, Ruth McClung, Editor. 1950. McClung's handbook of micro-scopical technique. Ed. 3. New York: Hoeber. Reprinted, 1961. New York: Hafner Publishing Co.

165. Julien, J. B. 1959. A pinchcock as an aid in flattening chromosome preparations. Stain Tech. 34: 47–48.

166. Jump, John Austin. 1941. The preparation of slides of the salivary gland chromosomes of *Drosophila*. Turtox News 19: 81–82.

167. Kempton, Rudolf T. 1958. A simple demonstration of the anal pore in *Paramecium*. Turtox News 36: 19.

168. Keyl, M. J. and Smith, J. W. H. 1958. An aid for injections subcutane-ous. Turtox News 36: 90.

169. Kingsbury, B. F. 1916. A convenient method of orientation in paraffin embedding when paper trays or boxes are used. Anat. Rec. 11: 294.

170. Kingsley, D. M. 1935. A new hematological stain. I. Constituents and methods of use. Stain Tech. 10: 127–33.

171. Kirby, Harold. 1950. Materials and methods in the study of protozoa. Berkeley and Los Angeles: University of California Press.

172. Klatzo, Igor and McMillan, G. C. 1952. A new technic for the rapid diagnosis of brain tumors using chlorazol black E. Lab. Invest. 1: 24–28.

173. Klinger, H. P. and Ludwig, K. S. 1957. A universal stain for the sex chromatin body. Stain Tech. 32: 235–244.

174. Klüver, H. and Barrera, E. 1953. A method for the combined staining of cells and fibers in the nervous system. J. Neuropath. 12: 400–403.

175. Knisely, Melvin Henry. 1936. A method of illuminating living struc-tures for microscopic study. Anat. Rec. 64: 499–524.

176. Knox, G. A. 1954. The benzidine staining method for blood vessels. Stain Tech. 29: 139–42.

177. Koenig, H., Groat, R. A., and Windle, W. F. 1945. A physiological approach to perfusion-fixation of tissues with formalin. Stain Tech. 20: 13–22.

178. Kornhauser, S. I. 1930. Hematein—its advantages for general labora-tory usage. Stain Tech. 5: 13–15.

179. Kornhauser, S. I. 1945. A revised method for the "quad" stain. Stain Tech. 20: 33–35.

180. Krutsay, M. 1960. A versatile resorchin-fuchsin formula: I. Combined with formaldehyde; II. Used after periodic acid; III. Used after HCL hydrolysis. Stain Tech. 35: 283–85.

181. La Cour, L. 1941. Aceto-orcein: A new stain-fixative for chromosomes. Stain Tech. 16: 169–74.

182. Lamkie, N. J. and Burstone, M. S. 1962. Vinylpyrrolidone-vinyl acetate copolymers as mounting media for azo and other dyes. Stain Tech. 37: 109–10.

183. Landing. B. H. 1954. Histologic study of the anterior pituitary gland. A compilation of procedures. Lab. Invest. 3: 348–68.

184. Landing, B. H. and Hall, H. E. 1956. Histochemical differentiation of

anterior pituitary cell types by contrasting azo-coupling and muco-protein stains. Stain Tech. 31: 193–96.

185. Larimer, J. L. and Ashby, E. A. 1964. Reduced methylene blue as a stain for crustacean nerves. Stain Tech. 39: 369–71.

186. Lavoie, Marcel E. 1958. The preparation of polyclad whole mounts. Turtox News 36: 45–46.

187. Le Masurier, H. E. 1935. (For making permanent preparations which demonstrate white and gray matter of the central nervous system). Arch. Neurol. Psychol. 34: 1065. Reported by Addison (*164*, p. 355).

188. Levene, Cyril. 1964. Critical staining of pancreatic alpha granules with phosphotungstic acid hematoxylin. Stain Tech. 39: 39–44.

189. Lewis, P. R. and Shute, C. C. D. 1963. Alginate gel; an embedding medium for facilitating the cutting and handling of frozen sections. Stain Tech. 38: 307–10.

190. Lillie, R. D. 1944. Various oil soluble dyes as fat stains in the super-saturated isopropanol technic. Stain Tech. 19: 55–58.

191. Lillie, R. D. 1947. Reticulum staining with Schiff reagent after oxidation by acidified sodium periodate. J. Lab. clin. Med. 32: 910–12.

192. Lillie, R. D. 1951. Simplification of the manufacture of Schiff reagent for use in histochemical procedures. Stain Tech. 26: 163–65.

193. Lillie, R. D. 1954. Histopathologic technic and practical histochemistry. New York and Toronto: Blakiston Co., Inc.

194. Lillie, R. D. and Ashburn, L. L. 1943. Supersaturated solutions of fat stains in dilute isopropanol for demonstration of acute fatty degeneration not shown by Herxheimer technic. Arch. Path. 36: 432–35.

195. Lillie, R. D. and Greco Henson, J. P. 1955. A new histological mounting medium of low refractive index. Stain Tech. 30: 133–34.

196. Lindner, L. A., Goldman, H., and Ruzicka, P. L. 1961. Simple method for rotifer culture. Turtox News 39: 74.

197. Lison, Lucien. 1954. Alcian blue 8G with chlorantine fast red 5B. A technic for selective staining of mucopolysaccharides. Stain Tech. 29: 131–38.

198. Lison, L. and Vokaer, R. 1949. Sur la détection histochimique du glycogène des cellules vaginales chez la femme. Ann. Endocr., Paris 10: 66–72.

199. Lockard, I. and Reers, B. L. 1962. Staining tissue of the central nervous system with Luxol fast blue and neutral red. Stain Tech. 37: 13–16.

200. Loomis, W. F. 1953. The cultivation of hydra under controlled conditions. Science 117: 565–66.

201. Loomis, W. F. 1954. Environmental factors controlling growth in hydra. J. exp. Zool. 126: 223–34.

202. Loomis, W. F. 1955. Glutathione control of the specific feeding reactions of hydra. Ann. N. Y. Acad. Sci. 62: 211–27.

203. Lorenzo, Michael A. 1959. A trimming jig for use in microtomy. Stain Tech. 34: 296–98.

204. Lynch, J. E. 1930. Eine neue Karminmethode für Totalpraparate. Z. wiss. Mikr. 46: 465–69.

205. Lynch, Matthew J. 1964. Staining reticulin with gold. Stain Tech. 39: 19–25.

206. MacNeal, W. J. 1922. Tetrachrome blood stain; an economical and satisfactory imitation of Leishmann's stain. J. Amer. med. Assoc., 78: 1112.

207. Makino, S. and Nishimura, I. 1952. Water-pretreatment squash technic. Stain Tech. 27: 1–7.

208. Maneval, W. E. 1934. Rapid staining methods. Science 80: 292–94.

209. Margolis, G. and Pickett, J. P. 1956. New applications of the Luxol fast blue myelin stain. Lab. Invest. 5: 459–74.

210. Marshall, W. H. 1940. An application of the frozen sectioning technic for cutting serial sections through the brain. Stain Tech. 15: 133–38.

211. Martin, B. F. and Jacoby, F. 1949. Diffusion phenomenon complicating the histochemical reaction for alkaline phosphatase. J. Anat., London 83: 351–63.

212. Matthews, D. C. 1954. A simple apparatus for truing paraffin blocks. Turtox News, 32, 78–79.

213. McClung, C. E. 1929, editor, Handbook of microscopical technique. Ed. I. New York: Hoeber.

214. McManus, J. F. A. 1946. The histological demonstration of mucin after periodic acid. Nature Lond. 158: 202.

215. McManus, J. F. A. 1948. Histological and histochemical uses of periodic acid. Stain Tech. 23: 99–108.

216. McNeil, C. W., Gibbons, R., Kinney, P. G., and Farner, D. S. 1958. The use of the urinary bladder of the leopard frog in the demonstration of peripheral circulation. Turtox News 36: 170–73.

217. Melander, Y. and Wingstrand, K. G. 1953. Gomori's hematoxylin as a chromosome stain. Stain Tech. 28: 217–223.

218. Melnyk, John. 1961. A tissue transfer device. Stain Tech. 36: 202–3.

219. Melvin, D. M. and Brooke, M. M. 1955. Triton X-100 in Giemsa staining of blood parasites. Stain Tech. 30: 269–75.

220. Menschik, Z. 1953. Nile blue histochemical method for phospholipids. Stain Tech. 28, 13–18.

221. Menzies, D. W. 1962. Paraffin-beeswax-stearic acid: an embedding mass for thin sections. Stain Tech. 37: 235–38.

222. Meyer, David B. 1960. Application of the periodic acid-Schiff technique to whole chick embryos. Stain Tech., 35: 83–89.

223. Milch, R. A., Rall, D. P., and Tobie, J. E. 1957. Bone localization of the tetracyclines. J. nat. Cancer Inst. 19: 87–93.

224. Miles, A. E. W. 1949. Test of the end point of decalcification of histological specimens. Brit. dent. J. 86: 297–99.

225. Mitchell, R. D. and Cook, D. R. 1952. The preservation and mounting of water-mites. Turtox News 30: 169–72.

226. Moffat, D. B. 1958. Demonstration of alkaline phosphatase and periodic

acid-Schiff positive material in the same section. Stain Tech. 33: 225–28.

227. Moment, G. B. 1944. A simple method for quieting Paramecium and other small organisms during prolonged observation. Science 99: 544.

228. Morrison, Warren. 1946. Opaque slide mounts. Turtox News 24: 106–7.

229. Moss, Melvin L. 1954. Vital staining of newly formed areas of compact bone with chlorazol fast pink. Stain Tech. 29: 247–51.

230. Nace, G. W. and Spradlin, P. 1962. Bleeding rabbits. Turtox News 40: 26–29.

231. Naik, Ramesh M. 1961. Pigeon breast muscle as an ideal test material for histochemical demonstration of glycogen. Stain Tech. 36: 247–48.

232. Nauta, W. J. H. and Gygax, P. A. 1954. Silver impregnation of degenerating axons in the central nervous system: a modified technic. Stain Tech. 29: 91–93.

233. Needham, George Herbert. 1958. The practical use of the microscope. Springfield, Ill.: Charles C Thomas.

234. Needham, James G. *et al.* Culture methods for invertebrate animals. Ed. 1. Dover Reprint. New York: Dover Publications, Inc., 180 Varick St.

235. Newcomer, Earl H. 1959. Feulgen staining of tissues prior to embedding and sectioning. Stain Tech. 34: 349–50.

236. Nicholas, J. S. and Barron, D. H. 1932. The use of sodium amytal in the production of anesthesia in the rat. J. Pharmacol. 46: 125–29.

237. Nissenbaum, Gerald. 1953. A combined method for the rapid fixation and adhesion of ciliates and flagellates. Science 118: 31–32.

238. Nultsch, Wilhelm. 1955. Ein neues Celloidin-Einbettungsverfahren unter Verwendung von Tetrahydrofuran als Intermedium. Mikroskopie 10: 25–29.

239. Obrecht, Carl B. 1948. A method of storage for delicate specimens. Turtox News 26: 31–32.

240. O'Brien, B. R. A. 1961. Identification of haemoglobin by its catalase reaction with peroxide and o-dianisidine. Stain Tech. 36: 57–61.

241. Packard, Charles E. 1947. Fun with the fire brat. Turtox News 25: 196–97.

242. Papamiltiades, M. N. 1961. Injection of lymphatics: with colored cedar oil; with plastic. Stain Tech. 36: 241–46.

243. Parker, G. H. 1939. General anesthesia by chilling. Science 90: 63.

244. Parrish, F. K. and Parrish, J. W. 1962. Demonstrating gregarines. Turtox News 40: 236–37.

245. Pauly, John E. 1956. Cutting frozen sections on a paraffin microtome. Stain Tech. 31: 35–37.

246. Pearl, Raymond. 1903. Worcester's formol-sublimate fixing fluids. J. appl. Micr. Lab. Methods 6: 2451.

247. Pearse, A. G. Everson. 1960. Histochemistry, theoretical and applied.

Ed. 2. London: J. and A. Churchill, Ltd. Boston: Little, Brown and Co.

248. Peary, Joseph Ygor. 1955. Freeze-dehydration for permanent mounts after aceto-orcein stain. Stain Tech. 30: 249–51.

249. Peers, J. N. 1941. A modification of Mallory's phosphotungstic acid hematoxylin stain in formaldehyde-fixed tissue. Arch. Path. 32: 446–49.

250. Peters, H. 1961. A glass sieve for carrying loose frozen and celloidin sections through all stages of processing. Stain Tech. 36:201.

251. Piatt, Jean. 1945. Modification of Faris' Janus green-neutral red stain for amphibian embryos. Personal communication.

252. Porter, R. W. and Davenport, H. A. 1949. Golgi's dichromate-silver method. I. Effects of embedding. II. Experiments with modifications. Stain Tech. 24: 117–26.

253. Potts, F. A. 1920. A note on vital staining. Proc. Camb. phil. Soc. 20: 231–34.

254. Powers, M. M. and Clark, G. 1963. A note on Darrow red. Stain Tech. 38: 289–90.

255. Powers, M. M., Clark, G., Darrow, M. A., and Emmel, V. M. 1960. Darrow red, a new basic dye. Stain Tech. 35: 19–21.

256. Puchtler, H. and Sweat, F. 1960. Commercial resorcin-fuchsin as a stain for elastic fibers. Stain Tech. 35: 347–48.

257. Puckett, William O. 1937. The dioxane-paraffin technic for sectioning frog eggs. Stain Tech. 12: 97–98.

258. Puckett, W. O. and Neumann, C. P. 1940. Vinylite resin in the preparation of corrosions of anatomical specimens. Anat. Rec. 78: 105–12.

259. Ralph, P. H. 1941. The histochemical demonstration of hemoglobin in blood cells and tissue smears. Stain Tech. 16: 105–6.

260. Ranvier, L. 1880. On the terminations of nerves in the epidermis. Quart. J. micr. Sci. 20: 456–58.

261. Ratliffe, J. L., Williams, W. L., and Mayberry, H. E. 1963. Effects of pH on post-mortem retention of trypan blue vital staining in tissues of mice. Stain Tech. 38: 329–33.

262. Reeve, R. M. and Makower, B. 1954. An adaptable heating stage with electrically conductive glass for biological microscopy. Stain Tech. 29: 201–5.

263. Rice, N. E. 1946. Commercial fertilizer in the culture of fresh-water algae. Science 104: 16–17.

264. Richards, Oscar W. 1937. Killing organisms with chromium as from incompletely washed bichromate-sulfuric cleaned glassware. The Collecting Net. 12: 218.

265. Richards, Oscar W. 1959. The effective use and proper care of the microtome. Buffalo, N. Y.: American Optical Co., Instrument Division.

266. Richards, O. W. and Jenkins, R. L. 1950. Static electricity elimination during sectioning with a microtome. Science 111: 624–25.

267. Riley, Vernon. 1960. Adaptation of orbital bleeding technic to rapid serial blood studies. Proc. Soc. exp. Biol., N. Y. 104: 751–54.

268. Riser, Nathan W. 1950. Notes on toto-mount technique. Proc. helminth. Soc. Wash. 17: 132.

269. Romeis, B. 1948. Mikroskopischen technik. Ed. 15. München: Leibniz Verlag.

270. Rothfels, K. H. and Siminovitch, L. 1958. An air-drying technique for flattening chromosomes in mammalian cells grown *in vitro*. Stain Tech. 33: 73–77.

271. Roudabush, Robert L. 1949. A new microscopic technique. Bio-Plastic whole mounts. Ward's Nat. Science Bull. 22: 63–66.

272. Rugh, Roberts. 1934. Induced ovulation and artificial fertilization in the frog. Biol. Bull. 66: 22–29.

273. Rugh, Roberts. 1937. Ovulation induced out of season. Science 85: 588–89.

274. Rugh, Roberts. 1937. A quantitative analysis of the pituitary-ovulation relation in the frog (*Rana pipiens*). Physiol. Zool. 10: 84–100.

275. Rugh, Roberts. 1941. Experimental embryology: A manual of techniques and procedures. New York University Bookstore. (18 Washington Place, New York)

276. Rugh, Roberts. 1950. A laboratory manual of vertebrate embryology. Minneapolis, Minn.: Burgess Publishing Co.

277. Ruth, E. B. 1946. Demonstration of the ground substance of cartilage, bone, and teeth. Stain Tech. 21: 27–29.

278. Salthouse, T. N. 1962. Luxol fast blue ARN: a new Solvent azo dye with improved staining qualities for myelin and phospholipids. Stain Tech. 37: 313–16.

279. Sams, Alice. 1963. A celloidin infiltration-frozen section sequence for enhanced preservation of phosphatases in bone. Stain Tech. 38: 1–8.

280. Schajowicz, F. and Cabrini, R. L. 1959. Histochemical demonstration of acid phosphatase in hard tissues. Stain Tech. 34: 59–64.

281. Schell, Stewart C. 1952. Class use of viable nematode eggs for a study of early cleavages. Turtox News 30: 132–34.

282. Schiff, H. 1866. Einer neurer Reihe organischer Diamine. Liebigs Ann. Chem. Pharm. 140: 92–137.

283. Schleicher, E. M. 1943. Amer. J. clin. Path. 7: 35–39. Quoted from Edwards (*164*, p. 247).

284. Schwartz, F. J. and Nagy, E. R. 1963. Feulgen stain stability in relation to three mounting media and exposure to light. Stain Tech. 38: 179–85.

285. Scott, H. R. 1952. Rapid staining of beta cell granules in pancreatic islets. Stain Tech. 27: 267–68.

286. Slater, D. W. and Dornfeld, E. J. 1939. A triple stain for amphibian embryos. Stain Tech. 14: 103–4.

287. Slifer, E. H. and King, R. L. 1933. Grasshopper eggs and the paraffin method. Science 78: 366.

288. Smith, Bertram G. 1914. Methods of preparing teleost embryos for class use. Trans. Amer. micr. Soc. 33: 54–55.

289. Snider, R. S. 1943. A rapid bulk Nissl method. Stain Tech. 18: 35–39.

290. Snodgrass, A. B., Dorsey, C. H., and Lacey, L. B. 1962. Luxol fast blue staining of degenerating myelinated fibers. Stain Tech. 37:60. Abstracted from Anat. Rec. 140: 83–90. 1961.

291. Snook, Theodore. 1939. Preservation of trypan blue and neutral red within the cells of loose connective tissue. Stain Tech. 14: 139–45.

292. Society of Dyers and Colourists. 1924. Colour Index. Edited by F. M. Rowe. Published by The Society. Bradford, Yorkshire, England.

293. Society of Dyers and Colourists. 1956. Colour Index. Ed. 2. Published by the Society of Dyers and Colourists, England, and the American Association of Textile Chemists, Lowell, Mass.

294. Sparano, B. M. 1961. The use of hypotonic citrate and aceto-orcein for squash preparations of mammalian chromosomes. Stain Tech. 36: 41–42.

295. Specht, H. 1935. The culture of Spirostomum ambiguum. Arch. Protistenk. 85: 150–52.

296. Speece, A. J., Jr. 1952. A rapid method in section mounting. Stain Tech. 27: 337.

297. Spurr, Arthur R. 1954. Polyvinyl alcohol with cadmium iodide and fructose as an aqueous mounting medium. Stain Tech. 29: 301–13.

298. Stagg, F. B. and Tappen, N. C. 1963. A device for cutting parallel-ended blocks from decalcified long bones. Stain Tech. 38: 343–44.

299. Steen, Edwin B. 1955. A technique for the study of the fruit fly, Drosophila melanogaster. Turtox News 33: 190.

300. Stegman, Le Roy C. 1958. Some simple techniques for collecting various invertebrate animals for class use. Turtox News 36: 8–11.

301. Stegman, Le Roy C. 1959. An excellent method for demonstrating living parasites of earthworms. Turtox News 37: 266–68.

302. Stilwell, Donald L. 1957. A Sudan black B myelin stain for peripheral nerves. Stain Tech. 32: 19–23.

303. Strike, Thomas A. 1962. A device for adapting the rotary microtome to frozen sectioning. Stain Tech. 37: 187–89.

304. Swan, Emery F. 1961. Some uses of colored materials in marine biological research. Turtox News 39: 290–93.

305. Swigart, R. H., Wagner, C. E., and Atkinson, W. B. 1960. The preservation of glycogen in fixed tissues and tissue sections. J. Histochem. Cytochem. 8: 74–75.

306. Tamate, H. and Kondo, Y. 1961. An improved staining of the three fundic gland cells of the mammalian stomach. Stain Tech. 36: 254.

307. Tappen, N. C. 1962. Block staining with hematoxylin, gelatin embedding and serial sectioning of decalcified bone. Stain Tech. 37: 161–63.

308. Tartar, V. 1950. Methods for the study and cultivation of protozoa; in Studies honoring Trevor Kinkaid, pp. 164–67. Seattle: University of Washington Press.

309. Templeton, McCormick. 1961. A simple macrotome for soft tissue. Stain Tech. 36:255–56.

310. Thompson, E. C. 1961. Simultaneous staining of reticulocytes and Heinz bodies with new methylene blue N in dogs given iproniazid. Stain Tech. 36: 38–39.

311. Timm, Richard W. 1953. The study of free-living nematodes. Turtox News 31: 170–72.

312. Tjio, J. H. and Whang, J. 1962. Chromosome preparations of bone marrow cells without prior *in vitro* culture or *in vivo* colchicine administration. Stain Tech. 37: 17–20.

313. Turbyfill, C. L., Peterson, R. P., and Soderwall, A. L. 1962. The cardiac puncture in adult, fetal and young golden hamsters. Turtox News 40: 162–63.

314. van Breeman, V. L. and Marx, R. 1958. Use of hypothermia in preparing tissues for electron microscopy. Stain Tech. 33: 300–301.

315. van Duijn, P. and Oort, J. 1962. Stirring during freeze-substitution. Stain Tech. 37: 116–18.

316. Van Herwerden, M. A. 1920. A method for fixing films of human blood cells during the ameboid movement of leucocytes and thrombocytes. J. exp. Med. 32: 135–37.

317. Viehoever, Arno. 1935. Daphnia propagation for experimental use. Amer. J. Pharm. 107: 1–28.

318. Viehoever, Arno. 1936. Daphnia—the biological reagent. J. Amer. pharm. Ass. 25: 1112.

319. von Borstel, R. C. and Lindsley, D. L. 1959. Insect embryo chromosome techniques. Stain Tech. 34: 23–26.

320. Wachstein, M. and Meisel, E. 1959. The histochemical demonstration of secretory capillaries in the pancreas with the aid of substrate-specific phosphatases. J. Biophys. Biochem. Cytol. 6: 119–120.

321. Wade, H. W. 1952. Notes on the Carbowax method of making tissue sections. Stain Tech. 27: 71–79.

322. Waerhaug, Jens. 1954. Control of the end-point of decalcification by fluoroscopy. Stain Tech. 29: 213–15.

323. Waldbauer, Gilbert P. 1955. Freezing: a method of preservation of insects. Turtox News 33: 186.

324. Walls, G. L. 1936. A rapid celloidin method for the rotary microtome. Stain Tech. 11: 89–92.

325. Ward's Service Bulletin No. 5. 1950. The use of latex and vinyl acetate in the injection of the circulatory system. Ward's Natural Science Establishment.

326. Watts, R. H. 1953. Selective staining of eosinophil leucocytes in blood films. Stain Tech. 28: 159.

327. Weatherell, J. A. and Hobbs, G. 1960. Chlorazol fast pink as an *in vivo* stain for unmineralized bone and tooth matrix. Stain Tech. 35: 139–43.

328. Weber, D. D. and Ridgeway, G. J. 1962. The deposition of tetracycline

drugs in bones and scales of fish and its possible use for marking. The Progressive Fish-Culturalist 24: 150–55.

329. Welshons, W. J., Gibson, B. H., and Scandlyn, B. J. 1962. Slide processing for the examination of male mammalian meiotic chromosomes. Stain Tech. 37: 1–5.

330. West, W. T. and Gorham, L. W. 1962. Injection of the arterial system of the mouse. Stain Tech. 37: 99–103.

331. White, Lowell E., Jr. 1960. Enhanced reliability in silver impregnation of terminal axonal degeneration—original Nauta method. Stain Tech. 35: 5–9.

332. Whiting, A. R. 1950. A modification of the Schmuck-Metz wholemount technic for chromosome study. Stain Tech. 25: 21–22.

333. Wichterman, R. 1952. A method for obtaining abundant dividing stages of Paramecium. Trans. Amer. micr. Soc. 71: 303–5.

334. Wichterman, Ralph. 1953. The biology of paramecium. New York: The Blakiston Co., Inc.

335. Williams, T. D. 1957. Mounting and preserving serial celloidin sections. Stain Tech. 32: 97.

336. Woods, P. S. and Pollister, A. W. 1955. An ice-solvent method of drying frozen tissue for plant cytology. Stain Tech. 30: 123–31.

337. Yunker, Conrad. E. 1959. An improved method for storage and shipment of small invertebrate specimens. Turtox News 37: 294–95.

338. Ziegler, E. E. 1944. Arch. Path. 37: 68–69. Quoted from Edwards (164, p. 242).

339. Zinn, D. J. and Morin, L. P. 1962. The use of commercial citric juices in gold chloride staining of nerve endings. Stain Tech. 37: 380–81.

340. Zirkle, Conway. 1934. Butyl alcohol and cytological technique. Science 80: 481.

341. Zuck, Robert K. 1959. Double and triple cover glass mounting technics. Turtox News 37: 57.

342. Zweifel, Frances W. 1961. A handbook of biological illustrations. Phoenix Science Series. Chicago: University of Chicago Press.

343. Zwemer, R. L. 1933. A method for studying adrenal and other lipoids by a modified gelatin embedding and mounting technique. Anat. Rec. 57: 41–44.

INDEX

INDEX